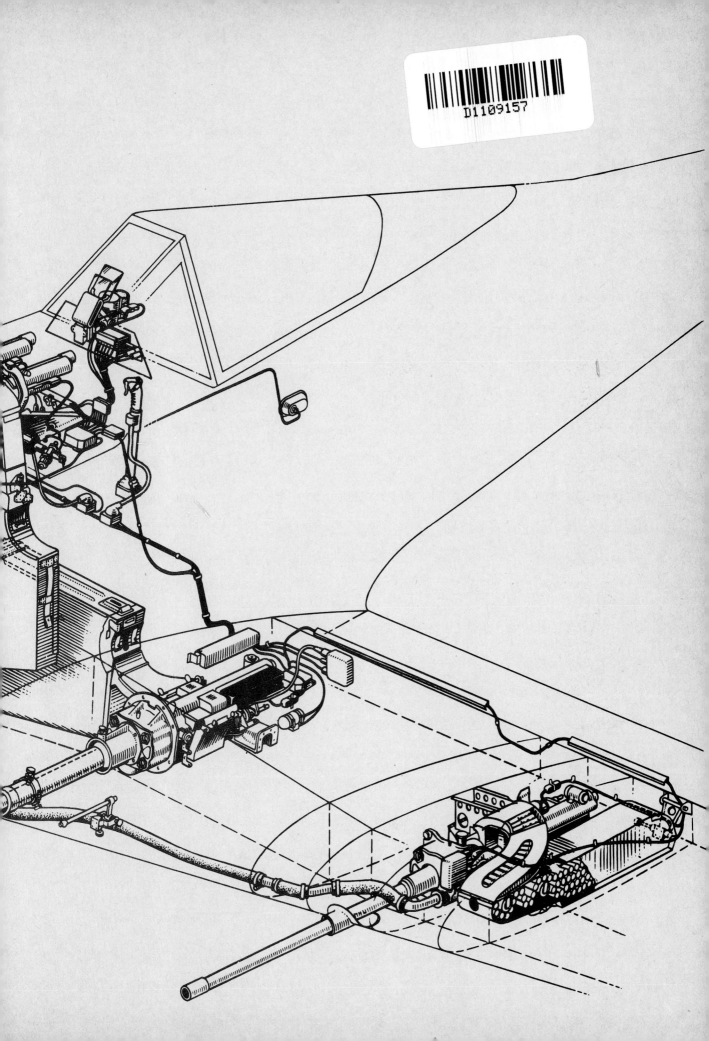

The Illustrated Encyclopedia of 20th Century
WEAPONS AND WARFARE

The Illustrated Encyclopedia of 20th Century

WEAPONS AND WARFARE

COLUMBIA HOUSE/New York

Editor: Bernard Fitzsimons
Consultant Editors: Bill Gunston (Aviation)
                    Ian V. Hogg (Land Weapons)
                    Antony Preston (Naval)
Deputy Editor: Suzanne Walker
Copy Editor: Michael Maddison
Assistant Editors: Will Fowler, Richard Green,
                   Corinne Benicka, John
                   Liebmann, Michael de Luca
Editorial Assistant: Julie Leitch
Art Editor: David Harper
Assistant Art Editor: John Bickerton
Design Assistants: Jeff Gurney, John Voce
Production: Sheila Biddlecombe
Picture Research: Jonathan Moore
Contributors: David Brown, Norman Friedman, Ian Friel,
                  Michael J. Gething, Bill Gunston, Mark Hewish,
                  Ian V. Hogg, John Jordan, David Lyon, Pamela D.
                  Matthews, Kenneth Munson, Malcolm Passingham,
                  Antony Preston, John A. Roberts, C. J. Ware,
                  Anthony J. Watts, John S. Weeks, M. R. Wilson
Illustrator: John Batchelor

Cover Design: Harry W. Fass
Production Manager: Stephen Charkow

"In war there is no substitute for victory."
—Douglas MacArthur

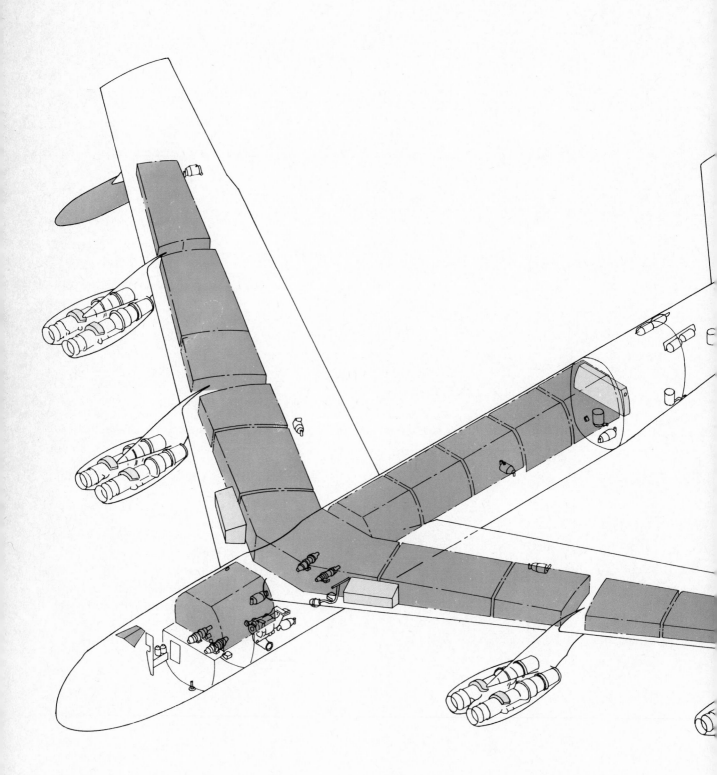

INTRODUCTION

Volume 22 of *The Illustrated Encyclopedia of 20th Century Weapons and Warfare* spans the whole range of military aviation, from First World War biplanes to jet-powered interceptors and strategic bombers, and includes a number of types which were among the first and best of their kind.

The French **Spad** series of biplane fighters, many of which equipped American Expeditionary Force squadrons in 1917-18, were among the finest of their day, while the Supermarine **Spitfire** was one of the first classic monoplane fighters. Derived from the 1931 Schneider trophy-winning S.6B seaplane, the fastest aircraft of its time, the Spitfire will always recall the desperate days of the Battle of Britain, but it went on to be developed through a whole series of models. It was the only Allied fighter to remain in production throughout the Second World War, and was a remarkable testimony to the soundness of the original design.

The advent of jet propulsion enabled a new order of performance. The Douglas F4D **Skyray** incorporated another innovation, the delta wing, the first such aircraft to be built in the United States, while the USAF's first all-weather interceptor, the Lockheed F-94 **Starfire,** had an unusual history of development. It developed from the F-80 Shooting Star via the T-33 trainer in one of the rare instances of a two-seat conversion having better performance than the original single-seat fighter. Another extreme of aerodynamic design is represented by the same company's F-104 **Starfighter**—"the missile with a man in it"—which combined a needle-like fuselage with wings of the smallest possible area to achieve its outstanding performance.

Bombers, too, are well represented, from the German **Staaken R** heavy bomber series of the First World War, via the Boeing B-29 **Superfortress,** the most advanced bomber of the Second World War. Boeing continued their tradition of heavy bomber design with one of the first generation of US jet bombers, the B-47 **Stratojet,** one of the few truly revolutionary airplanes, incorporating not only jet propulsion but also swept wings. And the B-52 **Stratofortress,** whose basic design was worked out in the space of a long weekend in a hotel room in Chicago. The Stratofortress was originally intended to serve for just five years; remarkably, it is still in service more than 25 years after its first flight. It has been adapted to new roles never envisaged when it was designed, and, following the cancellation of the Rockwell B-1, may well serve until the end of the century.

One type which also deserves a mention is the Ilyushin I1-2 **Sturmovik,** a specialized Soviet ground attack machine built in greater numbers than any other Soviet aircraft and so effective that it became known to German tank crews as the Black Death.

On land, Volume 22 deals with small arms from the **Smith & Wesson** and **Springfield** companies, the **Steyr** and **Solothurn** subsidiaries of Rheinmettal, used for design and production of new weapons during Germany's period of clandestine rearmament, the **Sten** submachine gun, and the remarkable designs of Eugene **Stoner,** who suffered the irony of having his new 5.56-mm weapon system turned down in favor of the M16, which itself stemmed from one of his own designs.

Skyray, Douglas F4D

US carrier-based intercepter aircraft. The experimental work carried out on the delta wing by the German Dr Alexander Lippisch encouraged the US Navy to issue a requirement for a delta-wing aircraft to be used for a short-range carrier-based intercepter in 1947. Headed by Ed Heinemann, the Douglas design team at the El Segundo factory was offered the task, and began design work on an aircraft with a high speed and rate of climb, yet with sufficient range to intercept enemy attackers before they could reach their target. The final drawings were not for a pure delta-wing design but, like Lippisch's Messerschmitt Me 163 point-defence intercepter, were for a tailless monoplane with round-tipped, swept-back wings of very low aspect ratio. Like all delta-type designs it required a high angle of approach on landing, so the aircraft had a small tail wheel, built into a ventral fairing as well as the normal tricycle-type retractable landing gear.

Two prototypes designated XF4D-1 were ordered on December 16, 1948. The aircraft had, in fact, been designed around the untried Westinghouse J40 turbojet, but its development did not keep pace with that of the XF4D-1 and both the prototypes were fitted with 2268-kg (5000-lb) st Allison J35-A-17 jets, the air intakes being one each side of the fuselage, in line with the rear of the cockpit. The first flight was made on January 23, 1951, and the aircraft was named Skyray. Further test flights were made with the 3175-kg (7000-lb) st Westinghouse XJ40-WE-6 and the 5262-kg (11 600-lb) st (with afterburning) XJ40-WE-8 powerplant. With the latter installation a world air speed record of 1211.7 km/h (752.9 mph) was achieved during 1953, but since there were still delays with the production of the J40 engine Douglas decided to switch to the 6577-kg (14 500-lb) st (with afterburning) Pratt & Whitney J57-P-2 for the production aircraft which had been ordered. This powerplant was itself superseded on some later aircraft by the 4763-kg (10 500-lb) st J57-P-8B.

First flight of a production model was made on June 5, 1954. Deliveries to the US Navy and Marine squadrons did not commence until April 1956, although some 38 machines had been completed before this date and were awaiting a decision on the engines to be used. During 1956 production stepped up rapidly. Basic armament of the F4D-1 Skyray was four 20-mm (0.79-in) cannon in the wings, and although it was intended as an intercepter, provision was also made for it to carry 1814 kg (4000 lb) of bombs, rockets, missiles or jettisonable fuel tanks on six underwing stores points.

The Skyray more than proved itself in service as a fighter. It claimed international records for rate of climb and time to height, one of which was for a climb to a height of 15 240 m (50 000 ft) in 2.6 minutes from a static start. Production ended in December 1958 after a total of 420 aircraft had been built. Under the redesignation system of 1962 they became known as F-6As, although by this time they had been relegated to second-line duties with reserve wings. First-line operational service was shortened as a result of the long delay in the engine development, followed by the introduction of larger and heavier single-seat naval fighters, which could carry the larger, more advanced weapon loads and electronic equipment by then required.

The Douglas F5D-1 Skylancer, powered by a J57-P-12 turbojet, was one intended replacement for the Skyray. Sixty-seven were ordered, but only a few of these had flown when the plans for its development were cancelled.

(F4D-1) *Span:* 10.21 m (33 ft 6 in) *Length:* 13.92 m (45 ft 8 in) *Gross weight:* 11 340 kg (25 000 lb) *Maximum speed:* 1118 km/h (695 mph)

Skytrain, Douglas US name for Douglas C-47 transport aircraft See **Dakota**

Skywarrior, Douglas A-3

US carrier-based attack bomber. The advent of the jet engine and nuclear weapons towards the end of the Second World War opened up different design standards for all types of aircraft, allowing smaller aircraft to achieve adequate power and operational facilities. Proposals for a carrier-based strategic bomber were put to the Douglas company by the Bureau of Aeronautics on behalf of the US Navy in 1947, and Douglas produced a design within the next two years. It was for a high-wing monoplane with 36° sweepback and was of all-metal construction with the wing centre section passing through the fuselage over the internal bomb bay. It had a fully retractable three-wheel undercar-

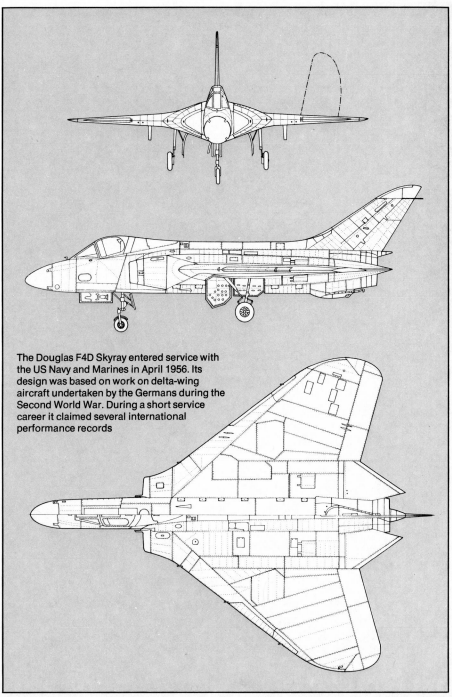

The Douglas F4D Skyray entered service with the US Navy and Marines in April 1956. Its design was based on work on delta-wing aircraft undertaken by the Germans during the Second World War. During a short service career it claimed several international performance records

SLAM, Vickers

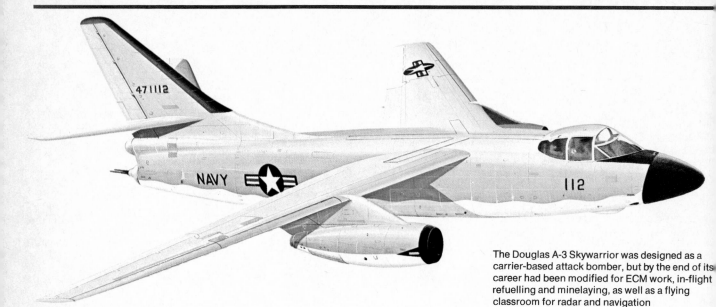

The Douglas A-3 Skywarrior was designed as a carrier-based attack bomber, but by the end of its career had been modified for ECM work, in-flight refuelling and minelaying, as well as a flying classroom for radar and navigation

riage. The engines were to have been two Westinghouse J40s, housed in pods, one under each wing. A pressurized cockpit was provided for the three-man crew and there was a remotely controlled gun barbette in the tail housing two 20-mm (0.79-in) cannon. An internal conventional or nuclear bombload of 5443 kg (12000 lb) could be carried. Two prototypes were ordered on March 31, 1949, designated XA3D-1, both of which were fitted with 3175-kg (7000-lb) st Westinghouse XJ40-WE-3 engines; the first one made its maiden flight on October 28, 1952.

The Westinghouse powerplant was proving troublesome and the J40 programme was eventually abandoned, but since orders for the Skywarrior had already been placed with Douglas it was decided to use two 4400-kg (9700-lb) st Pratt & Whitney J57-P-6 engines. Production models were designated A3D-1 and the first flight was made on September 16, 1953, full deliveries to the US Navy beginning to heavy attack squadron VAH-1 at the end of March 1956. Fifty of these aircraft were built. In 1962 they were redesignated A-3A, by which time they had been relegated to conversion training duties. The A3D-1 was used to evaluate the use of such a heavy aircraft from a carrier base: one was modified as the prototype of a photo-reconnaissance model, the YA3D-1P (YRA-3A); a further five were registered as four-seat YA3D-1Qs and A3D-1Qs (YEA-3A; EA-3A) with the tail barbette being replaced by an ECM (electronic countermeasures) installation. Some were later fitted with dual control trainers and redesignated TA-3A.

The main production version in the series was the Skywarrior A3D-2 (originally A3D-1B, later A-3B), powered by 5625-kg (12400-lb) st Pratt & Whitney J57-P-10 turbojets. Alterations were made to the weapons bay to enable a larger range of stores, including mines, to be carried. For in-flight refuelling a 4923-litre (1083-Imp gal) fuel tank could occupy the bay instead of weapons. This variant entered service in 1957 with VAH-2 and the production total of 164 machines eventually equipped eight heavy attack squadrons on the US aircraft carriers *Essex* and *Midway*. The specialized tanker version was known as the KA-3B, and about

30 other aircraft became multipurpose ECM/strike/tanker models designated EKA-3B, both these models seeing considerable service in the war in Vietnam. A few A-3Bs were fitted as VA-3B high-speed personnel transports.

Following the A3D-2 the navy ordered 30 A3D-2Ps (RA-3Bs). These had a redesigned pressurized fuselage/bomb bay, which could carry up to a dozen oblique and vertical cameras. They equipped heavy photographic squadrons VAP-61 and -62 which were embarked by carriers as and when required, operating in conjunction with the US Navy's carrier air wings. The largely similar A3D-2Q (EA-3B) variant flew for the first time on December 10, 1958. This also had a fully pressurized fuselage and carried four electronics engineers to operate the forward- and side-looking radar countermeasures and other electronic reconnaissance installations; 25 of these were built and served with the fleet reconnaissance squadron VQ-1 where required. After a first flight on August 29, 1959, 12 examples were built of the A3D-2T (TA-3B). They had a pressurized fuselage to accommodate the pilot, an instructor and six radar/navigation trainees. They saw service with VAH-3 and VAH-R123, together with A3D-1 (TA-3A) trainer conversions.

(A3D-2/A-3B) Span: 22.1 m (72 ft 6 in) *Length:* 23.27 m (76 ft 4 in) *Gross weight:* 37195 kg (82000 lb) *Maximum speed:* 982 km/h (610 mph)

SLAM, Vickers

British naval surface-to-air missile system. SLAM (submarine-launched airflight missile), based on the Short Blowpipe weapon, has been developed by Vickers Shipbuilding to allow submarines to attack fast patrol boats, hovercraft, hydrofoils, helicopters and merchant shipping. Development began in early 1968, and initial trials were carried out with the aid of a specially built land vehicle. A prototype system was then temporarily installed in HM Submarine *Aeneas* for testing and customer demonstrations; nine rounds were fired in October 1972, five of these scoring direct hits on floating and tethered airborne targets.

The cluster of six Blowpipes in their sealed launch tubes is mounted on top of a retractable mast in the submarine's bridge fin, which is elevated for firing. The missiles surround an optronics enclosure containing a television camera used for guidance and an infrared sensor to gather the rounds after launching. Targets are acquired with the aid of the submarine's attack periscope, the launcher mast is raised so that the head protrudes above the surface, and the operator searches for his objective. The missile is gathered automatically onto the operator's sightline and he then assumes command, using a joystick to steer the weapon. Manoeuvre instructions are transmitted over a radio link.

SLAM is known to have been fitted in the Israeli navy's German-built submarines, and the system may also have been supplied to other operators.

SLBM

Chinese submarine-launched ballistic missile. China is reported to be developing a two-stage SLBM powered by solid-propellant rocket motors, similar to early models of the US Navy's Polaris. The Chinese navy operates one submarine of the Soviet 'Golf' Class, which is equipped with three vertical missile-launch tubes, and is building nuclear-powered boats of indigenous design. Whether the latter can be armed with SLBMs or are intended solely for the attack role is not clear.

SLCM US submarine-launched cruise missile
See **Tomahawk**

Sleipner

Norwegian torpedo boat class, built 1935-40. Six light destroyers or torpedo boats were ordered from 1935 onwards: *Sleipner, Aeger, Gyller, Odin* and *Balder* from Horten naval yard, and *Tor* from Frederikstad Mekaniske Verkstad.

When Norway was invaded in 1940 *Sleipner* escaped to England, where she served in the reconstituted Royal Norwegian

Navy. *Aeger* was sunk by bombers at Stavanger on April 9, 1940, and *Balder, Gyller, Odin* and *Tor* all fell into German hands, the first-named being still incomplete at Horten. They were partially rearmed and were renamed *Leopard, Löwe, Panther* and *Tiger*. They retained one of the 100-mm (3.9-in) Bofors in Y position but the ones in A and X positions were replaced by 20-mm (0.79-in) AA guns, and the 40-mm (1.57-in) Bofors AA was suppressed. Towards the end of the war the torpedo tubes were removed.

In 1945 the German boats were ceded back to Norwegian ownership and were given their original names. With the *Sleipner* they served in the postwar navy. *Sleipner* was scrapped in the late 1950s but the other four were refitted as frigates (pendant numbers *F.301-304*), with three single US Navy 3-in (76-mm) AA, two 40-mm Bofors AA and a Hedgehog ASW weapon.

Displacement: 597 tons (standard), 708 tons (full load) *Length:* 74.1 m (243 ft 9 in) oa *Beam:* 7.8 m (25 ft 6 in) *Draught:* 3.7 m (12 ft) max *Machinery:* 2-shaft geared steam turbines, 25 000 shp=30 knots *Armament:* (in German service) 1 100-mm (3.9-in) DP; 2/4 20-mm (0.79-in) Flak 38 (2/4×1); 2 8-mm (0.315-in) MG 34 machine-guns (2×1); 2 53-cm (21-in) torpedo tubes (1×2) *Crew:* 72

Slinger

British catapult trials vessel. In 1916, the Admiralty invited tenders to design and construct various types of catapult gear for launching aircraft from ships. The Tyneside engineering firm of Armstrong Whitworth & company produced a simple compressed-air device which was accepted for trials aboard a newly built steam hopper barge, purchased in May 1917 by the Royal Navy for the purpose and named *Slinger*.

The catapult consisted of a 18.3-m (60-ft) box girder, supported above the hopper's well-deck by pillars and webs, down which a launching trolley was drawn by wires running back through sheaves to a pneumatically driven piston. The trolley, intended for launching floatplanes, was capable of reaching an end-speed of 96 km/h (60 mph) with a 2550-kg (5500-lb) load, the speed being varied by the pressure released by the piston.

The first dead-load trial was carried out in September 1917, in the Tyne, and after further trials using unmanned aircraft while alongside and underway, *Slinger* was transferred to the Isle of Grain, where the Royal Naval Air Service's shipboard flying experimental station had been taken over by the Royal Air Force. Fairey floatplanes were used for manned trials, with considerable success, but the catapult was not adopted for service at this time, the Royal Navy preferring to continue to use turret-mounted flying-off platforms. The latter could be readily dismantled and were cheaper and, as long as aircraft weights and takeoff speeds did not increase too much, gave the same results.

Slinger was taken out of commission early in 1919 and her catapult removed. In October of the same year she was sold commercially and employed for the miscellaneous cargo carrying for which she had been built.

Displacement: 875 grt *Length:* 59.6 m (195 ft 6 in) *Beam:* 10.8 m (35 ft 6 in) *Draught:* 4.4 m (14 ft 6 in) *Machinery:* 1-shaft vertical triple expansion, 10 knots *Armament:* none *Crew:* not known

Slugger

US tank destroyer. The first successful US tank destroyer was the M10, which used the M4 Sherman basic hull with an open-topped turret mounting a 3-in (76mm) gun. By late 1942 it was apparent that a better weapon than the 3-in was going to be needed, and work began on modifying the M10 to take a 90-mm (3.54-in) gun derived from the service AA gun. Since this gun weighed some 132 kg (290 lb) more than the 3-in, it would not balance properly in the turret without the addition of counterweights; this solution was adopted by the British Army when they fitted the 17-pdr gun into the M10, calling it Achilles, but the US Ordnance Department felt that a better solution would be a new turret with power controls and improved sights. In December 1942 the design was approved as the 90-mm Gun Motor Carriage T71, though the turret still had to have a large 'bustle' at the rear in order to balance the gun.

Pilot models were built, tested, modified and tested again, and in November 1943 Fisher Body, who were making M10A1s, were told to produce 500 T71s by converting M10A1s on the production line. By that time, though, much of the M10A1 production had gone too far to be modified, and Fisher were only able to make 300 T71s, which they completed in July 1944. To meet the demand, M10A1s were withdrawn from service and sent to Massey Harris to be converted, using turrets made by Fisher, and by the end of 1944, 500 conversions had been completed.

In July 1944 the design had been standardized as the M36, nicknamed Slugger, which entered service the same year, and after the invasion of Europe in June it became obvious that this was the only US tank destroyer capable of facing up to the German Tiger and Panther tanks. As a result, more production was demanded, and eventually 2324 vehicles were built. Subsequent modifications included the provision of a folding armour top for the turret, a muzzle brake on the gun, and an extended suspension and track to reduce the ground pressure. The M36 proved to be an excellent weapon, but some of the crews were too enthusiastic and tried to fight the vehicle as a tank rather than as a self-propelled gun. It was this, as much as anything, which finally convinced the US Army that tank destroyers, as such, were anachronisms, and that effort would be better spent producing tanks.

The M36 continued to serve with US forces until 1954, and was used in Korea. Many were exported, and some of those were still in use in the late 1970s.

Weight: 28.12 tonnes *Length:* 6.15 m (20 ft 2 in) *Width:* 3.05 m (10 ft) *Height:* 2.72 m (8 ft 11 in) *Armour thickness:* 102-19 mm (4-0.75 in) *Armament:* 1 90-mm (3.54-in) Gun M3; 1 0.5-in (12.7-mm) machine-gun *Powerplant:* Ford V-8 gasoline, 500 bhp at 2600 rpm *Speed:* 48 km/h (30 mph) *Range:* 240 km (150 miles) *Crew:* 5

S.M.72, Savoia-Marchetti

Italian three-engined high-wing monoplane bomber. The S.M.72 was in effect an enlarged militarized version of the S.M.71 airliner which operated on Ala Littoria domestic routes in the mid-1930s, carrying ten passengers in considerable comfort. The cantilever wing was of wood and the fuselage built up with steel tubing: both were fabric covered. The prototype first flew in 1934 and failed to impress the Italian air ministry, although it promptly established a payload-to-altitude record, lifting 5000 kg (11 023 lb) to 6400 m (21 000 ft).

The prototype was flown to the Far East and demonstrated to members of the Chinese Nanking government, who were anxious to build up their air arm to fight the Japanese aggressor, and 20 production machines for China were nearly all completed by the end of 1935. Powered by three 550-hp Bristol Pegasus II radial engines, they had dorsal and ventral defensive machine-guns and carried a substantial bombload internally. There is little evidence of large-scale operational use by the Chinese and it seems likely that they were employed as VIP or freight transports.

Span: 30 m (98 ft 5 in) *Length:* 19.3 m (63 ft 4 in) *Gross weight:* 12 773 kg (28 160 lb) *Maximum speed:* 295 km/h (183 mph)

S.M.79, Savoia-Marchetti Italian medium bomber   See **Sparviero**

The Savoia-Marchetti S.M.72 was ordered by the Chinese in the 1930s, but though it could carry a substantial bombload of up to 5000 kg (11 023 lb) it was used as a VIP transport

S.M.84, Savoia-Marchetti

S.M.84, Savoia-Marchetti

Italian medium bomber. In his design for a new bomber to replace the remarkable S.M.79 Sparviero, Alessandro Marchetti of the Società Italiana Aerei Idrovolante (Savoia-Marchetti) set out to eliminate the inherent faults of the earlier design. The S.M.84 prototype, serial number MM.22395, followed an experimental Sparviero fitted with a twin fin and rudder assembly. This was incorporated in the standard S.M.84 which also had a low-set, smooth upper surface to the fuselage. Upper defensive armament was provided by a Lanciani Delta E dorsal turret just aft of the pilot's cabin, with a 12.7-mm (0.5-in) Scotti-Isotta Fraschini machine-gun, the 360° firing arc being blocked only by the twin fins and rudders, but which could ward off attacking aircraft coming from immediately astern. Other differences from the S.M.79 included the location of the bomb-aimer's position, a retractable gondola being installed under the nose, rendering cooperation with the pilot easy at critical moments during an attack. The rear ventral gondola was thus small, containing only the free-mounted 12.7-mm machine-gun, for rear defence. The bomb bay was a new design, up to 1000 kg (2205 lb) of bombs being stowed horizontally instead of vertically. There was easy access from the pilot's cockpit right back to the two lateral defensive positions, each with a free mounted 12.7-mm gun.

Tests with the prototype were successful, following the initial flight on June 5, 1940, in the hands of the experienced Alessandro Passaleva, though weaknesses appeared when the early production machines went into service during 1941. The 1000-hp Piaggio P.XI radials, giving greatly increased overall power compared with the S.M.79, proved notoriously unreliable, and the relatively small surface area of the twin fins and rudders caused considerable instability, particularly at takeoff which was already fairly hazardous due to the high wing loading. Nevertheless, production continued and 309 S.84 and S.84 bis aircraft were built up to June 1943.

The 41° Gruppo Bombardamente Terrestre was the first to re-equip with the S.M.84, and after working up transferred to the island aerodrome at Gadurra in the Aegean. Thence they operated with limited success in both the bombing and torpedo-bombing roles. Like the S.M.79, the S.M.84 never used its theoretical capability of carrying two torpedoes. The 36° Stormo AS (Aerosiluranti, torpedo-bombers) which comprised the 108° and 109° Gruppi was next to convert to the S.M.84, its aircrew training in both conventional and torpedo-bombing techniques. Anticipating a heavily escorted British convoy from Gibraltar to Malta, the 36° Stormo moved to Decimomannu in Sardinia during September 1941. On September 27, the S.M.84s went into the attack. Six aircraft with experienced crews were lost, since the S.M.84s made their torpedo runs without air cover, and one British fighter was shot down. A considerable amount of damage was inflicted on the British vessels by the S.M.84s and other Axis aircraft, but the expected intervention by Italian ships never materialized. The greatest achievement by S.M.84s was heavy damage inflicted on the British

battleship Nelson, which was out of action for some six months afterwards.

During 1942 production switched to the S.M.84 bis, which differed from the S.M.84 in having wing dihedral and revised side glazed panels in the pilot's cabin, affording greater visibility downwards to the front and rear.

S.M.84s were issued to other Squadriglie and continued in the bombing and torpedo-launching roles up to the armistice of September 8, 1943. A number subsequently equipped transport units of the cobelligerent Italian air arm.

Span: 21.13 m (69 ft 4 in) *Length:* 17.93 m (58 ft 10 in) *Gross weight:* 13 288 kg (29 295 lb) *Maximum speed:* 432 km/h (268 mph) at 4000 m (13 000 ft)

S.M.85, Savoia-Marchetti

Italian dive-bomber. The prototype of this twin-engined single-seat shoulder-wing monoplane was flown by Adriano Bacula, the well-known Savoia-Marchetti test pilot, on December 19, 1936. Development was, however, rather protracted and a second prototype was not followed by the 32 series machines until 1939.

The S.M.85 was an all-metal aircraft, covered largely in plywood; it was nicknamed 'flying banana' owing to its rounded nose, deep fuselage beneath the raised, glazed pilot's cockpit and sharp taper thence to the extreme tail. It had the astonishingly poor armament of a single 12.7-mm (0.5-in) machine-gun fixed in the nose, and a single 250-kg (550-lb), 500-kg (1100-lb) or 800-kg (1764-lb) bomb was carried in the bomb bay. Power was provided by two 500-hp Piaggio P.VII RC 35 radial engines. The main wheels retracted backwards into the engine nacelles, remaining partially exposed, and the totally obsolete tail skid was retained.

When Italy entered the Second World War in June 1940, the S.M.85 was its only dive-bomber. It equipped the 96° Gruppo Bombardamento a Tuffo (dive-bomber group) which was moved forward to the island base at Pantelleria at the outbreak of hostilities. A number of inadequacies were soon apparent, and after two abortive missions the type was replaced by Junkers Ju 87s obtained from Germany. At the end of the second mission three aircraft jettisoned their 500-kg (1100-lb) bombs before landing, as the pilots were far from satisfied with the reliability of the S.M.85's undercarriage.

Span: 14 m (45 ft 11 in) *Length:* 10.5 m (34 ft 5 in) *Gross weight:* 4190 kg (9237 lb) *Maximum speed:* 368 km/h (229 mph) at 4000 m (13 000 ft)

S.M.1019A, Savoia-Marchetti

Italian general-purpose aircraft. In 1968 the Italian firm of SIAI-Marchetti of Sesto Calende undertook a redesign of the US Cessna O-1 Bird Dog liaison aircraft to extend its active life and the variety of roles in which it could operate. The result was the S.M.1019 which retained the general configuration of the original design, being a high-wing monoplane with a raised all-round-vision glazed crew canopy. The wing was braced either side by a single strut and the fixed undercarriage main wheels had single

cantilever struts. The tailplane was of a new design with angular surfaces and the nose was longer. Power was provided by a 317-shp Allison 250 B15G propeller-turbine engine, driving a three-bladed propeller.

The first of two prototypes flew initially on May 24, 1969, and extensive tests soon showed its superb qualities. It retains the excellent STOL characteristics of its predecessor and can carry a variety of loads on two underwing racks. These can include up to 225 kg (496 lb) of bombs or rockets, or alternatively two camera packs. The Italian army ordered 100 S.M.1019s in 1972, delivery being completed within two years.

Span: 10.97 m (36 ft) *Length:* 8.52 m (27 ft 11 in) *Gross weight:* 1270 kg (2800 lb) *Maximum speed:* 313 km/h (194 mph)

Smith

US destroyer class, built 1906-10. Following the lack of success with the *Bainbridge* Class the US Navy followed the lead of the Royal Navy and went for a slower but more robust hull. The five vessels of the *Smith* Class authorized in 1906-07, DD.17-21, had a raised forecastle for improved seaworthiness and 2 knots less speed than the previous class. They also introduced the well-known 'four-stacker' silhouette of the First World War.

Smith (DD.17), *Lamson* (DD.18)—built by Cramp & Son, Philadelphia
Preston (DD.19)—built by New York shipbuilding
Flusser (DD.20), *Reid* (DD.21)—built by Bath Iron works

They and their successors were known in the USN as the 'flivvers' after the Model T Ford. All except *Smith* had four widely spaced funnels, but *Smith* herself had the second and third funnels closer together. One 3-in (76-mm) gun on the quarterdeck was removed in 1918 to make way for depth-charge racks. All were sold for scrap in 1919, except *Smith*, which was sold in 1921.

Displacement: 700 tons (normal) *Length:* 89.5 m (293 ft 9 in) oa *Beam:* 7.9 m (26 ft) *Draught:* 2.4 m (8 ft) *Machinery:* 3-shaft steam turbines, 10 000 shp=28 knots *Armament:* 5 3-in (76-mm) QF (5×1); 6 18-in (46-cm) torpedo tubes (3×2) *Crew:* 86

Smith Gun

British Home Guard weapon. The Smith Gun, or Ordnance Smoothbore, 3-in (76-mm) Mark 1 was one of the many private-enterprise weapons which were developed in 1940, when numerous engineering concerns set about arming the Home Guard with home-made artillery. It was designed by a Mr Smith, Chief Engineer of the Trianco company, and was first tested in July 1940.

The gun consisted of a smoothbore barrel with a simple swinging-block breech, mounted through an axle which supported two large disc wheels. One wheel was concave on its outer face, the other convex; to place the gun into action, the whole equipment was tipped over onto the concave wheel, which then acted as a platform and allowed the gun to be traversed through 360°.

Smith & Wesson

The other wheel acted as an overhead shield, and a light steel shield between the wheels served to protect the gun detachment from frontal fire. The sights consisted simply of a V rear sight and four blades on the foresight to allow for aim-off against moving targets. The projectile was a cast-iron cylinder fitted with a percussion fuze and filled with explosive, and the propelling charge was contained in a shallow tin canister which used a 0.38-in (9.7-mm) revolver blank cartridge as the primer. On firing, the front section of the charge case detached from the rear section and followed the projectile up the barrel, acting as a gas-check.

The Smith Gun was turned down by the Directorate of Home Forces in September 1940 on the grounds that it was unsafe and did nothing which could not be done better by other weapons. But Smith improved the design, and early in 1941 the gun was officially adopted for the Home Guard. It had now acquired a hollow-charge antitank bomb, converted from the standard 3-in mortar shell, which gave it a good performance against armour. Formal approval for service with the army was granted in September 1941 and it was used by both army and RAF Regiment units guarding airfields in Britain. Its principal use, however, was with the Home Guard, and it was usually towed into action by a private car with a towing hook.

Although the Smith Gun looks somewhat comical, it was undoubtedly the best of the home-made weapons which were provided to the Home Guard during the war, and it was not declared obsolete until December 1945.

Weight in action: 274 kg (605 lb) *Length of gun:* 1.37 m (54 in) *Elevation:* −10° to +40° *Traverse:* 360° *Recoil system:* 11 rubber bands between barrel and axle *Projectile weight:* 3.63 kg (8 lb) *Muzzle velocity:* 122 m/sec (400 ft/sec) *Maximum range:* 457 m (500 yards)

The Smith & Wesson .45 M1917 revolver was a commercial .45 Hand Ejector model adapted to take the service .45 auto pistol cartridge

The Smith & Wesson .38 was also known as the 'British Military' or '38/200' Model and fired British 0.38-in (9.65-mm) ammunition

The Smith & Wesson .44 Magnum Model 29 fires a powerful cartridge developed by Remmington with a velocity of 470 m/sec (1540 ft/sec)

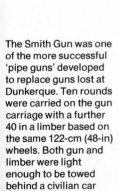

The Smith Gun was one of the more successful 'pipe guns' developed to replace guns lost at Dunkerque. Ten rounds were carried on the gun carriage with a further 40 in a limber based on the same 122-cm (48-in) wheels. Both gun and limber were light enough to be towed behind a civilian car

Smith & Wesson

US small-arms. The first Smith & Wesson revolver to attain military service officially (many of their 0.22-in (5.59-mm) pocket pistols were carried unofficially during the American Civil War) was the 0.44-in (11.2-mm) 'Russian' model of 1870. In 1870 the company had produced a .44 revolver with hinged frame and automatic extraction of the fired cartridge cases; this caught the eye of a Russian purchasing commission seeking a revolver to equip cavalry and artillery troops, and after requesting some modifications they ordered 215704 revolvers. The modifications were relatively minor, except for a major redesign of the ammunition in order to improve the accuracy and striking energy of the bullet. This enormous order kept the company occupied for five years but so tied up the manufacturing capacity that it left little to spare to deal with the home market; as a result, the Colt company reaped the benefit as the American West was being opened up. A .44 rimfire version of the Russian revolver was also manufactured for Turkey in the late 1870s.

The first orders from the US military forces came in 1900, when the US Army and US Navy each ordered 1000 0.38-in (9.65-mm) Hand Ejector models to be chambered for the .38 Long Colt cartridge. The Hand Ejector was a solid-frame double-action revolver which had the cylinder carried on a side-swinging 'crane'. By pressing a catch on the frame, the cylinder could be swung out of the frame and the empty cases ejected by pushing on the central ejector rod. To celebrate this order, and also the fact that these revolvers were being bought by police forces, the model became known as the Military & Police, and in slightly improved form it is still made today. Present versions are used by the US Air Force.

A heavier-calibre Hand Ejector was made in .44 rimfire chambering in 1908; the extra power of the cartridge led to the adoption of an additional locking catch, in the front of the frame, to hold the cylinder in place in addition to the existing front and rear catches. This led to the model being also called the Triple Lock and it was one of the finest revolvers in existence. In 1915 the British Army, anxious for more service revolvers, purchased 15 000 of these, chambered for the 0.455-in (11.6-mm) Webley cartridge. Unfortunately, service use showed that the triple lock was too delicate for the mud and dirt of the trenches, and only about 2000 of this type were made. The remainder reverted to the more simple double-lock pattern.

In 1917, when the US entered the First World War, the US Army were short of pistols and contracted with both Colt and Smith & Wesson for a supply of revolvers to be chambered for the standard .45 Colt Auto Pistol cartridge. Since this was a rimless case, it meant that the cartridges had to be loaded into the chamber linked together by half-moon spring clips into two groups of three. In this way the extractor plate had something upon which to act so as to eject the spent cases. In fact the Smith & Wesson revolver could be fired without the spring clips, since the chambers were bored with a slight step which halted the cartridge-case mouth and positioned the base correctly. These revolvers were modified .44 Hand Ejectors of the double-lock pattern and were officially known as the M1917 pattern; they were withdrawn to store after the war and re-issued in 1941, being principally used by military police and rear-echelon troops.

In 1940 the British Purchasing Mission ordered a .38 revolver, to be chambered for the standard British .38 200-grain bullet. Smith & Wesson made these by slightly modifying the current Military & Police model, and 1 125 000 were made for supply to British and Commonwealth forces. They remained in service for several years after the war and were very popular guns with their users.

A similar pistol produced for use by US forces, police and security agencies was the .38 Victory model, a wartime version of the Military & Police with a utility finish.

Early in 1939, with the prospect of war

The Smith & Wesson 9-mm (0.354-in) Light Rifle Model 1940 with the collapsible butt designed and developed by Enfield in 1942

The .44 American was similar to the Russian model which was ordered in vast numbers at the end of the nineteenth century for the Russian army

ahead, Smith & Wesson looked briefly at the submachine-gun market and then decided to make a self-loading carbine in 9-mm (0.354-in) Parabellum calibre. This was offered to the US Army who tested it and (foreseeably) rejected it, asking for a fully automatic .45-calibre version instead. Early in 1940 the gun was offered to the British; they rejected it at first on the grounds of fragility, but after some modifications had been made it was accepted by the Royal Navy in 1941. The number manufactured and supplied is not known, but is not believed to exceed 10 000; all the appropriate tools, gauges and surplus parts were sent to Britain with the guns, and the company took no further interest in the design.

The Light Rifle Model 1940 as it was known was a simple blowback weapon with a wooden stock; its only unusual feature was the magazine housing-cum-ejector tube. The forward half was a vertical chute down which the empty cases were ejected. As might be expected from Smith & Wesson, the standard of workmanship was of the highest order. A number of these weapons were converted to use a form of collapsible butt, designed and made in Enfield in 1942.

In the late 1960s the company briefly returned to the submachine-gun field with a modified Carl Gustav firing an electrically ignited caseless 9-mm cartridge, but the idea was not taken beyond the prototype stage.

(.44 Russian) *Calibre:* 0.44 in (11.2 mm) *Weight:* 1.14 kg (2 lb 8 oz) *Length:* 305 mm (12 in) *Barrel length:* 165 mm (6.5 in) *Magazine:* 6-round cylinder *Muzzle velocity:* 228 m/sec (750 ft/sec)

(.455 Triple Lock Hand Ejector) *Calibre:* 0.455 in (11.6 mm) *Weight:* 1.08 kg (2 lb 6 oz) *Length:* 298 mm (11.7 in) *Barrel length:* 165 mm (6.5 in) *Magazine:* 6-round cylinder *Muzzle velocity:* 182 m/sec (600 ft/sec)

(.38/200 British Service) *Calibre:* 0.38 in (9.65 mm) *Weight:* 680 g (1 lb 8 oz) *Length:* 258 mm (10.2 in) *Barrel length:* 127 mm (5 in) *Magazine:* 6-round cylinder *Muzzle velocity:* 200 m/sec (655 ft/sec)

(Model 1940 Light Rifle) *Calibre:* 9 mm (0.354 in) *Weight:* 3.92 kg (8 lb 10 oz) *Length:* 845 mm (33.3 in) *Barrel length:* 247 mm (9.7 in) *Magazine:* 20-round box *Muzzle velocity:* 378 m/sec (1240 ft/sec)

Snapper

Soviet antitank missile. The AT-1 Snapper was the Soviet Union's first operational ATGW, entering service in about 1960, and is comparable with the West's Nord SS.10 or Bölkow Cobra. The weapon is thought to be designated PUR-61 or 3M6 by the Soviet forces and to be known as Shmell (bumblebee). Snapper has been seen deployed on two types of vehicle: the GAZ-69 light cross-country type, which carried four rounds; and the triple-launcher BRDM-1 amphibious reconnaissance car. On the latter the missiles were protected by an armour casing when not in use, which slid down the sides of the vehicle to expose the launcher rails. The BRDM-1/Snapper combination has in most cases been superseded by the same type of vehicle armed with the later AT-2 Swatter or AT-3 Sagger. Although Snapper would normally be controlled by an operator sitting inside the launch vehicle, the missile could also be steered by means of a remote aiming unit up to 50 m (165 ft) from the launchers. An infantry-portable version may additionally have been deployed.

Snapper is powered by a single-stage solid-propellant rocket motor and is steered manually by the operator, who tracks the target with an optical sight, and moves a joystick to initiate commands for transmission down railing wires. Spoilers on the trailing edges of the cruciform wings steer the round in flight. Overseas operators have included most of the Warsaw Pact members, Yugoslavia, Mongolia, Egypt, Syria, Afghanistan and possibly Zaïre.

Length: 1.13 m (3 ft 8 in) *Span:* 75 cm (29.5 in) *Diameter:* 14 cm (5.5 in) *Weight:* 22.25 kg (49 lb) *Range:* 2330 m (2550 yards) *Speed:* 325 km/h (200 mph) *Warhead:* 5.25 kg (11.5 lb)

Snark, Northrop

US strategic cruise missile. The SM-62A Snark was one of the breed of long-range air-breathing missiles which proliferated in the 1950s. Their development was started at a time when the ballistic missile still had to prove its superiority, although the ICBM and SLBM later ousted most cruise missiles. Ironically, many of the advantages claimed at the time for 'unmanned bombers'—comparative cheapness and small size, for example—have since been resurrected to justify 1980s-vintage cruise missiles such as Tomahawk and ALCM-B. Snark was intended to be fired from fixed or mobile launchers on mass raids coordinated with manned bombers, the missiles both attacking enemy defences in the path of the bombers and striking major targets themselves. Much of this role was later to be assumed by the air-launched SRAM.

Northrop's work on guided missiles began in the mid-1940s, leading to Snark via a series of test vehicles. The SM-62A was of conventional aeroplane layout and construction, with a 45° swept wing carrying elevons for control; the tail comprised only a vertical stabilizer. The wings could be detached, allowing the weapon to be transported in a C-124 Globemaster cargo aircraft. Snark was fired from a zero-length launcher with the aid of two solid-propellant booster motors, each producing 59 000 kg (130 000 lb) of thrust for four seconds before being jettisoned. The missile would then climb to cruise altitude powered by a single Pratt & Whitney J57-P-17 turbojet running at 4770 kg (10 500 lb) thrust at sea level. Snark carried 2270 kg (5000 lb) of fuel in external pylon-mounted tanks, which were jettisoned when empty, plus 9525 kg (21 000 lb) internally—sufficient for a ten-hour mission.

Northrop also developed the stellar-updated inertial-guidance system, which was test-flown more than 200 times in North American B-45 bombers. A digital computer at the launch site fed preflight guidance information into the missile; this included instructions for the on-board star tracker, which continuously took celestial fixes on reference stars and compared them with the computer's predictions, allowing the guidance system to be updated. As the missile approached its target the nuclear warhead would have separated from the fuselage and followed a ballistic path to impact, leaving the rest of the body to break up in flight. In this way the designers avoided the need to stress Snark's structure for a terminal dive.

The SM-62A entered limited production at a rate of two missiles a month, although Northrop claimed that this could be raised to 36 per month without any increase in capacity being necessary. The first Snark unit, the 556th Intercontinental Guided Missile Squadron of the USAF's Strategic Air Command, was activated at Patrick AFB, Florida, in December 1957. The weapon was not deployed operationally until February 1961, however, when about 30 missiles of the 702nd Strategic Missile Wing were declared combat-ready at Presque Isle AFB, Maine. In his special defence budget message of March 28, President Kennedy directed that Snark should be phased out, as it was declared "obsolete and of marginal military value", and the operational missiles were deactivated in June of that year.

Length: 20.98 m (68 ft 10 in) excluding nose probe *Span:* 12.87 m (42 ft 4 in) *Weight:* 23 000 kg (50 000 lb) excluding boosters *Speed:* Mach 0.93 *Range:* 9660 km (6000 miles) *Warhead:* nuclear

Snipe, Sopwith

British fighter aircraft. The Sopwith 7F.1 was a single-seat fighter developed in 1917 to use the newly available 230-hp Bentley B.R.2 nine-cylinder rotary engine. The first prototype bore a strong resemblance to the Camel, though the fuselage was deeper in order to accommodate the bigger engine, and on the third prototype two-bay wings of increased span replaced the single bay wings the first two had inherited from the Camel. During trials in February 1918 this machine demonstrated a better rate of climb than the Camel and good manoeuvrability without the vices of the earlier fighter, and was selected for production as the Snipe Mark I in preference to a number of rival designs. Armament consisted of two Vickers machine-guns in a

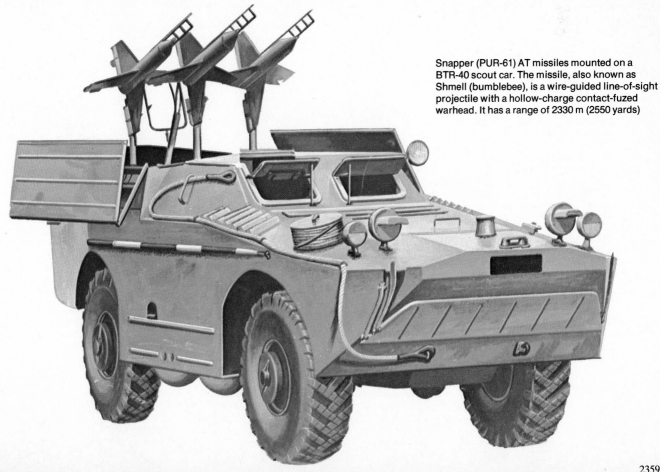

Snapper (PUR-61) AT missiles mounted on a BTR-40 scout car. The missile, also known as Shmell (bumblebee), is a wire-guided line-of-sight projectile with a hollow-charge contact-fuzed warhead. It has a range of 2330 m (2550 yards)

Snipe, Sopwith

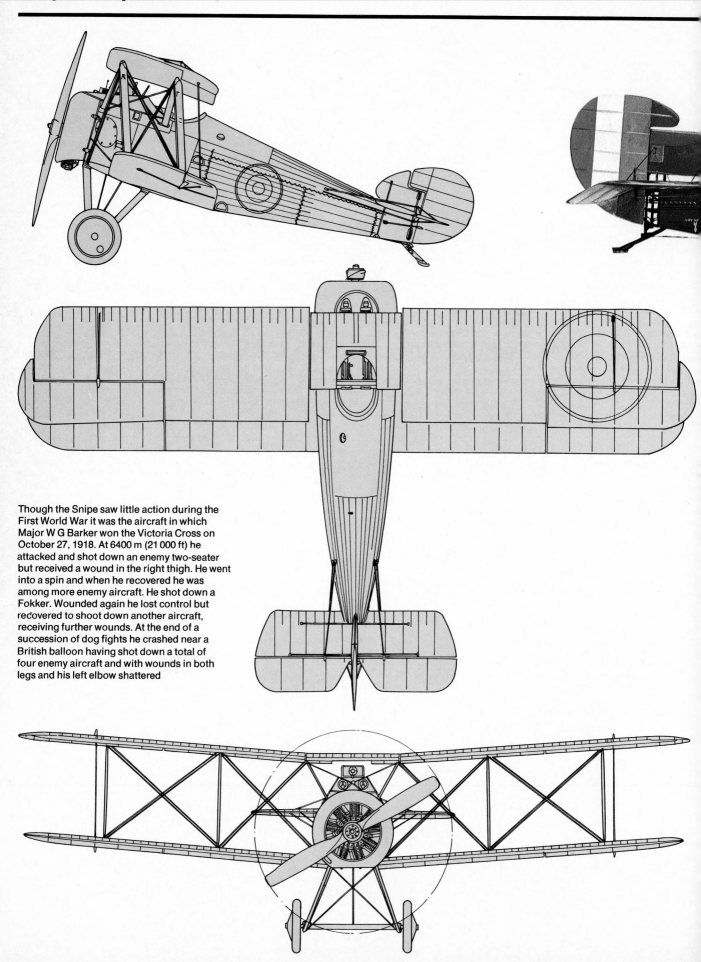

Though the Snipe saw little action during the First World War it was the aircraft in which Major W G Barker won the Victoria Cross on October 27, 1918. At 6400 m (21 000 ft) he attacked and shot down an enemy two-seater but received a wound in the right thigh. He went into a spin and when he recovered he was among more enemy aircraft. He shot down a Fokker. Wounded again he lost control but recovered to shoot down another aircraft, receiving further wounds. At the end of a succession of dog fights he crashed near a British balloon having shot down a total of four enemy aircraft and with wounds in both legs and his left elbow shattered

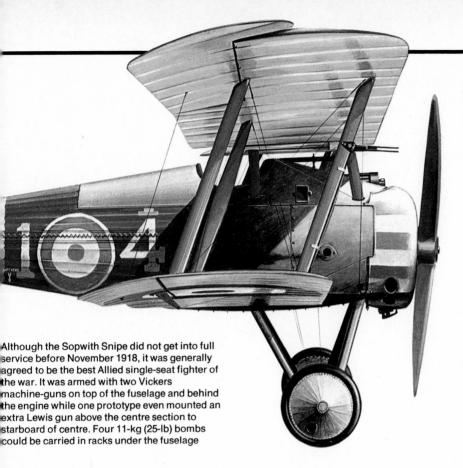

Although the Sopwith Snipe did not get into full service before November 1918, it was generally agreed to be the best Allied single-seat fighter of the war. It was armed with two Vickers machine-guns on top of the fuselage and behind the engine while one prototype even mounted an extra Lewis gun above the centre section to starboard of centre. Four 11-kg (25-lb) bombs could be carried in racks under the fuselage

hump-like fairing above the forward fuselage similar to that which had gained the Camel its name; an additional Lewis gun was mounted above the upper wing on the third prototype, but this secondary armament was eventually discarded. Four 9-kg (20-lb) bombs or one of 51 kg (112 lb) could be carried below the fuselage.

A special long-range version with additional fuel tankage and slightly swept wings was developed as an escort for the bombers of the Independent Force of the RAF on their long-range bombing raids. Designated 7F.1A, this variant had an endurance of four and a half hours against the three hours of the standard Snipe, and entered service in February 1919. Some experiments were carried out with navalized Snipes. One or two were fitted with flotation bags, hydrovanes, arrester hooks and other equipment for shipboard operation, but the Snipe never took the place of the Camel as a ship-borne fighter.

Another Snipe development was the Sopwith Dragon, which originated as a 320-hp ABC Dragonfly-engined Snipe in the spring of 1918. This had a top speed of 251 km/h (156 mph) and substantial numbers were ordered and built, but the type never achieved front-line service.

Over 1800 Snipes were ordered from several manufacturers during 1918, and deliveries to the RAF began in the summer of that year. By the end of October, however, only 97 had been delivered to France, equipping three squadrons, but by the end of the war these had done enough to demonstrate that the Snipe was the best Allied fighter of the war, and it remained in production and service after the war as the RAF's first standard fighter of the postwar period. It equipped a number of squadrons, serving both at home and in India, Egypt and Iraq,

and was not withdrawn from front-line service until 1926, though newer fighters such as the Siskin, Woodcock and Grebe had begun to replace it in 1924-25.

During its postwar service, some 40 examples were converted to two-seat dual-control trainers, and these remained in service even after the fighters had been retired.

Span: 9.17 m (30 ft 1 in) *Length:* 6.02 m (19 ft 9 in) *Gross weight:* 916 kg (2020 lb) *Maximum speed:* 195 km/h (121 mph)

SNCAC French fighter-bomber aircraft
See **NC 900**

SNCASE French naval fighter aircraft
See **Aquilon, Mistral**

SNJ, North American US Navy version of North American T-6 Texan basic trainer aircraft
See **Texan**

Snögg Norwegian missile strike craft
See **Storm**

Sola

The Sola submachine-gun was introduced in 1954 and manufactured by the Société Luxembourgoise d'Armes SA of Ettelbruck. The firm was one of many who tried to break into the potentially profitable postwar arms market, but there were too many submachine-guns being made at that time and the venture was a failure.

The Sola was a conventional gun offering very little that was not already well catered for in other designs. The only point of difference was that the number of parts was cut to 38, including all pins and springs. The

design was aimed at cheapness and simplicity of manufacture, and it used the greatest possible number of stampings and pressings. It was rather long and outwardly resembled the Belgian Vigneron, with a very similar telescoping wire stock, but the internal parts were different. One useful feature, probably copied from the US M3, was a dust cover over the ejection port with a safety stud on it so that the bolt was held when the cover was closed.

This model did not sell at all well, though some countries bought trials quantities, so the firm simplified the design yet further in 1957 and offered the result as the Light Model. In this they eliminated the dust cover, reduced the parts in the trigger housing still further, did away with the muzzle compensator, and generally sacrificed everything possible in order to cut down costs on the shop floor. The resulting gun was still perfectly practicable and would reputedly have cost less than $20 US each for a large order, though none was forthcoming. A few thousand guns are said to have been made for the FLN in Algeria before the firm abandoned arms manufacture.

(Sola Model Super) *Calibre:* 9 mm (0.354 in) *Ammunition:* 9-mm Parabellum *Weight:* 2.9 kg (6 lb 6 oz) unloaded *Length:* 889 mm (35 in) *Barrel length:* 305 mm (12 in) *Magazine:* 32-round box *Rate of fire:* 550 rds/min (cyclic) *Muzzle velocity:* 425 m/sec (1394 ft/sec)

(Sola Light Model) *Calibre:* 9 mm *Ammunition:* 9-mm Parabellum *Weight:* 2.72 kg (6 lb) unloaded *Length:* 789 mm (31.1 in) *Barrel length:* 200 mm (7.9 in) *Magazine:* 32-round box *Rate of fire:* 550 rds/min (cyclic) *Muzzle velocity:* 365 m/sec (1200 ft/sec)

'Soldati'

Italian destroyer class, built 1905-10. Two groups of boats were built by Ansaldo. The first group of six (*Artigliere, Bersagliere, Corazziere, Garibaldino, Granatiere* and *Lanciere*) had coal-fired boilers. The remaining four (*Alpino, Carabiniere, Fuciliere* and *Pontiere*) had oil fuel.

Pontiere ran aground off Sardinia on September 14, 1911, and had to be rebuilt and relaunched on November 1, 1913. The only war loss was the *Garibaldino*, sunk in collision with a British warship off Villefranche on July 16, 1918. They were all used on escort duty in the Tyrrhenian Sea and the Adriatic during 1915-18. *Artigliere, Bersagliere* and *Lanciere* were discarded in 1923, *Carabiniere* in 1925 and *Granatiere* in 1927.

Displacement: 400 tonnes (normal) *Length:* 65.07 m (213 ft 6 in) oa *Beam:* 6.11 m (20 ft) *Draught:* 2.11 m (6 ft 11 in) *Machinery:* 2-shaft reciprocating steam, 6000 ihp=28.5 knots *Armament:* 4 3-in (76-mm)/40-cal (4×1); 3 45-cm (17.7-in) torpedo tubes (3×1) *Crew:* 50-55

'Soldati'

Italian destroyer class, built 1934-42. A series of big destroyers based on the *Alfredo Oriani* Class was started in 1937, known as the 'Soldati' Class because they were named after warriors ancient and modern. The first group comprised 12 ships:

Solothurn

Alpino, Fuciliere—built by Cantieri Navali Riuniti, Ancona
Artigliere, Ascari, Aviere, Camicia Nera, Corazziere, Geniere—built by Odero-Terni-Orlando, Livorno
Bersagliere, Granatiere—built by Cantieri Navali Riuniti, Palermo
Carabiniere, Lanciere—built by Cantieri dell Tirreno, Riva Trigoso

They were big, handsome ships with a single wide funnel. All had twin 120-mm (4.7-in) guns forward and aft but Carabiniere, Camicia Nera, Geniere and Lanciere mounted a fifth single gun amidships. They were also provided with a 120-mm/15-cal howitzer for firing starshell, a feature unique to Italian ships of this period. The ships of this group were all completed in 1938-39.

A second group was started in 1940-41:

Bombardiere, Mitragliere—built by Cantieri Navali Riuniti, Ancona
Carrista, Corsaro, Legionario, Squadrista, Velite—built by Ordero-Terni-Orlando, Livorno

The hull was the same, and all were completed with the fifth gun amidships except Velite, which had four. Like the first group many had a set of torpedo tubes replaced by two additional 37-mm (1.46-in) AA and eight to ten 20-mm (0.79-in) AA guns were mounted on completion in 1942-43.

As with the rest of the Italian navy war losses were heavy. Alpino was sunk by bombing at La Spezia on September 19, 1943. Artigliere was sunk by British surface forces on October 12, 1940. Ascari was mined on March 24, 1943. Aviere was torpedoed by HM Submarine Splendid on December 17, 1942. Bersagliere was sunk by bombs in Palermo on January 7, 1943. Corazziere was scuttled at Genoa on September 9, 1943, and although refloated by the Germans was sunk again on September 4, 1944. Geniere was sunk by bombs in Palermo on March 1, 1943. Lanciere foundered in a storm on March 23, 1942. Bombardiere was torpedoed by HM Submarine United on January 17, 1943. Corsaro sank after hitting two mines on January 9, 1943. Squadrista was renamed Corsaro in July 1943, fell into German hands on September 1943 and was sunk by bombing on September 9, 1944. The incomplete Carrista had her bow cut off to repair the damaged Carabiniere and her stern cut off to repair Velite; the hull named TA.34 was scrapped by the Germans.

Seven of the class survived. Camicia Nera (blackshirt) had been renamed Artigliere after the downfall of Mussolini, and was ceded to the USSR in February 1949; as Z.12 she served in the Black Sea until about 1958. Fuciliere went to the USSR as the Z.20 in January 1950 and was scrapped about the same time as her sister. Legionario, Mitragliere and Velite were ceded to France in 1948 and renamed Du Chaffault, Jurien de la Graviere and Duperre; they served until 1954-61. Carabiniere and Granatiere were retained in the postwar Italian navy and were reclassified as frigates in 1957. Granatiere was stricken in 1958 but her sister was used to test new weapons.

Displacement:1715-1846 tonnes (normal), 2290-

Fuciliere and **Alpino**, two 'Soldati' Class destroyers of the Italian navy during the early years of the Second World War

2550 tonnes (full load) Length: 106.74 m (350 ft 2 in) oa Beam: 10.15 m (33 ft 4 in) Draught: 3.58 m (11 ft 9 in) Machinery: 2-shaft geared steam turbines, 50 000 shp=25 knots Armament: 4/5 120-mm (4.7-in)/50-cal (2×2, 1×1); 1 120-mm/15-cal howitzer; 1 37-mm (1.46-in)/54-cal AA; 8/12 20-mm (0.79-in)/65- or 70-cal AA (8/12×1); 6 53-cm (21-in) torpedo tubes (2×3) Crew: 216-219

Solothurn

Swiss small-arms. The Swiss company Solothurn AG was established by Rheinmetall in 1929 and functioned primarily as the development engineering plant for weapons designed in Germany by Rheinmetall. The majority of weapons so developed were marketed through the Steyr organization in Austria (and thus took the Steyr name) or appeared as Rheinmetall weapons after German rearmament had ceased to be clandestine. However, some weapons were produced and sold under the Solothurn name.

The Solothurn Model 1929 machine-gun was designed by Stange of Rheinmetall. It was a short-recoil gun, using a side-mounted magazine, and was the first production gun to be laid out in the straight-line configuration, with the stock a continuation of the line of the barrel and receiver. This reduced the tendency for the gun to lift its muzzle when firing automatic. Breech locking was done by a fermeture nut similar to that used on the light Hotchkiss machine-gun; the circular nut with interrupted threads surrounded the mouth of the chamber and was partially rotated by cams as the barrel recoiled. The bolt carried locking lugs which, when the nut was turned, could pass through the interrupted thread and thus chamber the cartridge. As the barrel returned to the firing position, the nut was turned and the lugs

locked the bolt to the chamber for firing.

Although the Model 1929 had some good points it did not sell, and Stange redesigned it to become the Model 1930 or MG30. This used a similar layout, but changed the bolt mechanism to use simple bolt rotation, controlled by cam grooves in the receiver. The barrel could be quickly changed by removing the butt, shaking out the bolt and barrel, and replacing a fresh barrel into the jacket. About 5000 of these guns were bought by Austria and Hungary in the late 1930s, many of the components being made by Steyr. A number were also bought by the German army but they were dissatisfied with it and asked Mauser to redesign it; this resulted in the MG34.

The Solothurn S1-100 submachine-gun was developed, also from a design by Stange, in 1929-30. It was subsequently marketed by the Steyr company and it is more often known as the Steyr-Solothurn gun. In outline it resembles the original Bergmann, with a wooden stock and perforated barrel jacket, side-mounted magazine and no pistol grip. The mechanism differs but slightly from the Bergmann, using a long recoil spring contained within the butt and controlling the bolt by means of a long metal arm. A sliding catch on the side of the stock fore-end allows single shots or automatic fire. An unusual feature of the S1-100 is the provision of a magazine filler in the magazine housing; most of these were chambered for 7.63-mm (0.30-in) Mauser or 9-mm (0.354-in) Mauser cartridges, which were normally supplied in ten-round chargers. So that these could be inserted quickly into the magazine, the top of the housing had a slot cut in it; the empty magazine could be clipped underneath and the chargers of cartridges inserted into the slot, the cartridges then being stripped down into the magazine.

S1-100 guns in 7.63-mm Mauser calibre were supplied to most South American countries and in small numbers to Japan; in 9-mm Steyr chambering it was supplied to the Austrian police, and in 9-mm Mauser calibre it became the MP34 of the Austrian army. The Portuguese army purchased them in both 7.65-mm (0.301-in) Parabellum and 9-mm Parabellum calibres, and the latter weapons were still in use in the 1970s by the Portuguese Guarda National and Guarda Fiscal.

In about 1930 Rheinmetall began work on antitank rifles and eventually passed this over to Solothurn; the result was the 20-mm (0.79-in) Solothurn S8-100 rifle. The weapon was a recoil-operated semiautomatic feeding from a ten-shot side magazine, and a number were sold to the Hungarian army. However, the performance was marginal at 600 m/sec (1968 ft/sec) muzzle velocity, and the weapon was redesigned to fire a more powerful cartridge. This became the S18-1000 model, which was adopted by the Swiss and Italian armies. It was fitted onto a variety of small wheeled carriages or could be carried in a convenient vehicle. Heavy and cumbersome, it was nevertheless an efficient weapon and was used by the Italians in 1940-41.

(MG30 machine-gun) Calibre: 7.92 mm (0.312 in) Weight: 10.59 kg (23 lb 6 oz) Length: 117.5 cm (45.8 in) Barrel length: 585 mm (23 in) Magazine: 25-round detachable box Rate of fire: 800 rds/min Muzzle velocity: 760 m/sec (2500 ft/sec)

(S1-100 submachine-gun) *Calibre:* 9 mm (0.354 in) *Ammunition:* 9-mm Parabellum *Weight:* 3.87 kg (8 lb 9 oz) *Length:* 850 mm (33.5 in) *Barrel length:* 195 mm (7.7 in) *Magazine:* 32-round detachable box *Rate of fire:* 500 rds/min *Muzzle velocity:* 380 m/sec (1250 ft/sec)

(S18-1000 antitank rifle) *Calibre:* 20 mm (0.79 in) *Weight:* 54.7 kg (120 lb 9 oz) *Length:* 216 cm (85 in) *Barrel length:* 142 cm (55.9 in) *Magazine:* 10-round detachable box *Rate of fire:* single shot *Muzzle velocity:* 832 m/sec (2730 ft/sec) *Weight of shot:* 150 g (5.3 oz) *Penetration:* 35 mm (1.4 in) at 300 m (330 yards)

Sólyom, Weiss-Manfred W.M.21

Hungarian tactical reconnaissance aircraft. The W.M.21 Sólyom (falcon) was descended from the famous Fokker C.V via the W.M.16 Budapest reconnaissance aircraft. Aircraft HA-SAI was modified as the W.M.16B and became the prototype for the W.M.21. Flights began in May 1937 and 36 production aircraft were ordered for the Hungarian air arm in July the following year, 12 to be built by each of three factories; Weiss-Manfred, MAVAG and MWG. Later orders brought total production to 128 machines, final deliveries being made in the spring of 1941.

The W.M.21 was an unequal-span single-bay biplane. The wings were of wood with plywood covering, and had N-bracing struts. The fuselage was a welded tube structure, again with plywood covering. The movable control surfaces were metal-framed and covered with fabric. The pilot's and observer/gunner's cockpits were in tandem, each with a plexiglas windshield, the observer's position had glazed panels in the fuselage sides and floor. The divided main undercarriage units each had three struts, that with the shock absorber being very long and connecting with the upper wing main spar. A tail wheel was discarded in favour of a tail skid to facilitate shorter landings. Power was provided by an 870-hp Weiss-Manfred W.M. K-14 radial engine in an NACA cowling driving a three-bladed propeller.

Defensive armament comprised two fixed synchronized Gebauer GKM 7.9-mm (0.311-in) machine-guns plus a further GEM 7.9-mm gun on a mounting operated by the observer/gunner. There were two small internal bomb bays, one for 12 10-kg (22-lb) antipersonnel bombs and the other for 120 1-kg (2.2-lb) incendiary bombs. There were no external racks.

W.M.21s served with six front-line squadrons of the Hungarian air arm. They first went into action against Yugoslavia in April 1941, and then the following June against the Soviet Union in support of the Hungarian VIIIth army corps. After a number of reconnaissance missions they were turned to bombing and ground attack as the Axis troops penetrated further into Soviet territory. Attrition was high, due more to accidents than to enemy activity. Later, Sólyoms were used to patrol the Hungarian border to prevent penetration by partisan units. Their last sorties were in August 1943. Gradually they were transferred to training duties and almost all were destroyed on the ground when the Germans withdrew from Hungary in the spring of 1944.

Span: 12.9 m (42 ft 4 in) *Length:* 9.64 m (31 ft 8 in) *Gross weight:* 3450 kg (7606 lb) *Maximum speed:* 320 km/h (199 mph)

Somers

US destroyer class, built 1935-39. *Somers* (DD.381) and *Warrington* (DD.383), two large destroyers or squadron leaders of the *Porter* Class, were redesigned to accommodate major improvements specified for the three ships DD.394-396 scheduled for Fiscal Year 35. A major effort was made to reduce topweight to allow offensive power to be increased over the *Porter* design, the torpedo reloading gear being omitted in favour of a third bank of tubes; the heavy tripods replaced by two pole masts, and the after director omitted. *Somers* and *Warrington*, built by Federal shipbuilding, Kearney, had quadruple tubes, but even a slight increase in beam was insufficient to offset the increase in topweight; *Sampson* (DD.394), *Davis* (DD.395), and *Jouett* (DD.396), built by Bath Iron Works, were reduced to triple tubes.

They were handsome single-funnellers, with a prominent boiler casing on which was placed the forward set of torpedo tubes. The problem of increasing antiaircraft armament was even more acute than it had been in the *Porter*s. In accordance with orders from the Chief of Naval Operations in September 1941, the after set of tubes was removed. It was hoped to fit a twin 40-mm (1.57-in) Bofors AA mounting in place of B 5-in (127-mm) gunhouse, but this was not done. Instead they underwent piecemeal conversion starting with the removal of the after superfiring 5-in twin mounting and the installation of two twin Bofors, offset to port forward and to starboard aft. A third twin Bofors was positioned behind B 5-in gun. *Davis* and *Jouett* were modified in 1944 with a single dual-purpose 5-in aft; *Davis* was also given a conical top to her funnel.

The five ships were all heavily involved in the fighting in the Pacific. *Warrington* foundered in a hurricane off the Bahamas on September 13, 1944, probably because of instability. The other four were sold for scrap in 1946-47.

Displacement: 1850 tons (standard), 2900 tons (full load) *Length:* (*Somers* Group) 116.2 m (381 ft 3 in) oa; (*Sampson* Group) 119.2 m (391 ft) oa *Beam:* (*Somers* Group) 11.1 m (36 ft 6 in); (*Sampson* Group) 11.3 m (37 ft) *Draught:* 5.4 m (17 ft 9 in) *Machinery:* 2-shaft geared steam turbines, 52 000 shp=37.5 knots *Armament:* 8 5-in (127-mm)/38-cal (4×2); 8 1.1-in (28-mm)/75-cal AA (2×4); 2 0.5-in (12.7-mm) machine-guns (2×1); 9/12 21-in (53-cm) torpedo tubes (3×3/4) *Crew:* 194-235

Somua

French tank. The Somua derived its name from the manufacturer, the Société d'Outillage Mechanique et d'Usinage d'Artillerie of St Ouen and it was built in response to a demand from the French cavalry. After being accepted for cavalry use, it was decided to adopt the design as the standard medium tank of the French army as the Char S-35, and eventually some 500 were built.

The Somua is generally considered to be the best prewar French tank design, though it

had some defects. The hull and turret were both cast, the first time this was done on a major production tank, and the turret carried a 47-mm (1.85-in) gun and coaxial machine-gun, the latter being unusual in having free traverse of some 10° away from the gun's axis. Mobility was also good, with a reasonably powerful engine and good suspension. But the cast hull was made up of three pieces, since casting the entire hull was beyond the company's ability, and a lucky shot on one of the joints could split the tank in half. The turret, as with all French tanks of the period, only accommodated one man who had to operate the machine-gun, load and fire the 47-mm gun, give orders to the driver and radioman, and command the tank in action. Neverthless, in 1940 the Somua was more than a match for any German tank and would have given a good account of itself but for the tactical ineptitude of the higher command.

An improved version, the S-40, was about to go into production when the German invasion took place in 1940. It had a more powerful engine and improved suspension but retained the defects of the S-35.

Weight: 20 tonnes *Length:* 5.46 m (17 ft 11 in) *Width:* 2.11 m (6 ft 11 in) *Height:* 2.69 m (8 ft 10 in) *Armour thickness:* 56-15 mm (2.2-0.6 in) *Armament:* 1 47-mm (1.85-in) gun; 1 7.5-mm (0.295-in) machine-gun *Powerplant:* V-8 gasoline, 190 bhp at 2000 rpm *Speed:* 37 km/h (23 mph) *Range:* 260 km (160 miles) *Crew:* 3

Sonar

Underwater sensor derived from the original Asdic of 1920. The pooling of Allied antisubmarine efforts in 1917-18 resulted in the passing of British secrets to the US Navy, and so the QB sonar set which came into service in 1931 followed the same lines as the British Asdic. However, the US Navy did not give priority to ASW in the 1930s and development lagged behind the British, particularly in the design of the dome.

After the entry of the United States into the Second World War this attitude changed rapidly, and after the war a great effort was put into finding an answer to the Soviet submarine fleet. Great emphasis was placed on big passive sonars for long-range detection in hunter-killer submarines and on bow sonars for surface escorts, but towed arrays and variable-depth sets have been developed as well. The variable-depth sonar can be streamed at a preselected depth to get below a thermal gradient which reflects transmissions from a hull-mounted sonar, while a towed array has the advantage of 'listening' well clear of hull and propeller noise.

The US Navy used the following systems:
BQQ-2: Made by Raytheon and introduced in 1960, it is an active/passive set used in nuclear submarines such as the *Tullibee* and the *Permit* Class. It contains a BQR-7 conformal hydrophone array.
BQQ-5: An improved version of BQQ-2 made by IBM and mounted in the *Los Angeles* Class nuclear submarines.
BQQ-6: A passive version of BQQ-5 used in the *Ohio* Class to come into service in 1979.
BQR-15: Towed passive array with BQR-23 processor, fitted in *Lafayette* SSBNs.
BQR-19: Short-range, rapid-scanning set for SSBNs introduced 1970.

Sonar

BQR-21: Digital multibeam steering (DIMUS), designed by Honeywell for SSBNs for passive detection.

BQS-4: An active/passive system introduced in 1955 for diesel/electric submarines and the older nuclear boats. It contains a BQR-2B passive array, and is made by EDO.

BQS-8, 14 and 20: Sets for navigating under ice and detecting mines, fitted in the newer nuclear submarines. Made by EDO and Hazeltine and introduced in 1960.

BQS-11, -12 and -13: Replaced BQS-6 as a spherical array in the bow dome of BQS-2 and -5. Introduced in 1960 and manufactured by Raytheon.

BQG-4: A fire-control system known as passive underwater fire-control system (PUFFS), and introduced in 1963 in GUPPY submarines and the *Permit* Class.

WAA: Wide aperture array, under development for future nuclear hunter-killers, with three widely separated arrays on either side of the hull.

SQQ-23: Passive/active integration retrofit, a modified SQS-23 introduced in 1972 for modernized *Charles F Adams* Class DDGs.

SQS-23: Made by Sangamo and introduced in 1958 for *Forrest Sherman* Class DDs, also fitted in attack carriers and cruisers.

SQS-26: Exists in various modifications for use in surface ships.

SQS-35: Variable-depth, used in *Knox* Class.

SQS-53: A version of the SQS-26CX digitally interfaced with the Mk 116 underwater fire-control system. Used in nuclear cruisers and *Spruance* Class.

SQS-56: Improved digital version of SQS-23, used in *Perry* Class frigates.

SQQ-14: Minehunting sonar.

SQS-14: To replace SQQ-14 around 1985. It has side-scan and other advanced features.

SQR-17: Acoustic processor for LAMPS.

SQR-18: Tactical towed array sonar (TAC-TAS) for passive long-range detection, used in *Knox* Class.

SQR-19: Improved TACTAS used in *Spruance* and *Perry* Classes etc.

After 1949 the Royal Navy also adopted the term sonar to conform to NATO terminology, and all current Asdic sets were included in the list. Following the Type 147, the last wartime set in service, the following sets are known to exist:

Type 184: Standard active/passive set fitted in *Rothesay*, *Leander* Classes and other frigates. Admiralty design.

Type 184M: Solid-state version of Type 184 developed by Graseby.

Type 193: The world's first minehunting set, capable of identifying and classifying objects on seabed. Fitted in *Shoulton* in the 1960s.

Type 193M: Improved version of 193 developed by Plessey. Used in *Brecon* Class MCMVs and West German *Lindau* Class.

Type 195: Helicopter-mounted dipping set developed from Plessey PMS26/27 range.

Type 2016: Hull-mounted multiple-frequency set used in *Broadsword* Class frigates.

Type 2020: Submarine-mounted, for new nuclear *Trafalgar* Class, to be retrofitted to *Superb* Class and back to *Courageous*.

It is interesting to see that the Royal Navy has never favoured the bow position for big sonars, for it is claimed that in rough weather the bulb lifts clear of the water and slams down violently. The only exception has been the 7.6-m (25-ft) diameter bow

A variable-depth sonar (VDS) partially deployed from the stern of HMS *Hermione*. Sonar equipment can be used for minehunting as well as for submarine detection

A US Navy SH-3D helicopter with a 'dunking sonobuoy'. Combined with A/S weapons these sonar receivers make the helicopter the submarine's most lethal enemy

dome fitted in HMS *Matapan*; this contained at least two big sets, believed to have led to the 2016 and 2020 sets coming into service in 1979.

The pioneers in variable-depth sonar were the Canadians, and the AN/SQS-505 series has been sold to the Netherlands and Belgian navies. Australia is producing the Mulloka sonar as US and British sonars are not suited to the range of temperatures and salinity found in the south-west Pacific. West Germany is also developing its own DSQS-21 BZ surface-ship sonar to cope with Baltic conditions, in its new *F-122* type frigates.

The other Western country pursuing an independent line of sonar research is France. French surface ships carry the very large DUBV-23/43, a combination of hull-mounted and variable-depth sets. The DUUA-2 series of passive sonars are made for submarines, and Thomson-CSF and CIT-Alcatel market many commercial derivatives of French navy sonars, as well as their own designs for small ships. The DUBM-21A is a minehunting sonar similar in conception to the British Type 193, and is used for the new Tripartite minehunter built in Belgium, France and the Netherlands.

The variable-depth sonar is considered by some navies to be more trouble than it is worth, with many yards of cable trailing astern and the risk of losing the 'fish'. The helicopter with a dipping sonar is claimed to be more effective, but many navies used both methods. Whereas sonar development was for many years under the patronage of navies, many commercial derivatives are now sold by firms like Graseby, Plessey, EDO, Raytheon, Westinghouse and Thomson-CSF

Sopwith British aircraft See **B.1, Baby, Camel, Cuckoo, Dolphin, Dragon, Pup, Salamander, Schneider, Seaplane, Snipe, Tabloid, Triplane**

Sopwith 1½ Strutter

British fighter and bomber. Deriving its name from the unusual W-strut arrangement that supported the upper wing above the fuselage, the Sopwith 1½ Strutter was a two-seat biplane designed by Herbert Smith for the

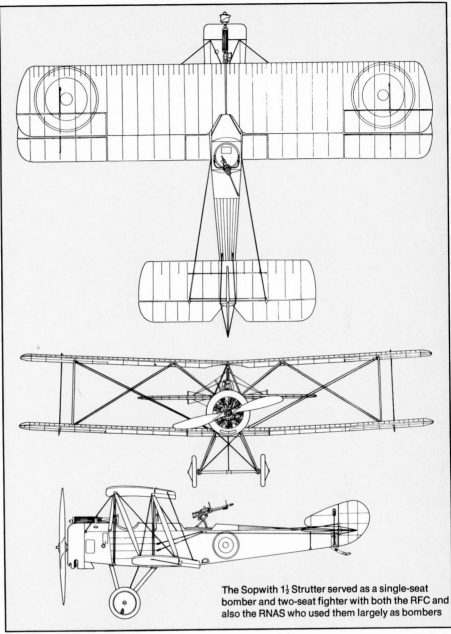

The Sopwith 1½ Strutter served as a single-seat bomber and two-seat fighter with both the RFC and also the RNAS who used them largely as bombers

The Sopwith 1½ Strutter was not only used by the RFC, but built in France and flown by the Russians, Belgians and Americans. The King of the Belgians flew over the front lines on July 6, 1917 in a 1½ Strutter piloted by Jacques de Meeûs, and Belgium's leading ace Willy Coppens scored his first victories in one

Royal Naval Air Service. The unarmed prototype was completed in December 1915 with a Clerget 9Z engine, and the first production aircraft for the RNAS appeared early in 1916, with armament of a single synchronized Vickers machine-gun above the engine and a pillar- or ring-mounted Lewis gun in the observer's rear cockpit. These entered service with the Admiralty designation Type 9700 in April 1916, serving as escort fighters and bombers with up to 73 kg (160 lb) of bombs.

With the introduction of the new Scarff ring mounting for the Lewis on early production aircraft the 1½ Strutter became the first British two-seat fighter to provide effective armament for both pilot and observer, as well as the first to enter service with a synchronized forward-firing machine-gun. The Scarff ring was such an improvement on earlier flexible machine-gun mountings that it remained in service almost until the start of the Second World War, while almost all the early British synchronizing mechanisms were fitted, the Scarff-Dibovsky type becoming standard on RNAS machines, while in RFC service the Sopwith-Kauper gear was generally used.

A single-seat conversion had the rear cockpit converted to an internal bomb bay for four 29.5-kg (65-lb) bombs; in this configuration a forward-firing Lewis with a single drum of ammunition was sometimes added above the upper wing, and the normal ammunition supply of 300 rounds for the Vickers was increased to 500 rounds. In this form the 1½ Strutter became one of the first strategic bombers, carrying out a number of raids against targets inside Germany from mid-1916. As well as serving on the Western Front, RNAS 1½ Strutters were used in the Aegean, Italy and Macedonia, and carried out antisubmarine patrols over Home Waters and in the Mediterranean. Others were modified for shipboard service aboard the aircraft carriers Furious, Argus and Vindex, while both single-seat and two-seat versions were carried on turret platforms by a number of battleships and battlecruisers.

During the build-up to the Battle of the Somme a number of 1½ Strutters were transferred to the Royal Flying Corps, and the type was subsequently ordered from several contractors for the RFC. The small numbers in service at the start of the Somme offensive on July 1 enjoyed a considerable degree of success as fighters, as well as carrying out bombing and reconnaissance missions, but by the following autumn were beginning to be outclassed by the new German Albatros and Halberstadt D-types.

Poor performance at altitude was partially remedied by the substitution of 130-hp Clerget 9B engines, and the type remained in service on the Western Front until mid-1917. Thereafter some were used for Home Defence, often as single-seaters with the pilot in the rear cockpit and one or two Lewis guns on Foster mounts above the upper wing replacing the forward-firing Vickers. The RAF's remaining 1½ Strutters were declared obsolete in 1921.

Altogether, almost 1500 1½ Strutters were built in Britain, of which the majority were used by the RNAS, but production on an even larger scale was carried out in France. The first examples to be used by the French

were transferred in the early autumn of 1916; at the same time production by Darracq, Hanriot, Lioré et Olivier and Sarazin began to get under way. An eventual total of 4500 were completed by French manufacturers, the single-seater being designated Sop.1B.1 and the two-seater Sop.1B.2. Powerplant was a 135- or 145-hp Clerget or 135-hp Le Rhône. Unfortunately, the bulk of these did not become operational with bomber and reconnaissance squadrons, until the second half of 1917, by which time they were becoming outclassed, and from January 1918 they began to be relegated to training duties, continuing in this role for a time after the war.

Over 500 1½ Strutters were supplied to the American Expeditionary Force in the spring of 1918, and while most were used for training a few were flown by operational units. After the war a small number were carried during exercises on US Navy battleships. Other users of the type included Belgium, Holland, Japan, Latvia, Romania, and USSR. The Belgian Aviation Militaire had three Escadrilles of 1½ Strutters, and a few were bought by Holland after being interned there during the war. Combat service in USSR included action with the British Expeditionary Force during the post-revolutionary civil war, when some were fitted with ski undercarriage, and with the Japanese forces during the intervention in Siberia in 1918.

(Two-seater, 110-hp Clerget) Span: 10.21 m (33 ft 6 in) *Length:* 7.7 m (25 ft 3 in) *Gross weight:* 1008 kg (2223 lb) *Maximum speed:* 161 km/h (100 mph)

Söridderen

Danish torpedo boat class, built 1911. A prototype, *Söridderen,* was ordered from Yarrow, followed by *Flyvefisken* and *Soulven* from Burmeister & Wain, Copenhagen to the same design. They were two-funnelled craft with a raised forecastle. Two single torpedo tubes were sided in the well between the forecastle and bridge, as in German torpedo boats. The other tubes were sited in the bow and sided on the upper deck aft, while the guns were mounted singly forward and aft. In 1920 the boats were renumbered *16 (Söridderen), 15 (Flyvefisken)* and *14 (Soulven)*; in 1923 they became *D.1-3* and in 1929 *O.1-3*. They were stricken in 1937.

Displacement: 271 tons (normal) *Length:* 55.4 m (181 ft 9 in) wl *Beam:* 5.5 m (18 ft) *Draught:* 1.9 m (6 ft 3 in) *Machinery:* 2-shaft steam turbines, 5000 shp=27.5 knots *Armament:* 2 75-mm (2.95-in) QF (2×1); 5 45-cm (17.7-in) torpedo tubes (1 bow, 4 deck) *Crew:* 33

Soryu

Japanese fleet carrier. The problem which exercised the minds of Japanese carrier designers was not so much the Treaty limitation on the tonnage of individual ships as the overall national limit for the type, in Japan's case 83000 tons. With 52900 tons used by *Akagi* and *Kaga,* considerable restraint had to be shown and after attempting the almost impossible with *Ryujo,* they were left with only 20000 tons. Two large ships were

included in the 1931-32 Imperial Japanese Navy Programme and one was laid down in 1934. The Japanese then declared their intention to withdraw from the naval treaties, so freeing themselves from restraint after December 31, 1936.

The 1934 ship had been designed with the limits in mind and her standard displacement was declared at just under 16000 tons. For such a light ship she was remarkably long and had two hangar decks, giving her a capacity of 63 aircraft, while maintaining a low profile, having a freeboard at the flight deck of only 12.8 m (42 ft)—the same as the British single-hangar *Illustrious* Class. The penalty was low hangar overhead clearance, with only 4.6 m (15 ft) in the upper hangar and 0.3 m (1 ft) less below. Three centreline lifts served both hangars and the wood-planked flight deck.

A cruiser hull of very fine form was used, with a waterline length to beam ratio of 10:1. The machinery was similar to that installed in the *Mogami* Class heavy cruisers, the 152000 shp giving a maximum speed of over 34 knots, making the carrier one of the fastest ever built. The light weight and high speed could only be obtained with some sacrifice, and in this case it was protection, for the only armour was 55-mm (2.17-in) plating over the magazines and 25-mm over the machinery; the 21.3-m (70-ft) beam did not permit any antitorpedo voids, and the only underwater protection behind the 46-mm (1.8-in) protective plate (not armour) on the waterline was a splinter bulkhead.

Named *Soryu* (grey-blue dragon), the carrier was built at the Kure navy yard, being launched on December 23, 1935 and completed just over two years later, on December 29, 1937. Armed initially with Mitsubishi A5M Claude fighters, Aichi DIA biplane dive-bombers and Nakajima B5N Kate torpedo-bombers, she was still equipped with Kates, but Mitsubishi Zeros and Aichi Vals were serving in the fighter and dive-bomber units.

With *Hiryu,* she formed Carrier Division 2 and after Pearl Harbor was in action at Wake Island, in the Netherlands East Indies, against Darwin and Ceylon, and took part in the fateful Midway operation. At 1026 hours on June 4, 1942, she was attacked by 17 Douglas Dauntless dive-bombers of USS *Yorktown's* Bombing Squadron 3 (VB-3), which scored direct hits with three 454-kg (1000-lb) bombs, on the centreline of the flight deck. The first bomb exploded in the hangar and lifted out the forward lift, the next set fire to the many aircraft on deck and the last exploded in the lower hangar, between the centre and after lifts. The fully fuelled and bombed-up aircraft, and the broken refuelling lines, stoked an uncontrollable blaze and the ship was ordered to be abandoned 20 minutes after the attack had begun. *Soryu* remained afloat for another eight hours and it was not until dusk that the fires reached her magazines and she blew up and sank, 314 km (195 miles) north-west of Midway Island.

Displacement: 15900 tons (standard), 19800 tons (full load) *Length:* 227.5 m (746 ft 6 in) oa *Beam:* 21.3 m (70 ft) wl, 26 m (85 ft 4 in) flight deck *Draught:* 7.6 m (25 ft) *Machinery:* 4-shaft geared turbines, 152000 shp=34.5 knots *Aircraft:* 63 *Armament:* 12 12.7-cm (5-in) DP (6×2); 28 25-mm (1-in) AA (14×2) *Crew:* 1100

Southampton

British cruiser class. The London Naval Treaty of 1930 restricted the total cruiser tonnage allowed to the major naval powers, and the maximum gun calibre in such ships to 6.1-in (155-mm). These limitations, which were in large part instigated by the British, were intended to bring a halt to the construction of the large 8-in (203-mm) gun cruiser type which the Admiralty had found to be too expensive to construct in sufficient numbers to meet the needs of the Fleet. Thus in the early 1930s the British began to construct small 6-in (152-mm) gun cruisers (*Leander* and *Arethusa* Classes) which were intended to provide the maximum number of ships possible within the overall treaty limit. The Japanese approached the problem in a completely different way, and instead of constructing small cruisers produced the *Mogami* design which carried 15 6.1-in guns on a displacement of 11 000 tons. The Japanese actually reported the displacement as 8500 tons which caused something of a stir and, despite the assurance from the Admiralty's design department that this was impossible, it seems that some were willing to believe that this figure was correct. The United States quickly reacted to the Japanese ships in producing the design for the *Brooklyn* Class (15 6-in guns, 10 000 tons) and the British soon felt compelled to follow suit.

The Admiralty's answer to the *Mogami* was the *Southampton* or 'Town' Class cruisers in which a smaller armament of 12 6-in guns was accepted, partly because of the ever-present need to produce numbers of ships, which necessitated a restriction in size, and partly because more guns than this was considered unnecessary. The new ships were given sufficient armour to provide defence against 6-in shells, a speed of 32 knots and displaced 9100 tons standard. The design was based on that of the Modified *Leander (Sydney)* Class and like those ships incorporated unit machinery but the increased size and markedly different profile with raked masts and funnels gave little indication of a connection. They were the first British cruisers to be designed with integral aircraft hangars (one being fitted on each side of the forefunnel) and a fixed cross-deck catapult—an indication of the increasing sophistication of naval aircraft. The main armament was mounted in the new triple Mk XXII turret, two forward and two aft, the guns having a designed rate of fire of 12 rds/min. In practice the rate of fire was about half this figure but it still gave the ships the capability of smothering a target with about 70 6-in shells per minute, and it was hoped that this would enable them to counter not only enemy 6-in gun cruisers but also the slower firing 8-in gun ships. The secondary armament consisted of four twin 4-in (102-mm) dual-purpose gun mountings fitted abreast the after superstructure while close-range AA defence was provided by a quadruple 2-pdr pom-pom mounted on the roof of each hangar and two quadruple 0.5-in (12.7-mm) machine-gun mountings fitted on the after superstructure. The main armament director was fitted above the bridge, a secondary emergency control position aft and an HA/LA director on each side of the bridge.

Two of the class (*Southampton* and *New-*

HMS *Glasgow*, a *Southampton* Class cruiser during the Second World War. She first saw action in the Norwegian campaign when she evacuated King Haakon following the German invasion

castle) were provided under the 1933 Programme and three more under the 1934 Programme. These five were laid down during 1934/35, launched in 1936 and completed in 1937. Another three, of slightly modified design (*Liverpool, Manchester* and *Gloucester*) were added under the 1935 Programme, laid down in 1936, launched in 1937 and completed in 1938. The last three were fitted with improved fire-control gear which included the addition of a second main-armament director aft, a new streamlined bridge with rounded front and machinery of 82 500 shp. They were also 300 tons heavier than the original ships and had 8 cm (3 in) more beam.

During the Second World War they saw extensive front-line service principally with the Home and Mediterranean Fleets, and they proved to be one of the best cruiser designs of the prewar period. *Southampton, Gloucester* and *Manchester* were lost. *Southampton* was heavily damaged and set afire during an air attack while escorting a Malta convoy on January 10, 1941. She had to be abandoned on the following day and was sunk by torpedoes from the cruisers *Gloucester* and *Orion*. On May 22, 1941, *Gloucester* was hit by four bombs and near-missed by three more during the battle for Crete and subsequently capsized and sank. *Manchester* was torpedoed by E-Boats during the night of August 12/13, 1942 while escorting the Malta convoy Pedestal. Extensive flooding was caused and she was rendered immobile and, as she was in enemy waters, the ship was abandoned and sunk with scuttling charges. Besides these losses *Liverpool* was out of action for a large part of the war owing to action damage. On October 14, 1940, while operating off Leros, she was hit in the bow by an aircraft torpedo. Extensive damage was caused by the detonation but worse was to follow. The torpedo explosion had damaged the aviation-spirit tank, positioned at the extreme forward end below water, and the bow structure was permeated with gasoline fumes. A short while after being hit these fumes were ignited by an electrical short circuit and the resulting detonation completely wrecked the fore end of the ship and left the remnants of the bow hanging into the sea. She was taken in tow by the cruiser *Orion* but progress was extremely slow until the bow finally broke away and sank. She was under repair until March 1942 but on June 14, 1942, she was again torpedoed while covering a Malta convoy. The torpedo struck abreast the after engine room, caused extensive flooding and put her machinery and steering gear out of action. She was eventually towed back to Gibraltar but on passage her damage was further increased by a number of near-miss bombs. Her repairs were completed by July 1943 but, presumably due to the manpower shortage, she was not commissioned and did not re-enter service until the war was over.

Early war modifications included the addition of between 6 and 9 20-mm (0.79-in) AA guns and the usual outfit of radar equipment for gunnery, air- and sea-warning (*Sheffield* became one of the first ships to be equipped with radar when she was fitted with an experimental air-warning set in 1938). During 1942-43 the 0.5-in (12.7-mm) guns were removed, and a number of twin 20-mm mountings substituted for some of the singles. In 1944 the need to still further improve the AA defence resulted in the removal of the aircraft equipment and X turret to provide the necessary space and weight. *Newcastle*, *Birmingham* and *Sheffield* received two extra and *Glasgow* and *Liverpool* four extra four-barrel pom-pom mountings while *Birmingham* and *Sheffield* also received two four-barrel 40-mm (1.57-in) Bofors. In addition the 20-mm armament was increased to between 11 and 18 guns per ship.

In most cases postwar service was limited to short periods and the class spent most of their time in reserve until sold for scrap during 1958-60. *Sheffield*, however, was extensively refitted during 1956-57 and was fitted with a lattice foremast, a uniform close-range armament of 18 40-mm (8×2, 2×1) and new AA directors. She therefore survived somewhat longer than her sisters and was not sold for scrapping until 1967.

Southampton—built by John Brown
Newcastle, Sheffield—built by Vickers-Armstrongs
Glasgow—built by Scotts
Birmingham, Gloucester—built by Devonport dockyard
Liverpool—built by Fairfield
Manchester—built by Hawthorn Leslie

Displacement: 9100 tons (load), 11 350 tons (full load) *Length:* 180.3 m (591 ft 6 in) oa *Beam:* 18.9 m (62 ft) *Draught:* 5.2 m (17 ft) *Machinery:* 4-shaft Parsons geared steam turbines 75 000 shp=32 knots *Protection:* 114 mm (4.5 in) sides, 52-25 mm (2-1 in) turrets, 38-25 mm (1.5-1 in) decks *Armament:* 12 6-in (152-mm) (4×3); 8 4-in (102-mm) (4×2); 8 2-pdr AA (2×4); 8 0.5-in (12.7-mm) AA (2×4); 6 21-in (53-cm) torpedo tubes (2×3) *Crew:* 750

Southampton, Supermarine

British general-purpose reconnaissance flying boat. The Southampton was one of the first new twin-engined flying boats to enter RAF service after the First World War. Developed from a civil type, the Supermarine Swan, to Air Ministry Specification R.18/24, it was built to carry a five-man crew. It had wooden framework and fabric covered wings, and the prototype and first six Southampton Mk I production models had a wooden hull. However, this proved unsatisfactory, and in the Mk II the hull was constructed from duralumin which considerably reduced the basic weight. The equal-span wings had vertical interplane bracing struts, with a stabilizing float beneath each outer bay.

Southamptons began entering RAF service in August 1925, with No 480 (Coastal Reconnaissance) Flight. They were powered by two 470-hp Napier Lion V engines, fitted halfway between the top and lower centre sections of the wings. Installed on removable mountings, each engine was a complete unit, with its own instruments, radiator, oil tank and cooler, and could be removed or replaced without disturbing the wing structure; the gravity-feed fuel tanks were situated in an accessible position beneath the upper wing. Armament comprised three Lewis machine-guns, each mounted on a Scarff ring, one in the front cockpit and the other two amidships. The bombload of 499 kg (1100 lb) was carried internally, and there was provision for one 18-in (46-cm) torpedo to be carried on each side of the hull. Two pilots sat in tandem open cockpits, with the navigational instruments in the rear one. Inside the hull there were cooking facilities and hammocks for use by the crew while the aircraft was afloat. When the metal-hulled Mk II entered service,

The Supermarine Southampton Mk 10 was powered by three Jupiter X engines and appeared in 1930. Though bearing the same name this aircraft differed considerably from all the other marks

metal wings were also developed, which could be interchanged with the existing type.

Whilst in service with the Royal Air Force during the late 1920s, Southamptons established many endurance records, perhaps the most famous being the Far East flight. Four Southamptons left Felixstowe on October 14, 1927, and followed an itinerary which took them to Australia via the Mediterranean, India and Singapore; after returning to Singapore they flew to Hong Kong and back again to Singapore. A total of 78 Southamptons were built, staying in service for more than 12 years. Eight of these were refitted with 450-hp Lorraine engines and exported to Argentina for naval use; others went to the Royal Australian Air Force and the Imperial Japanese Navy.

The Southampton IV, which first appeared in 1932, was a much modified aircraft powered by two 525-hp Rolls-Royce Kestrel IIIMS engines and became the prototype of the Scapa. The Southampton V of 1935 later went into production as the Stranraer.

(Mk II) Span: 22.86 m (75 ft) *Length:* 15.57 m (51 ft 1 in) *Gross weight:* 6895 kg (15 200 lb) *Maximum speed:* 174 km/h (108 mph)

South Carolina

US battleship class, built 1906-10. These two ships were designed as the first all big-gun battleships with no intermediate or secondary battery and so claim to be the first Dreadnoughts in the world. They were the outcome of a natural progression from heavy secondary batteries of 8-in (203-mm) guns, and adopted a uniform armament of four twin turrets in order to simplify long-range firing.

Although not as heavily armed as the *Dreadnought*, the arrangement of four twin turrets on the centreline was equally effective, for it gave the same broadside of eight guns. In only one respect were they inferior, with triple-expansion machinery instead of turbines. Like the British ship the anti-torpedo armament was restricted to 3-in (76-mm) guns, which proved rather light for the purpose, but as they were carried well clear of the waterline, at forecastle deck level between the funnels, they could be worked in rough weather.

Congressional approval for the ships was delayed, and so they were not laid down until two months after the completion of the *Dreadnought*. *South Carolina* (BB.26) was launched on July 11, 1908 by William Cramp and Son at Philadelphia, and *Michigan* (BB.27) was launched on May 26 the same year by the New York shipbuilding company. Their appearance was unique, with prominent caps on the two funnels, two 'cage' masts and staggered boat cranes. In the last two years of the First World War they mounted 3-in antiaircraft guns in place of searchlights on the after derrick posts.

South Carolina commissioned in March 1910 and took part in the annual manoeuvres and naval militia training. Between November 1910 and January 1912 she visited Europe with the 2nd Battleship Division and also took part in the 1911 Naval Review at New York. After a period of training cruises she was sent to the Gulf of Mexico to protect American interests. In 1914 she landed marines at Port au Prince, Haiti to protect the legation during unrest. She had recently completed a refit when war broke out in April 1917, and then became a gunnery training ship in Chesapeake Bay. In 1918 she was employed as an ocean escort for troop convoys to France, but had to return to the United States in September for repairs. After a further period on gunnery training she was used to repatriate troops from Europe; between February and July 1919, she made four trips and carried 4500 troops. After a period of training midshipmen she decommissioned at the end of 1921 and was stricken in 1924 and scrapped.

Michigan commissioned in January 1910 and went to the Caribbean for her shakedown cruise. In November 1910 she went on a two-month training cruise to Europe. In 1914 she was part of a squadron sent to Vera Cruz to land troops during a dispute with Mexico, and she landed a battalion of marines. In April 1917 she was with the Atlantic Fleet and was assigned to Battleship Force II. After a refit at Philadelphia navy yard in July she was relegated to training in Chesapeake Bay, but also escorted convoys leaving for Europe. In January 1918 her 'cage' foremast was flattened in a gale, killing six men. In December 1918 she was used as a transport, and from February to July 1919 she repatriated troops from France. She was stricken in October 1923 and scrapped at Philadelphia navy yard the following year.

Displacement: 16 000 tons (normal), 17 900 tons (full load) *Length:* 138 m (452 ft 9 in) oa *Beam:* 24.5 m (80 ft 3 in) *Draught:* 7.5 m (24 ft 6 in) *Machinery:* 2-shaft vertical triple-expansion, 16 500 ihp=18.5 knots *Protection:* 305-229 mm (12-9 in) belt, 305-203 mm (12-8 in) turrets *Armament:* 8 12-in (305-mm)/45-cal (4×2); 22 3-in (76-mm)/50-cal (22×1); 4 1-pdr (37-mm) QF (4×1); 2 21-in (53-cm) torpedo tubes (submerged, beam) *Crew:* 869

South Dakota

US battleship class, laid down 1920-21 but not completed. Construction of a class of very heavily armed battleships was

The USS *Michigan*, a *South Carolina* Class battleship. During a heavy storm in 1918 her forward lattice mast was so badly buckled that it was brought down on the deck. She was scrapped in 1924

authorized under the Navy Act of 1916. As first conceived they were to have been upwards of 80 000 tons, would have steamed at 35 knots and would have been armed with five triple 18-in (46-cm) gun mountings. The problems of docking such monsters and the fact that they could not pass through the Panama Canal resulted in a scaling down to half that size, and a speed of only 23 knots. Nevertheless they were the most powerful ships in the world, and were intended as part of a new navy which would wrest control of the seas from either the Germans or the British, whoever emerged victorious from the war.

Work was to have started in 1917, but construction was delayed because of the urgent need for destroyers. Six ships were laid down in 1920-21, *South Dakota* (BB.49) and *Indiana* (BB.50) by New York navy yard; *Montana* (BB.51) by Mare Island navy yard; *North Carolina* (BB.52) by Norfolk navy yard; *Iowa* (BB.53) by Newport News; and *Massachusetts* (BB.54) by Bethlehem.

The design was an expansion of the preceding *Colorado* Class, with triple 16-in (406-mm) guns in four mountings, double the installed power and heavier deck protection. They would have been the first US Dreadnoughts armed with 6-in (152-mm) guns, in double-storey casemates amidships. The preliminary model shows an ugly arrangement of four funnels, placed two abreast and trunked into one pyramid, but it might well have been modified as the design was not settled. Turbo-electric machinery was retained, with the boiler rooms outboard of the main engine rooms and the motor rooms aft. Two 28 000 kVA generators supplied 5000-volt current to four 11 200 kW motors, each coupled to a shaft. The unusual positioning of the boiler rooms was responsible for the unorthodox funnel arrangement.

When news of this class and the *Lexington* Class battlecruisers leaked out the Japanese weighed in with their own enlarged designs,

followed by the British in 1921. Faced by the prospect of a renewed arms race and by the likelihood of the new battleships being stopped by Congress the US Navy decided to call a halt through bilateral disarmament. Following the ratification of the Washington Treaty the first four ships were cancelled immediately in February 1922, although BB.53 and BB.54 were not cancelled until August 1923. They were broken up on the slipways, but some of the *Montana*'s plates were reported to have been used nearly 20 years later to protect the lock gates of the Panama Canal. The 16-in/50-cal guns were put into store for the next generation of battleships, and were considered for the *Iowa* Class in 1940 but not used.

Displacement: 43 200 tons (normal) *Length:* 208.5 m (684 ft) oa *Beam:* 32.3 m (106 ft) *Draught:* 10.1 m (33 ft) normal *Machinery:* 4-shaft steam turbo-electric, 60 000 shp=23 knots *Protection:* 343 mm (13.5 in) belt, 152-32 mm (6-1.25 in) decks, 457 mm (18 in) turrets *Armament:* 12 16-in (406-mm)/50-cal Mk II (4×3); 16 6-in (152-mm)/53-cal QF (16×1); 4 3-in (76-mm) AA (4×1); 2 21-in (53-cm) torpedo tubes (submerged, beam) *Crew:* 1616

South Dakota

US battleship class, built 1939-42. The design of this class was evolved in parallel with that of the *Washington* Class, as the 1939 battleships. Unlike the latter, they were intended to be protected against 16-in (406-mm) shellfire; but as they were under the constraints imposed by international treaty it was difficult to increase the weight of armour while retaining the same 28 knots speed and the nine 16-in guns of the *Washingtons*. The waterline length could be reduced to save weight, but improved protection demanded a beamier hull, and this in turn would need more power to achieve the same speed as before. The size of the machinery spaces was

South Dakota

USS *South Dakota* at sea in August 1943. After seeing extensive action in the South Pacific during the Second World War she was scrapped in 1962

successfully reduced, saving weight by having a shorter citadel. The shorter hull made for improved handling and manoeuvrability. The weight saved was used to increase armour protection and internal subdivision against torpedoes. In many ways the *South Dakota*s turned out to be the most cost-effective battleships built under the Washington Treaty limits, combining heavy armour, maximum armament and a reasonable turn of speed. Their main disadvantage was that they were too slow to work with the fast carriers, but this could not have been foreseen at the time of their design.

South Dakota (BB.57) was laid down at the Camden yard of New York Shipbuilding in July 1939; she was launched on June 7, 1941, and commissioned in March 1942. *Indiana* (BB.58) was laid down the following November at Newport News, was launched on November 21, 1941, and commissioned in April 1942. *Massachusetts* (BB.59) was laid down in July 1939 by Bethlehem at Fore River, launched on September 23, 1941, and

commissioned in May 1942. *Alabama* (BB.60) was laid down at Norfolk navy yard on February 1940, launched on February 16, 1942, and commissioned in August 1942.

South Dakota was sent to the Pacific soon after completing her shakedown, but grounded on a coral reef at Tangarebu in August 1942. Repairs were completed in time for her to take part in the Battle of Santa Cruz. On October 26, 1942, she claimed a record number of 26 aircraft shot down on the first occasion that proximity-fuzed shells were used at sea.

Her next action was the Battle of Guadalcanal on the night of November 14-15. She suffered a total loss of electrical power soon after the action started, when the blast of a 5-in (127-mm) gun mounting blew the ring main. Deprived of her radar, fire control and lighting, she blundered towards the Japanese battleline, and was soon engaged by the Japanese battleship *Kirishima* and the heavy cruisers *Takao* and *Atago*. She was saved by *Washington*, which fired steadily and exting-

uished the Japanese searchlights, allowing *South Dakota* to restore partial power and to fight back. She was hit 27 times by one 14-in (356-mm), 18 8-in (203-mm), six 6-in (152-mm), one 5-in and one of unknown calibre, but although damage was extensive it was superficial. She had 38 men killed and 60 wounded, and the damage took 62 days to repair. In 1943 she served in the North Atlantic with the British Home Fleet. On her return to the Pacific she took part in the operations against the Philippines, Okinawa

USS *Alabama* in 1945. Like her sisters, she supported US Navy carrier attacks on Japanese land targets during task force operations in the Pacific. At the end of the war she was decommissioned and handed over to Alabama as a state memorial. Since 1964 she has been anchored near Mobile

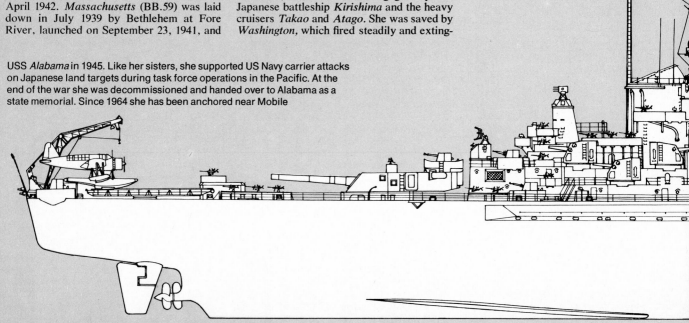

nd Iwo Jima, and bombarded the Japanese homeland.

Indiana replaced her damaged sister after he Battle of Guadalcanal, and covered the andings on Tarawa in 1943. In February 1944 he was badly damaged in a collision with *Washington,* and had to return to Pearl Haror for repairs. She returned in time for the ampaign against Hollandia and took part in he Marianas landings and the bombardment f Truk. With her sisters she was in action at he Battle of the Philippine Sea in June 1944, nd in 1945 covered the landings on Iwo Jima nd operations against the home islands.

Massachusetts was involved in the Allied nvasion of North Africa (Operation Torch), uring which she engaged the French battlehip *Jean Bart.* After a refit she went to the acific in 1943, taking part in operations gainst the Gilberts, Kwajalein, Truk, the arolines and Okinawa. She also took part in he Battles of the Philippine Sea and Leyte ulf.

Alabama, like *South Dakota,* served with he British Home Fleet in 1943 before being ent to the Pacific. In February 1944 during n engagement against Japanese aircraft one f her 5-in gun mountings inadvertently fired nto the back of another one, causing several asualties. Like her sisters she took part in he Philippine Sea and Leyte Gulf battles, nd covered operations in the Marianas and gainst the Japanese mainland.

The four ships were decommissioned early n 1947. In July 1954 a study was initiated to ind ways of increasing the speed of the *South Dakota*s and the *Washington*s. The roposal was to remove the after triple 16-in un turret to provide space for additional oilers. It was reported that 256 000 shp vould be needed to boost speed to 31 knots, ut in addition a major redesign of the after ull, rudders and propellers would have been eeded. As this would cost an estimated $40 nillion, excluding any updating of electronics r other systems on board, the project proeeded no further. All four were stricken in

1962; parts of *South Dakota* were salvaged for a war memorial, *Alabama* was preserved as a war memorial for the state of Alabama, *Massachusetts* was similarly saved by her name-state, but the other two were scrapped.

Displacement: 38 000 tons (standard), 44 000-45 000 tons (full load) *Length:* 207.3 m (680 ft) oa *Beam:* 33 m (108 ft 3 in) *Draught:* 11.1 m (36 ft 3 in) max *Machinery:* 4-shaft geared steam turbines, 130 000 shp=28 knots *Protection:* 311 mm (12.25 in) belt, 127-38 mm (5-1.5 in) decks, 457 mm (18 in) turrets *Armament:* 9 16-in (406-mm)/45-cal Mk 6 (3×3); 16/20 5-in (127-mm)/38-cal DP Mk 12 (8/10×2); 48/68 40-mm (1.57-in) Bofors AA (12/17×4); 40/52 20-mm (0.79-in) Oerlikon AA (40/52×1); 2 Kingfisher floatplanes, 2 catapults *Crew:* 2384

Spad VII

French fighter aircraft. Formed in 1915, the Société Anonyme pour l'Aviation et ses Dérivées preserved, and brought a new distinction to, the Spad acronym, previously applied to the prewar Société Provisoire des Aéroplanes Deperdussin (founded in 1910 as the Société pour les Appareils Deperdussin). Continuity between these companies was provided by Deperdussin's chief designer, Louis Béchereau, who became technical director of the 1915 concern. Béchereau had designed the prewar Deperdussin monocoque racing monoplanes, and it was a combination of his talents in 1915 with the extremely efficient V-8 aero-engine designed by Marc Birkigt of Hispano-Suiza that laid the foundation for one of the most famous lines of French fighters of the First World War. In the heyday of the rotary engine, Birkigt's water-cooled stationary engine, promising 150 hp in its early form, marked a turning point in aircraft powerplants. Its first alliance with a Béchereau airframe emerged in late 1915 in a tractor biplane known as the Spad V, forerunner of many thousands of Spads of various models to be turned out at the company's Surèsnes factory and elsewhere before the end of the war.

First of these to enter large-scale production was the Spad VII, whose prototype made its first flight at Villacoublay in April 1916, powered by a 140-hp Hispano-Suiza engine and armed with a single fixed, forward-firing 0.303-in (7.7-mm) Vickers machine-gun offset slightly to starboard in front of the pilot. In order to fire through the propeller disc, it had a synchronizing gear, also designed by Birkigt. An attractive, single-bay single-seat non-staggered biplane, the Spad

VII was of mixed construction (mainly wood and fabric), with a circular frontal radiator and characteristic louvred metal side panels enclosing the engine. It was quickly accepted by the French Aviation Militaire, which placed initial orders for 268 of the new fighters, fitted with the more powerful 150-hp Hispano-Suiza 8 Aa. In August 1916, one Spad VII (piloted by Lt Pinsard) was flown for operational evaluation on the Western Front, taking part in the Battle of the Somme. Official deliveries of the type began in early September 1916, initially to replace the Nieuport 11. Within a year some 500 had been built, and eventually French production reached about 5600, shared between eight factories. After the first batch, Spad VIIs had uprated (180-hp or 200-hp) Hispano engines, a slightly increased wing span of 8 m (26 ft 3 in), and larger rudders. Others were built in Britain, for the RFC and RNAS respectively, by the British Blériot and Spad (100) and Mann, Egerton (120) companies.

Although less nimble than the Nieuports which it replaced, the Spad VII was ruggedly built, could climb to 3000 m (9850 ft) in 15 minutes, and provided a steady gun platform. It equipped numerous French escadrilles on the Western Front, including the celebrated SPA 3 (*Cigognes,* cygnets) and French-built Spad VIIs were supplied to the Belgian Aviation Militaire (15), the Italian Corpo Aeronautica Militare (214), the Imperial Russian Air Service, and (in 1917-18) the United States (189). The British models in the end served only with the RFC (the RNAS exchanging its Spad VIIs for RFC Sopwith triplanes) but they arrived in France at a time when the British air forces had a particularly acute need to replace ageing and vulnerable pusher-engined aircraft. Three RFC squadrons in Mesopotamia also operated the type, some of which had the standard Vickers gun augmented by a wing-mounted Lewis of the same calibre. Other armament variations were seen in Russia, and some Russian airmen flew Spads carrying two strut-mounted Le Prieur rockets in addition to the fixed gun. Seven squadrons of the American Expeditionary Force received Spad VIIs, the rest of the US batch being sent across the Atlantic to serve as trainers.

Replacement by the Spad XIII began in mid-1917, but many of the earlier model survived the war. About 100, including rebuilt aircraft, went to the École Blériot flying school at Buc after the Armistice, and considerable numbers were exported postwar to Brazil, Greece, Peru, Portugal, Romania, USSR, Thailand and Yugoslavia. In 1917 one

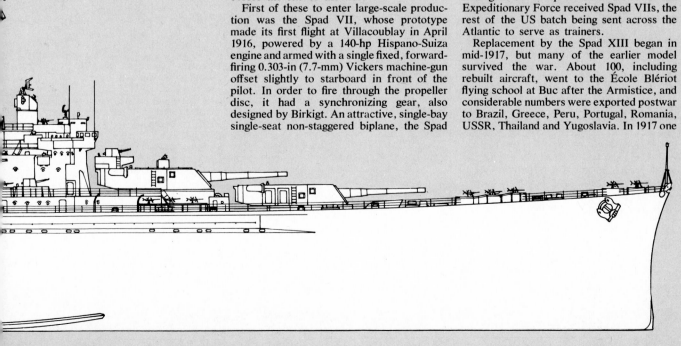

Spad XII

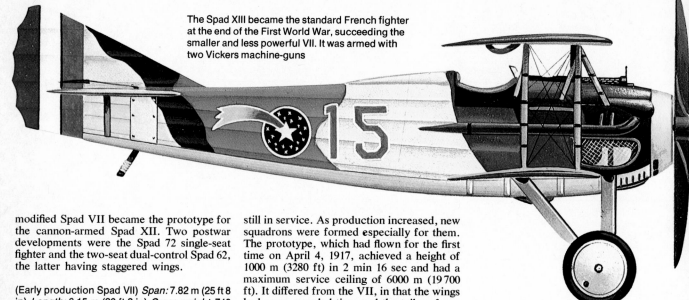

The Spad XIII became the standard French fighter at the end of the First World War, succeeding the smaller and less powerful VII. It was armed with two Vickers machine-guns

modified Spad VII became the prototype for the cannon-armed Spad XII. Two postwar developments were the Spad 72 single-seat fighter and the two-seat dual-control Spad 62, the latter having staggered wings.

(Early production Spad VII) *Span:* 7.82 m (25 ft 8 in) *Length:* 6.15 m (20 ft 2 in) *Gross weight:* 740 kg (1631 lb) *Maximum speed:* 192 km/h (119 mph)

Spad XII

French fighter aircraft. In January 1917, Captain Georges Guynemer of the French air arm suggested that the proven Spad VII be fitted with a 37-mm (1.46-in) cannon installed in the V-shaped space between the two cylinder banks of the Hispano-Suiza engine. This was to fire through the propeller disc and the existing synchronized Vickers 0.303-in (7.7-mm) machine-gun was to be retained. Thus equipped, the aircraft went for evaluation tests and was found to be satisfactory.

The XII had the same basic equal-span biplane configuration as the VII, being a single-seat single-engined aircraft with a fixed two-wheel front undercarriage plus a tail skid at the rear. The prototype, which made its maiden flight on July 5, 1917, became Guynemer's personal machine with which he achieved several scores against the enemy. The first machines off the production line were powered by a 200-hp Hispano 8 Bc V-type engine driving a two-blade propeller, but later a change was made to the 220-hp Hispano 8 Bec powerplant. On one of the later production models René Fonck claimed as many as 11 enemy aircraft destroyed.

Total production amounted to only 300 aircraft, built by the Blériot, Levasseur and Janoir companies. The major drawback of the Spad XII was the fact that the cordite fumes from the 37-mm cannon were likely to render the pilot unconscious. One aircraft was sold to the US in July 1918; the British Royal Naval Air Service acquired several Spad XIIs which they fitted with floats.

Span: 8.19 m (26 ft 10 in) *Length:* 6.3 m (20 ft 8 in) *Gross weight:* 835 kg (1841 lb) *Maximum speed:* 211 km/h (131 mph)

Spad XIII-24

French fighter aircraft series. Spad produced some of the most famous aircraft of the First World War, not the least of these being the XIII-24 series. Starting at the end of May 1917 the Spad XIIIs began to replace the VIIs

still in service. As production increased, new squadrons were formed especially for them. The prototype, which had flown for the first time on April 4, 1917, achieved a height of 1000 m (3280 ft) in 2 min 16 sec and had a maximum service ceiling of 6000 m (19 700 ft). It differed from the VII, in that the wings had more rounded tips, and the tail surfaces were enlarged. Increased power and range were provided by the installation of a 200-hp Hispano 8 B engine (in the initial production batch only) driving a two-blade propeller. Existing armament of a single Vickers 0.303-in (7.7-mm) machine-gun was supplemented by two more of the same type and calibre.

Aircraft of the second production run, started at the end of 1917, had less-rounded wingtips and were powered by the supercharged 220-hp Hispano 8 Be.

During the remainder of the war 81 French squadrons were equipped with Spad XIIIs, including some which were fitted with the 220-hp Hispano 8 Bec in 1918. As well as serving with two squadrons of the Royal Flying Corps, Spad XIIIs also served in two units of the Italian air arm. Thirty-seven were sent to Belgium, and after March 1918 a total of 893 served with the US forces; 435 of these were later re-engined with 180-hp Wright-built Hispanos and allocated to training duties as Spad 13Es.

Total production eventually reached 8440 machines at the time of the Armistice and outstanding orders for 10 000 more aircraft were cancelled. Six thousand of these had been for the US. Spad XIIIs were built by the Blériot, Levasseur, De Marcay, Kellner and Bernard companies. After the war, exports were made to Poland (40), Japan and Czechoslovakia, plus enough to equip three fighter groups for Belgium. A Rateau supercharger was fitted to one aircraft, which allowed the engine to retain full power at high altitudes.

The Spad X, a twin-float seaplane version of the Spad VII, came out in 1916, with a 180-hp engine. This became the prototype of the production model XIV, and it flew for the first time, off the Seine, on November 15, 1917. Production models, all built by the Levasseur company, were fitted with the 200-hp Hispano 8 Bc *moteur canon* engine, with one further machine-gun also fitted. The XIV had the same fuselage and wings as the XII, and was equipped with twin Tellier floats. Total production of this type was only 40 aircraft for the Forces Aériennes de Mer (French naval air arm), based on the northwestern coast of France, and they too were used in the fighter role. A prototype-only

variant of this was the Spad 24, a wheeled-undercarriage version intended for use on aircraft carriers, which made its maiden flight on November 5, 1918.

Produced as a fighter/photo-reconnaissance model, the Spad XVII was a modernized, stronger biplane version of the type XIII. Powered by a 300-hp Hispano engine, it had a maximum speed of 240 km/h (149 mph) and was designed by André Herbemant, who was to take over the continued development of Spad aircraft from Louis Béchereau. Twenty of these were built, some serving with the famous *Cigognes* Squadron. Two variants of this were developed, one being the Spad 21 of 1918, with modified wings and armament, but which was never built. (A racing seaplane built for the Schneider Trophy race of 1919 was also designated Spad 21.) The second variant was the Spad 22, the single example of which flew for the first time at Villacoublay towards the end of the war.

Another prototype was the Spad XVIII which was completed in April 1918 but never flew. It was a two-seat biplane fighter, with a distinctive swept upper wing (like the Spad 22) and ailerons on the lower wing only. The fuselage was of monocoque construction and the engine used was the 300-hp Hispano 8 Fbc *moteur canon*. Towards the end of the year the production version appeared, designated Spad XX, powered by 300-hp engine without the cannon, but armed with two forward-firing Vickers machine-guns and having a single Lewis gun in the rear cockpit. France received 100 of this model and a manufacturing licence was sold to Japan. After the war, when demand for such aircraft diminished, these and subsequent developments of the Spad XX were modified mostly for racing and the speed trials, which had their heyday during the 1920s.

(Spad XIII) *Span:* 8.05 m (26 ft 5 in) *Length:* 6.22 m (20 ft 5 in) *Gross weight:* 820 kg (1808 lb) *Maximum speed:* 222 km/h (138 mph)

(Spad XX) *Span:* 9.72 m (31 ft 11 in) *Length:* 7.3 m (23 ft 11 in) *Gross weight:* 1306 kg (2879 lb) *Maximum speed:* 217 km/h (135 mph)

Spad 51

French single-seat fighter aircraft. The Spad S.51 was built to a 1924 programme evolved by the French Air Ministry to replace the Nieuport 29 then in service. It employed a biplane configuration, with a straight leading edge and considerable sweepback on the upper wing, which had greater span than the lower wing. The staggered wings were of metal with fabric covering, and were braced with single I-struts either side. The rounded fuselage was of semimonocoque construction. Powered by a 420-hp Jupiter radial, the S.5101 prototype first flew on June 16, 1924. It was followed by the S.51-2 intended for the French 1925 fighter contest. It was not accepted by the Aéronautique Militaire, however, and 50 were exported to Poland, where they served with the 111th (Kosciusko) Squadron for several years.

Span: 9.47 m (31 ft 1 in) *Length:* 6.45 m (21 ft 2 in) *Gross weight:* 1311 kg (2890 lb) *Maximum speed:* 220 km/h (137 mph)

Spad 61

French single-seat fighter aircraft. Designed by André Herbemont, the prototype S.61 first flew on November 6, 1923. It was an unequal-span biplane, with staggered wings braced by I-struts and was powered by a 450-hp Lorraine water-cooled engine. The S.61-2 followed in 1924. It had a nose radiator and wooden wings with straight leading edges. Tests were impressive, and although no French orders were forthcoming Poland purchased 250 and Romania contracted to build 100 under licence at the I.A.R. factory to equip its air arm. A Polish S.61-2 won second place in the 1927 Coupe Militaire race over a specified circuit at Zurich. Poland also subsequently undertook licence production.

Experimental versions of the basic design included the S.61-3, S.61-4, S.61-5, S.61-6, S.61-7 and S.61-9. The Coupe Michelin was won by an S.61-6b in 1925 and an S.61-6d in 1927, both modified racing variants.

(S.61-2) *Span:* 9.53 m (31 ft 3 in) *Length:* 6.78 m (22 ft 3 in) *Gross weight:* 1531 kg (3375 lb) *Maximum speed:* 237 km/h (147 mph)

Spad 81

French single-seat fighter aircraft. The Spad S.81 biplane flew for the first time in prototype form on March 13, 1923, before either the S.51 or S.61. Like the Dewoitine D.1 parasol monoplane, it was built for the French air ministry 1922 fighter competition. In accordance with the basic requirement, it was powered by a 300-hp water-cooled Hispano-Suiza 8 Fb engine equipped with twin Lamblin radiators fitted under the nose. The unequal-span wings were braced with I-struts and had straight leading edges. As a result of tests, the Aéronautique Militaire accepted the S.81. Of the other competitors, the D.1 had slightly superior performance, but was felt to be insufficiently robust for escadrille service by the army due to its high-wing configuration. Eighty S.81s went into service from 1924, flying with the 2nd Regiment d'Aviation (Chasse) with headquarters at Strasbourg, and equipping the 5th Escadrille

The Spad 510 was armed with four machine-guns in the wings. It equipped French fighter units in the mid-1930s but by September 1939 it had been withdrawn for training and target defence

of the 2nd Groupe and the 9th Escadrille of the 3rd Groupe. Armament comprised two fixed light machine-guns in the cowling.

Variants tested included the S.81-3 (with retractable radiator), and André Herbemont produced the S.81*bis* racer, with reduced wing span and weight in 1923 with an eye to competing in the Coupe Michelin. Tests were disappointing, however, and the machine was subsequently converted into the S.61-6.

Span: 9.61 m (31 ft 6 in) *Length:* 6.4 m (21 ft) *Gross weight:* 1266 kg (2791 lb) *Maximum speed:* 245 km/h (152 mph)

Spad 510

French single-seat fighter aircraft. The Spad S.510 was a response to the requirements set out for a new fighter by the French Section Technique Aéronautique in 1930, which brought forth many contenders from the foremost firms in the home aviation industry of which the S.510 was the only biplane. The forward fuselage was built up of duralumin and steel and the rear fuselage was a duralumin monocoque. The equal-span metal wings were fabric covered. Wing bracing was by single I-struts either side and there was considerable sweepback on the upper wing leading edge. The fixed undercarriage struts were covered by fairings and the wheels were spatted. The water-cooled Hispano-Suiza 12Xbrs engine with a supercharger developed 690 hp and drove a two-bladed propeller. A frontal radiator was fitted. The pilot was accommodated in an open cockpit beneath the traditional cutout in the upper wing.

The first prototype flew initially on January 6, 1933, development having been delayed by negotiation of the prototype contract and financial problems faced by the parent Blériot company. Official tests showed poor longitudinal stability. The fuselage was therefore modified and slightly lengthened and the ailerons, fitted to both wings, were also altered. Some doubts had been cast on the newly revised prototype by service test pilots, but ace pilot Louis Massotte put the

aircraft through its paces on March 12, 1935, repeatedly pulling it out of spins with ease.

In order to determine whether series production should be started, the S.510 was tested against the low-wing Dewoitine D.510 and adjudged to be superior in manoeuvrability and angle of climb. As a result an official order for 60 aircraft was placed in August 1935. Series S.510s were armed with four MAC-1934 7.5-mm (0.295-in) machine-guns in the lower wings, as against the two synchronized guns of the prototype. In April 1937 the first fighter unit to equip with the S.510 was Groupe de Chasse II/7. By July the whole of the 7ᵉ Escadre had S.510s. Reports that several S.510s were supplied to the Spanish Republican government and served in the Civil War have never been confirmed. By the outbreak of the Second World War almost all the French S.510s had been relegated to flying schools and escadrilles regionales set up for target defence of cities and industrial complexes well behind the front line. The final Spad biplane was the single prototype S.710, with enclosed cockpit, retractable undercarriage and butterfly-type tail. It crashed on June 15, 1937, killing Louis Massotte.

(S.510) *Span:* 8.84 m (29 ft) *Length:* 7.46 m (24 ft 6 in) *Gross weight:* 1680 kg (3704 lb) *Maximum speed:* 372 km/h (231 mph)

Spada, Selenia

Italian surface-to-air missile system. Spada has been ordered by the Italian air force to defend its air bases and other important targets. The system comprises a search and interrogation radar associated with up to four tracking and illumination radars, each of which can be allocated three quadruple launchers. The missile is the Selenia Aspide, which is additionally used in the Albatros shipboard system and in the air-to-air role. A mobile version of Spada, known as Stiletto, was offered to the Italian army for defence of armoured columns but the Sistel Indigo-MEI has been selected in its place.

Spahi

Spahi

French destroyer class, built 1908-12. The need to improve on the 300-tonne type led to a new set of requirements being laid down in 1906. The first of these were seven ships of the new 450-tonne type. They worked out nearly 20% heavier than designed, and so were relatively slow.

Spahi—built by Forges et Chantiers de la Méditerranée, La Seyne
Hussard, Mameluk—built by Chantiers de la Loire
Carabinier—built by Penhoët, St Nazaire
Lansquenet—built by Dyle & Bacalan, Bordeaux
Enseigne Henry, Aspirant Herbert—built by Rochefort arsenal

The class was stationed in the Mediterranean from 1914. In May 1915 *Spahi* counterattacked a U-Boat attempting to torpedo the British cruiser *Amethyst. Carabinier* attacked *U21* in May 1915 near Gibraltar, while *Enseigne Henry* and *Aspirant Herbert* attacked the Austrian *U3* the following August. *Lansquenet* took part in the French raid on the island of Lissa (now Vis) in the Adriatic in November 1914. On the night of December 14, 1917 she, with *Spahi* and *Mameluk* sank *UC38* after the U-Boat had torpedoed the old cruiser *Chateaurenault; Lansquenet* and *Mameluk* then rescued over 1100 men, for which they were awarded the Croix de Guerre pendant. *Carabinier* was the only war casualty of the class, being wrecked near Lattakieh in Syria on November 13, 1918; she came under fire from Turkish artillery and had to be scuttled two days later. *Hussard* was condemned in 1922, but the others were not stricken until 1927-30.

Displacement: 530-550 tons (normal) *Length:* 64-65.8 m (210 ft – 215 ft 11 in) pp *Beam:* 6.05-6.6 m (19 ft 10 in – 21 ft 8 in) *Draught:* 2.5 m (8 ft 3 in) approx *Machinery:* 2-shaft reciprocating steam, 7500-9000 ihp=28 knots *Armament:* 6 65-mm (2.56-in)/45-cal Model 1902 QF (6×1); 3 45-cm (17.7-in) torpedo tubes, Model 1906 (3×1) *Crew:* 77-79

Spandau Popular name for German air-cooled aircraft-mounted version of the Maxim machine-gun   **See Maxim**

Spandau Allied nickname for Mauser MG42 machine-gun   **See Mauser**

Sparrow, Raytheon/General Dynamics

US air-to-air missile. Sparrow has proved to be one of the most accommodating missiles ever built, having evolved through beam-riding and active-radar versions in the United States to reach the later semiactive-radar variants; Britain and Italy have adopted the airframe as the basis of their Sky Flash and Aspide weapons respectively. Sparrow has additionally been developed for the surface-to-air role, both land-based and ship-borne. The AIM-7 (formerly designated AAM-N-6) Sparrow III model entered service as the AIM-7C in August 1958. The beam-riding AIM-7A Sparrow I had been deployed briefly

The French destroyer *Spahi*. She was one of seven ships built between 1908-12, all of which saw service in the Mediterranean during the First World War. *Spahi* assisted *Mameluk* when they sank *UC38* on the night of December 14, 1917 after the U-Boat had sunk the *Chateaurenault*

from 1955 on the US Navy's McDonnell F3H Demon fighters until replaced by the semiactive version. The active-radar AIM-7B Sparrow II was cancelled in 1957. The Sparrow III series has since progressed through the AIM-7D, -7E (Sparrow IIIB) and -7E2 to reach the -7F, an updated version developed for the new generation of USAF and USN fighters.

Sparrow is a single-stage missile powered by a solid-propellant rocket motor available from a number of sources; the AIM-7E can be fitted with an Aerojet Mk 52 or Rocketdyne Mk 38, while the longer-range AIM-7F uses either the Hercules Mk 48 or Aerojet Mk 65. The missile is steered by mid-body wings, and homes onto radar energy which is emitted by the launch aircraft and then reflected back from the target.

The -7F, development of which began in January 1972, entered service in the mid-1970s and incorporates a number of improvements. The maximum range is virtually doubled and a heavier warhead is carried, although the seeker is still not as advanced as those available in either Sky Flash or Aspide. This is to be rectified by the development of an advanced monopulse seeker (AMS), Raytheon having been selected as prime contractor for this homing head. The AMS, due to enter service in the early 1980s, will have greater resistance to electronic countermeasures and will allow Sparrow to snap down and intercept targets flying against a background of clutter.

Production of AIM-7F is shared by Raytheon and General Dynamics, with a total of some 19 000 rounds due to be built for the USAF and USN by 1985. Other missiles will be supplied for export. The AIM-7E version is operated by all users of the McDonnell Douglas F-4 Phantom and additionally arms the Aeritalia F-104S Starfighters of the Italian and Turkish air forces. The AIM-7F is replacing the earlier version on US fighters including the F-4 Phantom, F-14 Tomcat and F-15 Eagle, and is specified for the US Navy's F-18 Hornet.

(AIM-7E2) Length: 3.65 m (12 ft) *Span:* 1 m (3 ft 3 in) *Diameter:* 20 cm (8 in) *Weight:* 205 kg (450 lb) *Range:* 50 km (30 miles) maximum *Speed:* Mach 4 *Warhead:* 30 kg (66 lb) continuous-rod

(AIM-7F) Weight: 228 kg (500 lb) *Range:* 100 km (62 miles) maximum *Warhead:* 40 kg (88 lb) continuous-rod *(Dimensions* and *speed:* as AIM-7E2)

Sparrowhawk, Curtiss F9C

US Navy parasite fighter. The prototype of the Sparrowhawk was the XF9C-1 of 1930, designed to a Bureau of Aeronautics specification for a very small carrier-based fighter. In the event it was rejected by the US Navy as a carrier type, but at the time the new US Navy airships *Akron* and *Macon* were under construction. Their design incorporated a hangar and trapeze mechanism for carrying and launching fixed-wing aircraft, but no special aircraft had been designed for them: the hangar measured only 18.3×23.9 m (60×75 ft), and it appeared that the unwanted prototype might be a suitable fighter for the airships. Consequently, a second prototype, the XF9C-2, with a 438-hp Wright R-975-E3 Whirlwind engine, was begun by Curtiss. In October 1931 the first prototype began hook-on trials with an experimental trapeze fitted to the airship *Los Angeles*, and in the same month the second prototype was completed and six production F9C-2s were ordered. The first hook-up with *Akron* was made by the XF9C-1 in May 1932, and the following month the F9C-2 began preliminary trials with the airship.

Although a number of other types were used in trials, the Sparrowhawk was the only fighter to operate with *Akron* and *Macon*. Armament was two 0.30-in (7.62-mm) machine-guns. Once installed in the hangar they dispensed with their wheel undercarriage, and the large hook above and forward of the cockpit was their only means of recovery. No Sparrowhawks were aboard *Akron* when she was lost in the Atlantic in April 1933, but four were lost when *Macon* crashed and sank in the Pacific in February 1935, marking the end of the US Navy's aircraft-carrying airship programme. The three surviving Sparrowhawks were retained for a short time as utility aircraft.

Span: 7.75 m (25 ft 5 in) *Length:* 6.27 m (20 ft 7 in) *Gross weight:* 1256 kg (2770 lb) *Maximum speed:* 284 km/h (176.5 mph)

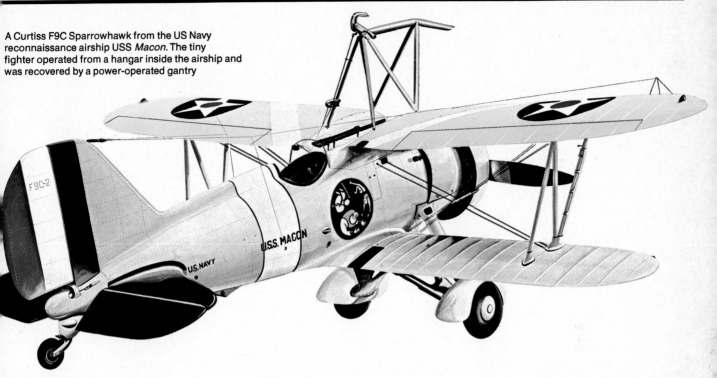

A Curtiss F9C Sparrowhawk from the US Navy reconnaissance airship USS *Macon*. The tiny fighter operated from a hangar inside the airship and was recovered by a power-operated gantry

Sparrowhawk, Gloster

British fighter and training aircraft. The name Sparrowhawk was given to three export versions of the Gloster Mars two-bay biplane, built for the air arm of the Imperial Japanese Navy in the early 1920s. The single-seat Sparrowhawk I (or Mars II) fighter is essentially the airframe of a Nieuport Nighthawk, with the latter's unsatisfactory ABC Dragonfly radial engine replaced by a 230-hp Bentley B.R.2 rotary. The RAF rejected it as a Snipe replacement since its performance was poorer, but 30 were supplied to the Japanese navy in 1922 for use as ship-borne fighters. In the same year these were joined by ten Sparrowhawk II two-seat trainers (Mars III) and ten Sparrowhawk III single-seaters, the latter similar to the Mk I but fitted with a hydrovane main undercarriage, and flotation gear to minimize the hazards of ditching in the sea. Armament of the two fighter models comprised a pair of fixed, forward-firing 0.303-in (7.7-mm) machine-guns, mounted in the upper engine decking to fire through the propeller disc. The Sparrowhawk I could climb to 3000 m (9850 ft) in 13 min 54 sec, and had an endurance of 3.2 hours.

Span: 8.53 m (28 ft) *Length:* 5.94 m (19 ft 6 in) *Gross weight:* 925 kg (2040 lb) *Maximum speed:* 195 km/h (121 mph)

Spartan, McDonnell Douglas

US antiballistic missile. The XLIM-49A Spartan was developed as the long-range exo-atmospheric intercepter for the Safeguard ABM system. In October 1965 Douglas was awarded a contract to develop an improved version of the DM15X-2/Nike Zeus missile, and by incorporating its experience gained during the earlier programme the company was able to deliver the first Spartan for firing trials beginning in March 1968 at Kwajalein Atoll in the Pacific.

Spartan was launched from a silo to intercept incoming warheads at altitudes of up to 480 km (300 miles). The first- and second-stage solid-propellant rocket motors, a Thiokol TX-500 and TX-454 respectively, boosted the weapon beyond the atmosphere, leaving the third-stage TX-239 to manoeuvre the missile for its interception. Spartan was guided by the missile-site radar (MSR), which simultaneously tracked both the missile and its target; the correct interception course was continuously computed, and steering instructions transmitted via the MSR. The thermonuclear warhead would have been detonated on command, also via the radar, its main destructive effect coming from hard X-rays.

In August 1970 Spartan intercepted its first operational-type target: a re-entry vehicle from a Minuteman I ICBM launched from Vandenberg AFB, 6760 km (4200 miles) away. A two-round salvo firing was successful in January 1971, and in December of that year a Spartan intercepted a dummy Polaris re-entry vehicle camouflaged by balloons and other penetration aids.

Length: 16.5 m (54 ft) *Span:* 3 m (9 ft 10 in) *Diameter:* 1.07 m (3 ft 6 in) *Weight:* 13 000 kg (28 600 lb) *Range:* over 640 km (400 miles) *Warhead:* 5-megatons thermonuclear

Sparviero

Italian auxiliary carrier. Just as British carrier successes in fleet actions led to the Italian navy's comprehensive conversion of a ship for the fleet carrier role (*Aquila*), so their successes escorting convoys to Malta (and the Italians' notorious lack of success on the Tripoli run) resulted in a ship being taken in hand to serve as an escort carrier. The ship chosen was the 30 418-grt *Augustus*, an 18-knot, diesel-engined transatlantic liner built in 1927 and similar in most respects to the *Roma*, which became the *Aquila*.

Augustus was taken in hand at Genoa in November 1942 and renamed *Falco*; not long

after, she was renamed *Sparviero* (sparrowhawk). In the ten months before the Italian armistice, work progressed no further than the removal of the superstructure and with the German occupation on September 9, 1943, all work ceased. A year later, on October 5, 1944, the ship was scuttled at the entrance to Genoa harbour in order to deny the port to the Allies.

It had been intended that *Sparviero* should be a flush-decked carrier, with a 150-m (492-ft) flight deck built as a roof over the narrow hangar, which was only 14 m (46 ft) wide for much of its length. A 4.9-m (16-ft) wide takeoff deck extended forward for 46 m (151 ft) from the flight deck to the bows, over the open forecastle. This unique arrangement would have had considerable limitations and would have been extremely dangerous with the wind anywhere but from dead ahead, and it may be that it was intended that a catapult should be fitted at some stage, at the after end of the runway. The hangar opened on to the large quarterdeck, which served as a handling area for seaplanes, lowered and raised by cranes at the after ends of the hangar structure. Two T-shaped lifts were installed.

To provide some protection for the machinery and magazines, as well as to maintain stability, a deep bulge was added below the waterline over the midships section on each side of the hull. No other protection was to be fitted. Armament consisted of six single 152-mm (6-in) low-angle guns, three on each broadside, and four 102-mm (4-in) guns of uncertain antiquity in AA mountings, two on the forecastle and two on the quarterdeck; 20-mm (0.79-in) cannon or 13.2-mm (0.52-in) machine-guns were to have made up the close-range automatic armament.

The original 28 000-bhp diesels were to have been retained, although it is unlikely that *Sparviero* would have been able to attain the liner's 18 knots. She was the largest ship to be taken in hand for conversion as an escort carrier and although the score or so of aircraft which she could have carried would

Sparviero

have been of value for convoy protection in 1941, by the end of 1942, Allied air supremacy over the Mediterranean would have allowed *Sparviero* only a brief life.

Displacement: 30418 grt approx (20000 tons standard) *Length:* 219 m (718 ft 6 in) oa *Beam:* approx 32.5 m (106 ft 8 in) over bulges *Draught:* 9.2 m (30 ft 2 in) *Machinery:* 4-shaft diesel motors, 28000 bhp=18 knots *Aircraft:* 15-20 *Armament:* 6 152-mm (6-in); 4 102-mm (4-in) AA

Sparviero

Italian hydrofoil class. The contract for the name-vessel of this class was placed in October 1970 and it commenced trials in May 1973. The design is closely based on that of the US *Tucumcari*. The design requirement was for a vessel capable of operating in a wide variety of environments on both offensive and defensive missions. The fully submerged foil system is used. When not in use the after foils fold back against the side of the hull. The bow foil retracts forwards into a recess in the bow to preserve the hull lines. With the fully submerged canard foil arrangement almost two-thirds of the dynamic lift is provided by the two after foils with the remainder by the bow foil.

The vessel is equipped with a fully automatic control system incorporating aircraft-type gyros to sense pitch and roll, and yaw, with accelerometers measuring heave or vertical motion. An ultrasonic height detector ensures that the craft maintains flying height above the water. All data from the sensors is fed to a computer which automatically controls the foil attitudes.

When foil-borne the ship is propelled by a powerful water jet powered by a Rolls-Royce Proteus gas turbine. The pump sucks in water through inlets on the noses of the after foils and expels it through twin nozzles beneath the hull under the pump. While hull-borne, propulsion is provided by a diesel engine which powers a retractable, steerable, fixed-pitch propeller outdrive unit mounted on the centreline of the transom. Trials have shown the craft to be easily capable of meeting performance and design requirements.

Sparviero is armed with an OTO-Melara 76-mm (3-in) gun forward and Otomat surface-to-surface missiles aft. Fire control is by an Elsag NA-10 system incorporating the Orion RTN-10X radar. The radius of action is 15400 nautical miles.

Six sister-ships are due to be completed by Cantieri Navale Riuniti between 1979-81.

Displacement: 62.5 tons *Length:* 22.9 m (75 ft 2 in) *Beam:* 7 m (23 ft) *Draught:* 4.4 m (14 ft 5 in), 1.5 m (4 ft 11 in) foil-borne *Machinery:* 1 Rolls-Royce Proteus gas turbine, 5000 hp=50 knots; 1 General Motors diesel, 160 hp *Armament:* 1 3-in (76-mm); 2 Otomat launchers *Crew:* 10

Sparviero, Breda Meccanica

Italian antitank missile. Sparviero is a third-generation antitank weapon being developed for service in the 1980s and is unusual in that it dispenses with the need for trailing wires to carry steering corrections from the operator's sighting unit; such commands presumably being transmitted over a radio link. The missile is normally fired from a ground-based tripod launcher weighing some 70 kg (154 lb) when loaded with a round, and the Officine Galileo guidance system is assumed to use the semiautomatic command to line-of-sight principle—an infrared sensor aligned with the operator's optical sight measures the angle between the missile and its target, with the aid of flares on the round, and a small computer calculates steering corrections for transmission to the weapon. Sparviero is powered by solid-propellant rocket motors and is planned to arm vehicles and helicopters in addition to its infantry role.

Length: 1.38 m (4 ft 6 in) *Span:* 53 cm (1 ft 9 in) *Diameter:* 13 cm (5.1 in) *Weight:* 16.5 kg (36 lb 6 oz) *Range:* 75-3000 m (82-3280 yards) *Speed:* 1045 km/h (650 mph) *Warhead:* 4 kg (8 lb 13 oz) hollow-charge

Sparviero, Savoia-Marchetti S.M.79

Italian medium bomber. The S.M.79·Sparviero (hawk) was the most famous and successful Italian military aircraft of the Second World War. It began as a design by Alessandro Marchetti of the famous firm of Savoia-Marchetti at Sesto Calende for a fast long-range record-breaking aircraft and was then adapted for military purposes as a conventional bomber, finally becoming the outstanding land-based torpedo-bomber of its epoch. The first S.M.79P, civil registration I-MAGO,

The Italian hydrofoil *Sparviero* at speed. *Sparviero* is capable of 50 knots and carries an armament of a single OTO-Melara 76-mm (3-in) gun with two Otomat surface-to-surface missiles. The Italian navy plan a fleet of eight craft, six of which were due for completion in the late 1970s

Italian Navy

The ship's view of the Savoia-Marchetti S.M.79 Sparviero, Italy's most successful torpedo-bomber. Working with German medium and dive-bombers, the Sparviero was used in skilful and courageous attacks against Allied convoys in the Mediterranean during the Second World War

The S.M.79 made its name as a torpedo-bomber but at the beginning of the war saw extensive action as a medium bomber in Europe and Africa

was first flown in October 1934, and the first military version, MM260, followed on September 2 the following year. Later that month the civilian prototype established world records over 1000 km (621.4 miles) and 2000 km (1243 miles) with 500-kg (1100-lb), 1000-kg (2205-lb) and 2000-kg (4410-lb) payloads, during the course of which it averaged 381 km/h (237 mph). Power was provided by three 750-hp Alfa Romeo 125 RC 25 radial engines.

The S.M.79 was of mixed construction, the fuselage being built up of welded steel tubing. Covering forward and over the upper mid-fuselage was of dural sheet, while the rest of the fuselage and tail unit were covered with plywood and fabric. The wooden three-spar wing was built as a single unit and contained ten tanks, which with two others in the engine nacelles had a total capacity of 2550 kg (5620 lb) (approximately 3650 litres [800 Imp gal]) of fuel. Camber-changing flaps were fitted to the inboard trailing edge, while the ailerons outboard could also serve as flaps. Stability at low speed was maintained by Handley-Page leading-edge automatic slots. Pilot and copilot were seated side by side in the glazed control cabin. Immediately behind them were the flight engineer (to port) and radio operator (to starboard). Modifications for the bombing role included a dorsal fairing immediately behind the pilot which gave the bomber a characteristic appearance and the nickname *Gobbo Maledetto* (damned hunchback). Fixed to fire forward from the front of the fairing was a single 12.7-mm (0.5-in) Breda-SAFAT machine-gun with 350 rounds of ammunition. At the rear of the fairing under a sliding panel was a dorsal 12.7-mm gun on a free mounting with 500 rounds. A ventral gondola behind the wings accommodated the bomb-aiming position forward, complete with Jozza bombsight and retractable metal-plated 'leggings' for use by the bomb aimer during an attack. In the rear of the gondola was located a free mounting for a further 12.7-mm gun with 350 rounds. A 7.7-mm (0.303-in) SAFAT machine-gun on a sliding free mounting in the rear fuselage could be operated either to port or starboard, firing through hatches in the fuselage sides. The eight-passenger cabin of the civil S.M.79 was replaced in the bomber by a bay which could take up to 1250 kg (2700 lb) of bombs stored vertically.

The civil S.M.79s had distinguished careers, breaking records and winning prizes for Italy. Five S.M.79Cs plus a single military S.M.79 with ventral gondola deleted, took part in the prestigious Istres-Damascus-Paris race on August 21-22, 1937. Opposed by the British D.H.88 Comet, several French designs and Fiat's B.R.20A, the S.M.79Cs took the first four places, the winners, Fiori and Lucchini in S.M.79C registered I-FILU (like the other aircraft, taking its registration letters from the first syllables of the crew's surnames) reaching an average speed of 424 km/h (263.5 mph). Later exploits included a flight by three S.M.79T (for 'transatlantic') variants with extra fuel tankage from Rome to Rio de Janeiro on January 24-25, 1938, in just 24 hours 20 min flying time. All the record-breaking S.M.79s adopted the *sorci verdi* insignia, featuring three green mice painted on the forward fuselage.

The military S.M.79 passed its tests with flying colours and the first series aircraft reached the specially redesignated Squadriglie Bombardamento Veloce (fast bombing squadrons) in late 1936. During 1937 three Stormi, each with four Squadriglie of S.M.79s, were operational in Spain supporting the forces of General Franco and making heavy attacks on Mediterranean ports in government (Republican) hands. Powered by three Alfa Romeo 126 RC 34 radials, each of 780 hp, these initial production machines reached a maximum 430 km/h (267 mph) at 4000 m (13 100 ft). Savoia-Marchetti sold 45 S.M.79s to Yugoslavia. They equipped 7th Bombing Wing and the 81st Independent Group, most being destroyed during the German-Italian invasion in April 1941.

The S.M.79B prototype, which shared the general lines of the S.M. 79 and its retractable undercarriage, was an attempt to satisfy would-be foreign customers who were prejudiced against the three-engined layout for a bomber. It had twin 1030-hp Fiat A.80 RC 41 radials and a streamlined, glazed nose. Three S.M.79Bs went to Brazil and four to Iraq, who operated them against the invading British in 1941. Romania bought 24 examples and then a further 24 S.M.79JRs. The latter lacked the ventral gondola (which in the S.M.79B merely accommodated the lower rear gunner, the bomb-aimer being housed in the nose along with a flexibly mounted defensive gun), incorporated an entirely redesigned fin and rudder, and was powered by twin Junkers Jumo 211D liquid-cooled engines, each of 1220 hp. Sixteen more S.M.79JRs were subsequently built in Romania by the I.A.R. factory at Brasov. The S.M.79JRs saw widespread use during 1941-42 on the Soviet Front.

Total S.M.79 production for the Regia Aeronautica was 1215. When Italy entered the Second World War on June 10, 1940, its 594 S.M.79s equipped 14 Stormi. They served first of all against France, attacking targets in the Mediterranean coastal belt, and also in North Africa. They had already participated in the annexation of Albania in 1939 and from bases there supported the invasion of Greece from October 1940 to April 1941, in which month they were also involved against the Yugoslavs. Four Stormi were engaged in North Africa supporting the initial Italian offensive against the British and then suffer-

M B Passingham

Sphinx

ing heavy losses during the two British offensives before the Germans took overall command. Only 12 S.M.79s were available in East Africa when war broke out there, but they were reinforced by aircraft flown in by stages from Italy. All were lost when the Italian front finally collapsed in 1941.

Main activities of the S.M.79s, however, were directed to the Mediterranean sector proper. They formed the backbone of attacks on Malta from bases in Sicily and made courageous and very effective torpedo attacks on convoys and Allied naval vessels. Later production S.M.79s were mostly fitted with three 1000-hp Piaggio P.XI RC.40 radials. As the war progressed, influence was placed increasingly on the Aerosiluranti units, whose S.M.79s carried a single 45-cm (17.7-in) torpedo slung under the fuselage, offset'to port. S.M.79s played a crucial role in a number of engagements, most famous of which was Operation Pedestal when 74 Sparvieri were thrown against 14 merchantmen and a powerful naval escort (which included three British aircraft carriers) attempting to reach Malta from Gibraltar in August 1942. The 132° Gruppo A.S. led by Capitano Buscaglia claimed direct hits on a British battleship, a carrier and a number of other vessels. Other carriers were damaged and five destroyers sunk by S.M.79s in the period up to September 1943 when Italy signed the Armistice with the Allies. Numerous merchant vessels were also successfully torpedoed.

After September 1943 the Aviazione della Repubblica Sociale Italiana, the 'rump' Fascist regime cooperating with the Germans in northern Italy, retained the S.M.79 as a torpedo-bomber and concentrated its activities in the Gruppo Buscaglia, named after the hero who had by then been killed in a takeoff accident. It took on charge a number of the final variant of the S.M.79, fitted with more powerful Alfa Romeo 128 engines and differing externally from its predecessors in having no ventral gondola. Some 50 of the type, sometimes known as the S.M.79-III, were completed. Based at the airfields of Venegono and Gorizia, the Gruppo suffered heavy losses on the ground to enemy bombing and in the air to enemy fighters, four being shot down on April 7, 1944 by USAAF P-47 Thunderbolts while making a transfer flight to Perugia airfield. Three days later the S.M.79 of Capitano Faggioni, commanding the Gruppo, was shot down by antiaircraft fire while attacking the Allied naval force supporting the Anzio landings, and the unit was thereafter named Gruppo Faggioni in his honour. S.M.79s moved to Istres for a night attack on Gibraltar on June 4-5, 1944, when four freighters were sunk and two others damaged. Final torpedo operations were in January 1945 when another merchant ship was sunk.

After the Second World War surviving S.M.79s flew supply and training missions. As late as 1950 three reconditioned Sparvieri were supplied to the Lebanese air arm for transport duties, and a number remained in Spanish service for several years after 1945. The Italian Aviazione Militare re-acquired from the Lebanon the sole surviving S.M.79, which went on display at the Museo Aeronautica at Vigna di Valle near Rome.

Span: 21.2 m (69 ft 7 in) *Length:* 15.6 m (51 ft 2 in) *Gross weight:* 10 500 kg (23 160 lb) *Maximum speed:* 430 km/h (267 mph) at 4000 m (1300 ft)

Sphinx

Netherlands torpedo boat class, built 1901-07. Three small torpedo boats, *Sphinx*, *Minotaurus* and *Python*, of Yarrow design were laid down at Flushing in 1901, followed in 1905 by three similar vessels, *Draak*, *Krokodil* and *Zeeslang*, from the same yard. They were generally similar to the *Ophir* Class, with two funnels, single guns forward and aft and two 45-cm (17.7-in) torpedo tubes on deck aft. The *Draak* group had a bow tube and only one deck tube.

Sphinx, *Minotaurus* and *Python* left for the Dutch East Indies in August 1903, and were joined there by the other three at the end of 1907. The *Sphinx* group were scrapped in the early 1920s, but the later three were still in existence in 1931, virtually unchanged apart from a bridge built against the forefunnel and a light signalling frame above it. They were scrapped in the mid-1930s.

Displacement: 103 tons (normal) *Length:* 39.6 m (130 ft) oa *Beam:* 4.2 m (13 ft 9 in) *Draught:* 2.1 m (6 ft 11 in) *Machinery:* 1-shaft reciprocating steam, 1200 ihp=24 knots *Armament:* 2 1-pdr (37-mm) QF (2×1); 2 45-cm (17.7-in) torpedo tubes (2×1) *Crew:* 20

Spica

Swedish fast patrol boat class, built 1962-66. Under the *Marinplan* for 1960 six gas-turbine driven torpedo boats were ordered for the Royal Swedish Navy. *Spica* (T.121), *Sirius* (T.122) and *Capella* (T.123) were built by Gotaverken at Gothenburg, while *Castor* (T.124), *Vega* (T.125) and *Virgo* (T.126) were built by Karlskronavarvet at Karlskrona.

New methods of production were developed for the class by Gotaverken. Sheet-metal jigs and a system of subassemblies were used to permit welding under cover. Each subassembly was about 7 m (23 ft) long, and was lifted onto a special building berth; the finished hull was then 'launched' by crane. The boats were powered by three Rolls-Royce (Bristol) Marine Proteus gas turbines developing 4100 shp each, to give fast starting and to save space.

The armament comprised six 53-cm (21-in) torpedo tubes firing TP 61 hydrogen peroxide torpedoes with wire guidance, backed up by a single Bofors 57-mm (2.24-in) gun forward. The gun is controlled by a Hollandse Signaalapparaten M22 fire-control system, with its distinctive radome above the bridge. Four 103-mm (4.1-in) rocket flare launchers are positioned on the sides of the wheelhouse, and six 57-mm flare-launchers are mounted on the gun shield.

In 1970-76 a further 12 modified vessels were built by Karlskronavarvet: *Norrköping* (T.131), *Nynäshamn* (T.132), *Norrtälje* (T.133), *Varberg* (T.134), *Västerås* (T.135), *Västervik* (T.136), *Umeå* (T.137), *Pitea* (T.138), *Lulea* (T.139), *Halmstad* (T.140), *Stromstad* (T.141) and *Ystad* (T.142). They differ from the original *Spicas* in having the Swedish-designed Philips 9LV200 fire control, which is much lighter and more compact, and its associated I-Band radar. They also have the latest model Bofors 57-mm gun, with a rate of fire of 200 rds/min, firing prefragmented proximity-fuzed ammunition to achieve a high kill rate against aircraft and missiles.

The whole class is to be converted to missile craft, with two twin Harpoon canisters mounted aft in place of the after pairs of torpedo tubes. A new Saab missile was under consideration, but it was discarded on grounds of time and cost.

Lulea, a *Spica* Class fast patrol boat of the Royal Swedish Navy. *Spicas* are armed with six wire-guided torpedoes with a radar-controlled Bofors 57-mm (2.24-in) gun and flare launchers

Displacement: 200-230 tons (standard), 230-260 tons (full load) *Length:* 41 m (134 ft 6 in) wl *Beam:* 7.1 m (23 ft 4 in) *Draught:* 1.6 m (5 ft 3 in) *Machinery:* 3-shaft gas turbines, 12900 shp=40 knots *Armament:* 1 57-mm (2.24-in) DP L/70; 6 53-cm (21-in) torpedo tubes (6×1) *Crew:* 28

Spinne

German wire-guided torpedo. Spinne (spider) was a coast-defence weapon, intended to be controlled from a shore station. A fine insulated wire was paid out through the propeller boss of the torpedo, permitting command signals to be sent to control direction and depth-keeping. In daylight the torpedo could be made to surface briefly to help the operator to track it, and at night it would make a flashing signal.

Known also as T10, Spinne was used on the French coast in 1944 with observation posts on high cliffs. It had a range of 4900 m

(5400 yards) and a speed of 30 knots. There is no report of its effectiveness during the Normandy invasion, but it is known that the early postwar experiments with the Mk 23 torpedo were made using captured Spinne wire dispensers.

Spitfire, Vickers-Supermarine

British fighter. Probably the most famous fighter of its time, the Spitfire was born in an age of wood-and-fabric biplane fighters and faded from operational service in the age of swept-wing supersonic fighters. Early in its career, in concert with the Hawker Hurricane, it established the RAF's supremacy during the Battle of Britain, becoming a household name. The Spitfire began life before the Second World War, and was developed continuously during the war; production finally ceased in 1947. It was the only Allied fighter to remain in continuous produc-

tion during the war. Its RAF career spanned 19 years of operational service.

The ancestry of the Spitfire can be traced back to the series of Supermarine racing seaplanes designed by R J Mitchell to participate in the Schneider Trophy contest. On September 13, 1931, a Supermarine S.6B won the Trophy outright for Great Britain, at a speed of 547.3 km/h (340.08 mph); the same aircraft later that month pushed up the world speed record to 655.8 km/h (407.5 mph).

From the S.6B evolved the Supermarine F.7/30, which was a single-seat monoplane fighter with a gull wing, fixed undercarriage and open cockpit. It was powered by a Rolls-Royce Goshawk engine and armed with four 0.303-in (7.7-mm) machine-guns. Although meeting the official requirement, Mitchell considered he could improve on the design and set about a new private-venture fighter. This had an enclosed cockpit and retractable undercarriage, and was to be powered by the

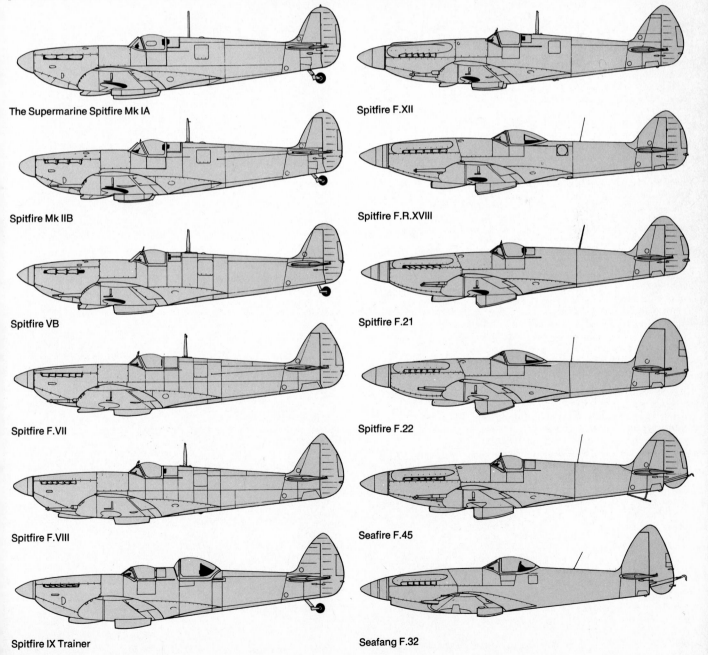

The Supermarine Spitfire Mk IA

Spitfire Mk IIB

Spitfire VB

Spitfire F.VII

Spitfire F.VIII

Spitfire IX Trainer

Spitfire F.XII

Spitfire F.R.XVIII

Spitfire F.21

Spitfire F.22

Seafire F.45

Seafang F.32

Spitfire, Vickers-Supermarine

Goshawk. Air Ministry Specification F.5/34, which called for eight rather than four machine-guns, was issued during his work; this, together with the announcement of the new PV-12 engine from Rolls-Royce, led to a further redesign. Placing the increased armament and new powerplant in a small airframe of a highly refined aerodynamic design resulted in what, in a moment of inspiration, was christened the Spitfire. About the same time, Rolls-Royce named their PV-12 the Merlin: it was to be a long and successful partnership.

The prototype Spitfire, built to Specification F.37/34, with a Merlin C installed, made its maiden flight on March 5, 1936, and soon displayed a performance described as second-to-none. In June 1936 an initial contract for 310 Spitfires had been placed, which by October 1939 had reached 4000. Just over a

year after the maiden flight, Mitchell died of tuberculosis and his place as chief designer was taken by J Smith, who remained with the Spitfire throughout its development and production.

Production of the Spitfire I commenced at Supermarine in 1937, and the production-standard aircraft incorporated further improvements. A tail wheel replaced the tail skid, ejector exhausts were fitted to the Merlin II (which had replaced the C), and the semicircular wheel fairings attached to the bottom of the undercarriage leg fairings were removed. First examples were armed with only four machine-guns, but this was soon changed to eight for the Mk IA. Later models also incorporated a new domed cockpit hood, and a de Havilland three-bladed variable-pitch propeller replaced the wooden two-bladed fixed-pitch propeller.

The Spitfire was very advanced in its aerodynamics, and was also the first all-metal fighter to be produced in Britain. The fuselage was built in three sections: the engine mounting of tubular structure with a horse-shoe-shaped cross member for strengthening; the centre fuselage of semimonocoque construction, with 15 frames and four longerons; and the rear fuselage and fin, which were an integral assembly with the fuselage frames extending upwards to become the fin spars (a most advanced design at this time).

Although each wing was built on two spars, the front spar took enough of the loads and stress for the Spitfire to be considered a single-spar aircraft. The leading-edge skin

and front spar combined to make a torsion box of great strength. The only design improvement that pilots of the Spitfire would have wished for concerned the undercarriage. Pivoted on the front spar, it retracted

outwards and slightly rearwards, giving the aircraft a narrow ground track, which many would have preferred to be wider.

The first Spitfires to enter RAF service were the four-gun Mk Is, which 19 Squadron took on strength in June 1938. Just over a year later, at the outbreak of the Second World War, the RAF had nine fully equipped and two partly equipped squadrons flying the Spitfire. On October 16, 1939, Spitfires of 602 and 603 Squadrons brought down two Hein-

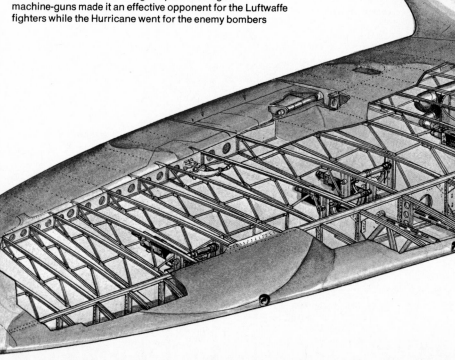

The Supermarine Spitfire Mk II the fighter which, with the Hawker Hurricane, became the mainstay of Britain's fighter defence during the Battle of Britain in the summer and autumn of 1940. Its excellent handling coupled with eight machine-guns made it an effective opponent for the Luftwaffe fighters while the Hurricane went for the enemy bombers

kel He 111 bombers over the Firth of Forth; they were the first enemy aircraft to be shot down over Britain since 1918. The Spitfire II entered service in late 1940, and was soon involved in Fighter Command's daylight offensive sweeps over occupied Europe, the first of which was carried out by 66 Squadron from Biggin Hill in December.

The suitability of the Spitfire for photo-reconnaissance soon became apparent, and it first operated in this role as early as December 1939. In this case, the aircraft was stripped of its armament, and a single vertically mounted F.24 camera was installed in each wing. With the introduction of the new F.52 camera in April 1940, these photo-reconnaissance missions began to pay dividends. Spitfire Is modified for photo-reconnaissance were known as PR Types A, B, C and D, while types E and F were put into production as the PR.IV, and type G was a service-modified Mk V for armed reconnaissance, known as the PR.VII.

Refined in the light of operational experience, the Spitfire Mk V made its appearance in March 1941 when it re-equipped 92 Squadron. The Mk V was produced in three main versions: those fitted with an A-type wing, with eight 0.303-in machine-guns; those with a B-type wing, with two 20-mm (0.79-in) cannon and four 0.303-in machine-guns; and those with a C-type wing, capable of taking the A or B armaments, or four 20-mm cannon. This version was also the first mark of Spitfire to be used as a fighter-bomber.

Spitfire VBs were the first of the type to be flown overseas, 15 being delivered to Malta in March 1942 by HMS *Eagle*; and by August 1942 there were three squadrons of Mk Vs in the Western Desert. This mark was also the first to operate in the Pacific, when in February 1943, 54 Squadron defended Darwin, Australia, against Japanese bombers. By October of that year, three squadrons were also operating in Burma.

With the appearance of the Fw 190 over Europe, the Spitfire V became outclassed, and a higher-altitude version, the Mk VIII, was put into development. As a stop-gap measure, the Merlin 61 engine was put in the Mk V airframe, which became the Mk IX—with the MK V, one of the most widely used versions of the Spitfire. It entered service with 64 Squadron in July 1942, and by VE-Day in May 1945 equipped not only eight home-defence units, but five squadrons of the 2nd Tactical Air Force on the Continent, and 22 squadrons of the Balkan and Desert air forces.

When the Spitfire VIII finally arrived, most were deployed to Italy (145 Squadron equipping in August 1943), and in Burma (155 Squadron receiving theirs in December 1943). Three main versions for low, medium and high altitudes were produced. The HF.VIII had an extended wing span with pointed tips, which was first used with Spitfire VI to help them reach high-flying German raiders. The other high-altitude version was the Mk VII, which was issued to squadrons at home and in the Middle East.

Apart from a service-modified version of the Mk IX, the next major photo-reconnaissance Spitfire was the Mk XI, which continued in service for some years after the war. Although out of numerical sequence, the PR.X was a pressurized version of the Mk XI and succeeded it, only 16

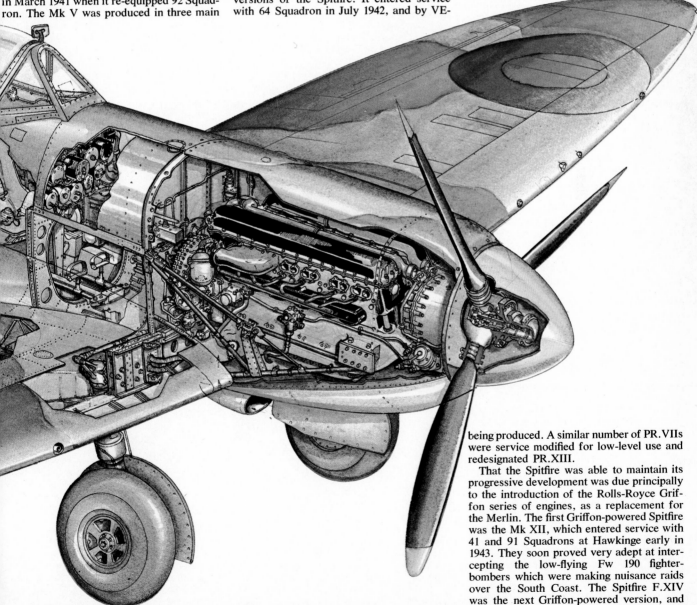

being produced. A similar number of PR.VIIs were service modified for low-level use and redesignated PR.XIII.

That the Spitfire was able to maintain its progressive development was due principally to the introduction of the Rolls-Royce Griffon series of engines, as a replacement for the Merlin. The first Griffon-powered Spitfire was the Mk XII, which entered service with 41 and 91 Squadrons at Hawkinge early in 1943. They soon proved very adept at intercepting the low-flying Fw 190 fighter-bombers which were making nuisance raids over the South Coast. The Spitfire F.XIV was the next Griffon-powered version, and

Spitfire, Vickers-Supermarine

although intended as an interim type until the arrival of the Mk XVIII it proved very effective in its own right. It entered service with 610 Squadron in January 1944, and by June that year was in action against FZG-76 (V-1) flying bombs. Of the 429 flying bombs claimed as shot down by home-defence Spitfire units, the Mk XIV wings claimed 300. This capability was mainly due to the Mk XIV's increased speed.

The Spitfire F.XIV was also used in the fighter-bomber and fighter-reconnaissance roles. In the former role, 33 F.XIVs of 229, 453 and 602 Squadrons made the biggest fighter-bomber attack of the war on V-2 sites on December 24, 1944, each aircraft delivering one 227-kg (500-lb) and two 113-kg (250-lb) bombs. The F.XIV was also a very effective high-altitude fighter, and an aircraft of 401 Squadron claimed the first jet-powered Messerschmitt Me 262 fighter to be shot down on October 5, 1944. By the time the war ended, however, the Mk XIV had only just reached 17 and 132 Squadrons in the Far East, and so they were not able to try their strength against their Japanese counterparts.

The last Merlin-powered version of the Spitfire to enter service was the Mk XVI, which was a Mk IX fitted with the US-built version of the Merlin. It entered service with the 2nd Tactical air force in 1944, and by VE-Day, equipped 11 squadrons, plus another four in Fighter Command. After the war, the Spitfire XVI equipped units of the Royal Auxiliary Air Force, and served with anti-aircraft cooperation units until 1950.

The end of the war coincided with the arrival of the fully redesigned Spitfire Mk XVIII. Although some went to the Middle East, most F.XVIIIs and fighter-reconnaissance FR.XVIIIs went to the Far East, including 28 Squadron, based at Kai Tak, Hong Kong. It was finally withdrawn from service in May 1955.

The final photo-reconnaissance version was the PR.XIX, which was produced to replace the PR.XI. The aircraft served with 2 Squadron in the British air force of occupation in Germany after the war, with 60 and 81 Squadrons in the Far East, and with four squadrons in England. It was to a Spitfire PR.19 (the use of Roman numerals in mark numbers was discontinued after the war) of 81 Squadron, based in Malaya, that the distinction of the last operational flight by an RAF first-line Spitfire went on April 1, 1954. The type continued in second-line duties as a meteorological aircraft until 1957, and in 1979 two examples were still flying with the RAF's Battle of Britain Memorial Flight.

The Spitfire underwent a major redesign during 1944, resulting in the F.21 which, although in production at the end of the war, did not see war service. After the war it entered service with five regular units and five RAF auxiliary squadrons, and was declared obsolete in May 1955. The Spitfire F.22 which followed was the mainstay of the auxiliary squadrons from 1946-51, serving with 12 squadrons, while the only regular RAF unit to fly them was 73 Squadron, based at Taquali, Malta.

The final version of the Spitfire was the F.24, which was basically an F.22 with several refinements. The first example was delivered to the RAF in April 1946 and entered service in November that year: the last Spit-

A Spitfire VC of the 352 (Yugoslav) Squadron RAF during operations in the Adriatic in 1944

A Spitfire PR.19 showing its five-bladed propeller and the Griffon engine installation

A Spitfire PR.19 of the RAF Battle of Britain Memorial Flight after the Second World War

fire F.24 was not released from the factory at South Marston until February 20, 1948. Intended for home service, 16 aircraft were delivered to 80 Squadron in Hong Kong in 1950, where they served for two years.

Apart from the naval variants of the Spitfire (known as Seafire), there were two attempts to produce a floatplane version of the Spitfire. The Norwegian campaign of April-May 1940 led to a requirement for a

floatplane to operate from sheltered waters and a set of Blackburn Roc floats were fitted to a Spitfire I. Flotation trials were not promising and the project was abandoned with removal of the requirement. It was restored in 1942, this time for use from sheltered tropical waters, and a Spitfire VB using Supermarine-designed floats was converted. The increased efficiency of the Japanese fighters later required use of a Mk IX

Spitfire, Vickers-Supermarine

A Spitfire Mk 22. It was powered by a Griffon 61/85, and had an improved Mk 21 airframe

The Supermarine Spiteful which was powered by a Griffon 65 rated at 2375 hp and flew in 1944

The Spitfire Mk 24 was the last Spitfire to be produced and had four 20-mm (0.79-in) cannon

served with the RAF, the Auxiliary air force, the USAF and the air forces of Australia, Canada, India, New Zealand, South Africa and the USSR. It was also flown by expatriate French, Czech, Polish and Yugoslav units. After the war, Spitfires flew with the air arms of many countries, including Belgium, Burma, Czechoslovakia, Denmark, Egypt, France, Greece, Holland, Ireland, Israel, Italy, Norway, Portugal, Southern Rhodesia, Sweden, Syria, Thailand and Turkey.

At the end of its development, the Spitfire had managed to increase its maximum speed by 35%, its weight by 90%, its rate of climb by 80%, and its power had been doubled. Such were the changes made that some authorities maintain the Spitfire Mk I and the F.24 are two different aircraft. However, the name was not changed and the Spitfire, of which 20336 were built, remains one of the fastest piston-engined fighters ever to have been produced. The following major variants were made.

Mk I Powered by Merlin II or III, rated at 1030 hp. First versions featured wooden two-bladed propeller, later replaced by de Havilland three-bladed variable-pitch or constant-speed propeller; four 0.303-in (7.7-mm) Browning machine-guns later increased to eight on the Mk IA; Mk IB experimentally armed with two 20-mm (0.79-in) Hispano cannon and four machine-guns; 1566 produced.

Mk II Powered by Merlin XII, rated at 1175 hp. Mk IIA armed with eight 0.303-in machine-guns and the Mk IIB with two 20-mm cannon and four machine-guns. Some converted to carry dinghy packs for air-sea rescue duties, and designated Mk IIC. Some later converted to Mk V standard; 920 produced.

Mk III Powered by Merlin XX, rated at 1260 hp. Developed as a private venture for experimenting with improvements incorporated in later versions.

PR.IV Powered by Merlin 45, rated at 1100 hp, or later series 46, 50, 55, 55A or 56. Developed as a production-standard fast reconnaissance aircraft. Unarmed. Fitted with either one F.52 vertical camera with 36-in lens, one F.24 with 14-in (35-cm) lens or two 20-in (50-cm) F.8 cameras; 229 produced.

Mk V Powered by Merlin 45, with increased rating of 1440 hp, and later series 46, 50 and 50A. Incorporated many refinements including an internal armoured windscreen, and a Vokes air filter mounted in a fairing under the nose for tropical operations. From 1943 many Mk Vs had wingtips clipped to improve handling at lower altitudes. Mk VA had eight 0.303-in machine-guns. Mk VB had two 20-mm cannon and four machine-guns. Mk VC which introduced universal wings, capable of taking either the VA or VB armament options or four 20-mm cannon, plus two 113-kg (250-lb) bombs. Both the VB and VC could take long-range belly fuel tanks mounted under the fuselage or a 227-kg (500-lb) bomb; 6479 produced.

Mk VI Powered by Merlin 47/49, modified for high-altitude operation and rated at 1415 hp. Evolved from the Mk V to combat high-flying Junkers Ju 86P reconnaissance aircraft. Featuring an extended wing span of 12.24 m (40 ft 2 in) basic cockpit pressurization and a four-blade propeller; 100 produced.

airframe, and considerable flight testing was carried out before it was finally abandoned in early 1945.

Another modification was a two-seat trainer variant. Although never used by the RAF, several Mk VIIIs and Mk IXs were converted after the war from surplus airframes for various foreign air forces, including Holland, Egypt and Ireland. The front cockpit was moved forward by 34 cm (13.5

in) and a second cockpit, with full instrumentation added behind, and additional wing tanks added.

The successor to the Spitfire, the Spiteful, was designed to F.1/43, but with the end of the war the contracts were cancelled. Powered by a Griffon 65, rated at 2375 hp, the first Spiteful flew in June 1944, but only 17 were built.

During the Second World War, the Spitfire

Mk VII Powered by Merlin 61/64/71 rated at 1660 hp, and fitted with a two-stage two-speed supercharger. High-altitude version featuring the extended wing span of the Mk VI, plus a retractable tail wheel. Late-production models had the pointed fin and rudder of the Mk XII. Both P.VII and HF.VII versions were produced, the latter having the Merlin 71 engines; 140 produced.

PR.VII Service-modified Mk V to produce an armed version of the PR.IV with eight 0.303-in machine-guns.

Mk VIII Powered by Merlin 61/63/63A (F.VIII); Merlin 66 (LF.VIII); and Merlin 70 (HF.VIII). Essentially an unpressurized Mk VII fitted with universal wing. F.VIII had the standard wing span; the LF.VIII had a 9.8 m (32 ft 2 in) span; and the HF.VIII the 12.2 m (40 ft 2 in) span. All aircraft were fully tropicalized, and had a retractable tail wheel. With modification, a single 227-kg (500-lb) bomb and two 113-kg (250-lb) bombs could be carried; 1658 produced.

Mk IX Powered by Merlin 61/63/63A, rated at 1660 hp. Produced initially as a conversion of the Mk VC. Produced in low-altitude (LF), medium altitude (F) and high altitude (HF) versions, and a service-modified photo-reconnaissance version all with a lengthened fuselage and additional radiator under the port wing. The Mk IXE was fitted with two 0.5-in (12.7-mm) Browning machine-guns in place of the four 0.303-in guns, but retained the twin 20-mm cannon; 5665 produced.

PR.X Powered by Merlin 64. Developed and produced after the PR.XI, as a long-range photo-reconnaissance aircraft. It combined the pressurization features of the PR.VII with the structure of the Mk IX. The wing leading edge was used as a fuel tank; 16 produced.

PR.XI Powered by Merlin 61/63/63A/70. Unpressurized, but tropicalized and with provision for a belly fuel tank; 471 produced.

F.XII Powered by Griffon III/IV, rated at 1735 hp. Specially strengthened Mk VC, with the same armament and 11.15-m (36 ft 7 in) clipped wing and the increased chord (or pointed) fin-and-rudder; 100 produced.

PR.XIII Converted from PR.VIIs, and fitted with 1620-hp Merlin 32 engine and a three-bladed de Havilland propeller. The cannon armament was removed, but the four 0.303-in machine-guns retained.

F.XIV Powered by Griffon 65/67, rated at 2050 hp, driving a five-bladed Rotol propeller. Based on the Mk VIII airframe. Fitted with a two-stage two-speed supercharger in a longer nose, offset by an increase in fin area and ailerons moved slightly inboard. Some late models which had the cut-down rear fuselage, full bubble canopy to increase rear view and universal wing with two 20-mm cannon and two 0.5-in machine-guns were designated F.XIVE; FR.XIVE had additional oblique F.24 camera in the rear fuselage; 957 produced.

F.XVI Based on Mk IX with US Packard-built Merlin 266, rated at 1705 hp. LF.XVI had clipped wings for low-altitude operations, and late-production models of each version had the cut-down rear fuselage and bubble canopy. Either the C- or E-type armament could be carried; 1054 produced.

F.XVIII This was the intended definitive version powered by two-stage Griffon 65; increased internal fuel capacity and strengthened wings and undercarriage. A fighter-reconnaissance version, with either an F.24 or F.52 vertical camera, was designated the FR.XVIII. Some were tropicalized and given increased fuel tankage, and some were pressurized; 300 produced.

PR.XIX Powered by Griffon 65 initially, then the Griffon 66. The former were unpressurized, and latter pressurized. This version was basically a Mk XIV fuselage with a universal camera installation fitted with Mk VC bowser wings for increased fuel capacity; 225 produced.

Mk XX Original Mk IV prototype redesignated for experimental purposes; powered by Griffon IIB.

F.21 Powered by Griffon 61, driving a five-bladed Rotol propeller. Increased area wing and new wing planform, wing strengthened spars; four 20-mm Hispano cannon, with no option for machine-guns of any calibre. Some were fitted with Griffon 85 engines driving two three-bladed contrarotating Rotol propellers; 122 produced.

F.22 Powered by Griffon 61/85, as on the F.21. Based on F.21 with the cut-down rear fuselage and redesigned bubble canopy, and a 24-volt electrical system (instead of 12-volt). Some late production models had the completely redesigned tail unit for the Spiteful; 278 produced (including 27 airframes produced to F.24 standard).

F.24 Powered by Griffon 61, rated at 2050 hp, or Griffon 85. Final production based on F.22 with the Spiteful tail assembly and provision for zero-length launchers for rocket projectiles under wings. Armament changed to four short-barrelled 20-mm Hispano Mk V cannon; 54 produced when production ended in February 1948.

(Mk 1A) Span: 11.23 m (36 ft 10 in) *Length:* 9.12 m (29 ft 11 in) *Gross weight:* 2624 kg (5784 lb) *Maximum speed:* 571 km/h (355 mph) at 5790 m (19 000 ft)

(LF.VB) Span: 9.8 m (32 ft 2 in) with clipped wings *Length:* 9.12 m (29 ft 11 in) *Gross weight:* 3016 kg (6650 lb) *Maximum speed:* 575 km/h (357 mph) at 1830 m (6000 ft)

(Mk IX) Span: 11.23 m (36 ft 10 in) *Length:* 9.45 m (31 ft) *Gross weight:* 3402 kg (7500 lb) *Maximum speed:* 657 km/h (408 mph) at 7620 m (25 000 ft)

(F.XIV) Span: 11.23 m (36 ft 10 in) *Length:* 9.96 m (32 ft 8 in) *Gross weight:* 3799 kg (8375 lb) *Maximum speed:* 721 km/h (448 mph) at 7925 m (26 000 ft)

(FR.XVIII) Span: 11.23 m (36 ft 10 in) *Length* 10.13 m (33 ft 3 in) *Gross weight:* 4990 kg (11 000 lb) *Maximum speed:* 711 km/h (442 mph) at 7925 m (26 000 ft)

(F.24) Span: 11.25 m (36 ft 11 in) *Length:* 10.03 m (32 ft 11 in) *Gross weight:* 4491 kg (9900 lb) *Maximum speed:* 731 km/h (454 mph) at 7925 m (26 000 ft)

Split

Yugoslav destroyer, built 1939-58. A large destroyer or flotilla leader was ordered from Chantiers de la Loire in October 1938 and laid down at Split shipyard in July 1939. She was launched and named *Spalato* in 1940, but work stopped when the Germans invaded Yugoslavia in 1941. The original design was to include five 138.6-mm (5.46-in) guns, six 55-cm (21.7-in) torpedo tubes and five twin 40-mm (1.57-in) Bofors guns. She would have resembled the *Fantasque* Class, but with less powerful machinery.

When work resumed after the war, the ship was renamed *Split* and the design was completely recast. The US supplied 5-in (127-mm)/38-cal single guns, fire control and radar, and the uptakes were trunked into a single funnel. Although the original long forecastle was retained, a continuous deckhouse replaced the torpedo tubes on the main deck to provide shelter for personnel and offices for the new equipment. A quintuple set of torpedo tubes of US Navy pattern was mounted a deck higher. Mk 37 fire control is provided for the 5-in guns, with Mk 12 and Mk 22 radars, while SC and SG-1 radars are provided on the tripod mast. She started her trials in July 1958.

The Yugoslav destroyer Split in May 1959. She was begun in July 1939 but construction was halted in 1940. She was still in service in 1977 as a flagship

The Springfield M1903 0.30-in (7.62-mm) rifle which equipped the US Army before the introduction of the semiautomatic M1 Garand

I V Hogg

Despite her age *Split* presents a modern profile, with a raked bow and a prominent funnel cap. At the end of 1977 she was still serving as flagship of the Torpedo Boat Brigade' or Division.

Displacement: 2400 tons (standard), 3000 tons (full load) *Length:* 120 m (393 ft 8 in) oa *Beam:* 11.1 m (36 ft 5 in) *Draught:* 3.8 m (12 ft 6 in) *Machinery:* 2-shaft geared steam turbines, 30000 shp=34 knots *Armament:* (as completed) 4 5-in (127-mm)/38-cal DP (4×1); 12 40-mm (1.57-in)/60-cal Bofors (12×1); 5 21-in (53-mm) torpedo tubes (1×5) *Crew:* 240

Springfield

US rifle. Springfield Armory, in Springfield, Massachusetts, was founded on George Washington's orders in 1795 and since that time has been the home of US military small-arms design and manufacture. Among the most famous of the early Springfield arms was the Trap-door rifle of 1868, a conversion of muzzle-loader to breech-loader along similar lines to the British Snider rifle. The rear of the musket barrel was cut away and a hinged block fitted. This could be lifted forward, exposing the breech and allowing a 0.45-in (11.4-mm) cartridge to be inserted. The block was then hinged down and locked, and a firing pin in the block was then aligned with the external hammer of the musket. Simple and robust, it was not only popular with the Army but also with hunters and trappers who purchased it in large numbers.

In the 1890s the US Army adopted a Krag-Jørgensen rifle, but during the Spanish-American war discovered that the Mauser was a better weapon. After testing and studying various Mauser designs, the Ordnance Department obtained a licence from Mauser to incorporate various features into their new design, and the first Springfield rifle was produced in 1900. The cartridge selected proved to be a poor one and both it and the rifle were redesigned, the rifle being shortened to the then-novel 'short rifle' concept, doing away with the division of 'long rifle' for infantry and 'carbine' for other troops. This was issued in 1903 as the Rifle .30 M1903, but has always been known as the Springfield. A further improvement appeared in 1906 with the adoption of a pointed bullet, since which time the standard US Army cartridge has invariably been called the '.30-06', relating its calibre and year of introduction.

The Mauser design was slightly modified in the Springfield rifle; a magazine cut-off was built into the bolt release catch, a two-piece firing pin was adopted, and a better rear sight installed. The US Army insist that it was the finest military bolt-action rifle ever made, but in this they are unlikely to find agreement from any foreign soldier.

The Springfield was produced in a number of variant models; the original M1903 was provided with an 'English' stock without pistol grip; the M1903 Mark 1 was modified for the Pedersen Device; the M1903A1 had a new stock with pistol grip; the M1903A2 was a barrel and action mounted on blocks so that it could be inserted into the barrel of an artillery piece and used as a subcalibre training device; the M1903A3 appeared in 1942 and was revised so as to make mass production easier. It also incorporated an aperture sight at the rear of the action instead of the original leaf sight above the chamber. The M1903A4 was the sniping version of the M1903A1; it was fitted with permanently mounted blocks for a telescopic sight and used the Weaver 330C sight as standard, though other commercial models were acceptable substitutes. No iron sights were fitted, which gives the exposed muzzle a curiously naked look.

(Rifle M1903A3) Calibre: 0.30 in (7.62 mm) *Weight:* 3.63 kg (8 lb) *Length:* 110.5 cm (43.5 in) *Barrel length:* 610 mm (24 in) *Magazine:* 5-round integral box *Muzzle velocity:* 853 m/sec (2800 ft/sec)

Sprint, Martin Marietta

US antiballistic missile. Sprint was the short-range intercepter in the Safeguard ABM system which was briefly operational in late 1975 before being deactivated. Martin had been awarded a feasibility-study contract for the weapon in October 1962 and full development was authorized a year later. A number of very difficult technical problems had to be overcome in the short time available: these included perfecting a new solid propellant with a very high burn rate and resistance to cracking at accelerations exceeding 100 g; developing a silica phenolic ablative material to coat the missile's skin; hardening the control electronics to withstand the effects of the electromagnetic pulse produced by a nuclear explosion; and providing a communications link through the ionized gases which enveloped the weapon in flight.

Sprint was first fired in November 1965, and in December 1970 the weapon intercepted a re-entry vehicle from a Minuteman ICBM launched from Vandenberg Air Force Base to the Safeguard test site on Kwajalein Atoll, 6760 km (4200 miles) away. Half the 38 development firings were deemed to have been successful, and sufficient Sprints to equip three Safeguard sites were ordered in December 1970, though only those at Nekoman AFB in North Dakota became operational.

Sprint was housed in silos, and was mounted on a piston which ejected the missile through a membrane covering the silo mouth. The weapon's Hercules solid-propellant first-stage motor then ignited, pro-

ducing 295000 kg (650000 lb) of thrust and accelerating to a final level over 100 g. Both the missile and its target were tracked by the missile site radar (MSR), which also transmitted steering commands to the weapon and ordered detonation of its nuclear warhead.

Martin began development of the improved Sprint 2, which was intended for the Site Defense of Minuteman ABM system (previously known as Hardsite), but the project was downgraded in 1974 to become a technology-demonstration programme.

Length: 8.2 m (27 ft) *Diameter:* 1.37 m (4 ft 6 in) *Weight:* 3400 kg (7500 lb) *Range:* 40 km (25 miles) *Warhead:* low-kiloton thermonuclear

A Martin Marietta Sprint blasts off during a test launch. The Sprint carries a nuclear warhead for intercepting incoming ICBMs

Martin Marietta

Spruance

Spruance

US destroyer class, begun in 1972. These vessels are built in a specially designed ship-building facility employing modular construction methods at the Ingalls division of Litton Industries, Pascagoula. *Spruance* (DD.963) was completed in 1975, followed by *Paul F Foster* (DD.964), *Kinkaid* (DD.965), *Hewitt* (DD.966), *Elliott* (DD.967), *Arthur W Radford* (DD.968), *Peterson* (DD.969), *Caron* (DD.970), *David R Ray* (DD.971), *Oldendorf* (DD.972), *John Young* (DD.973), *Comte de Grasse* (DD.974), and *O'Brien* (DD.975). Other ships under construction in early 1979 were *Merrill* (DD.976), *Briscoe* (DD.977), *Stump* (DD.978), *Conolly* (DD.979), *Moosbrugger* (DD.980), *John Hancock* (DD.981), *Nicholson* (DD.982), *John Rodgers* (DD.983), *Leftwich* (DD.984), *Cushing* (DD.985), *Harry W Hill* (DD.986), *O'Bannon* (DD.987), *Thorn* (DD.988), *Deyo* (DD.989), *Ingersoll* (DD.990), *Fife* (DD.991), and *Fletcher* (DD.992). The last of the 30 ships should complete in 1981.

The class is intended to fill the gap left by the disposal of Second World War construction. Seen by the US Navy primarily as ASW ships with the ability to operate as part of a fast carrier task force, the *Spruance* Class attracted considerable criticism because of their light armament. These cruiser-sized ships have, however, been specially designed to have sufficient weight and space in reserve to accommodate future developments in weapons technology. The first ships emerged with only two single light 5-in (127-mm)/54-cal guns fore and aft for surface or aerial engagement, but by 1979 some ships were fitted with two quadruple launchers for Harpoon surface-to-surface missiles just aft of the first funnel, and an eight-cell launcher for NATO Sea Sparrow short-range surface-to-air missiles above the after 5-in gun. It was also planned eventually to replace the forward gun by the 8-in (203-mm) lightweight mounting under development in the late 1970s, and to add two 20-mm (0.79-in) Vulcan Phalanx close-in weapon systems. The only above-water sensors fitted by 1979 were SPS-40 air-search radar and the new Mk 86 fire-control system, but the massive lattice masts have ample space for later developments.

The *Spruance* Class are the first large US ships to have all-gas-turbine propulsion. Four LM-2500 turbines, each rated at 20 000 shp, are paired en echelon to drive twin shafts with controllable-pitch propellers. The engine rooms are separated by no less than three bulkheads to minimize action damage. The generators, too, are gas-turbine driven, making the operation of the ships exceptionally quiet. This makes them difficult for submarines to detect and minimizes interference with the large SQS-53 bow sonar. The ASW weapons are an Asroc eight-cell launcher, with a large reload magazine beneath, and triple Mk 32 torpedo tubes concealed behind sliding doors in the hull beneath the flight deck. The capacious hangar houses either two Seasprite ASW helicopters or a single Sea King.

In 1978 two modified *Spruance* designs received Congressional approval. The DDG.47 design, intended to provide area-defence cover for fast carrier task forces, has twin-arm Mk 26 launchers for Standard SM-2

USS *Spruance* during builder's trials in 1975. Although designed for the ASW role, the destroyers of this class also carry Sea Sparrow SAMs and two 5-in (127-mm) guns

missiles, operating in conjunction with the advanced Aegis weapon control system; 16 ships are projected in addition to four (DD.993-996) which were laid down in 1978 for Iran, to be named *Kouroosh, Daryush, Ardeshir* and *Nader*. They have a similar armament to the DDG.47 design but have conventional sensors. DDH.997 is a single-ship design in which the hangar has been enlarged to carry four ASW helicopters.

Displacement: 7810 tons (full load) *Length:* 171 m (561 ft) *Beam:* 17.6 m (57 ft 9 in) *Draught:* 8.8 m (28 ft 11 in) *Machinery:* 4 LM-2500 gas turbines, 80 000 hp=33 knots *Armament:* 2 5-in (127-mm)/54-cal Mk 45 DP (2×1); 1 Asroc launcher; 6 Mk 32 torpedo tubes (2×3); 8 Harpoon SSM launchers (2×4); 8 Sea Sparrow SAM launchers (1×8); 2 SH-2 LAMPS helicopters or 1 SH-3 Sea King *Crew:* 296

Squalo

Italian submarine class. The four *Squalo* Class submarines were virtually repeats of the *Bandiera* Class with the bow raised and blisters added; dimensions were identical but the *Squalo*s had a slightly lower displacement. All four boats were built by Cantieri Riuniti dell'Adriatico, Monfalcone. Diesel machinery in the two classes was identical but CRDA electric motors replaced the Savigliano model of the *Bandiera*s. Slightly reduced bunkerage in *Squalo* gave a radius of

action of 8500 nautical miles at 8 knots surfaced and 72 nautical miles at 4 knots submerged. Armament was identical in the two classes.

The four submarines were stationed in the Dodecanese when Italy entered the Second World War and remained in that area until 1941 when they returned to Italian bases. *Tricheco* was responsible for accidentally sinking the Italian submarine *Gemma* in the Aegean Sea on October 8, 1940, and was herself sunk on March 18, 1942, off Brindisi by the British submarine *Upholder*. The remaining three submarines were subsequently relegated to training and transport duties, running supplies to North Africa. On one such trip *Narvalo* was sunk off Tripoli on January 14, 1943 by the British destroyer *Pakenham* and escort *Hursley* assisted by aircraft. *Delfino* was accidentally lost off Taranto on March 23, 1943. *Squalo* survived the war to be laid up in February 1948 and subsequently scrapped.

Name	completed
Delfino	6/31
Narvalo	12/30
Squalo	10/30
Tricheco	6/31

Displacement: 857/1142 tons (surfaced/submerged) *Length:* 69.8 m (229 ft) oa *Beam:* 7.2 m (23 ft 8 in) *Draught:* 5.2 m (17 ft) *Machinery:* 2-shaft diesels/2 electric motors, 3000 bhp/1300 hp=17/8.5 knots (surfaced/submerged) *Armament:* 1 4-in (102-mm); 2 machine-guns; 8 21-in (53-cm) torpedo tubes (4 bow, 4 stern), 12 torpedoes *Crew:* 54

Squid

British antisubmarine mortar. As early as 1932 the Royal Navy's experimental antisubmarine research unit at Portland recommended the development of a mortar capable of firing projectiles ahead of a ship to enable the Asdic (sonar) to remain in contact with the submarine during the final stages of the attack. The first efforts to implement these recommendations began in 1940 and resulted in the Hedgehog multiple spigot mortar. But Hedgehog's bombs were only impact-fuzed, and it was recognized that the hydrostatically-fuzed depth charge had a bigger lethal radius and that near-misses also helped to demoralize U-Boat crews.

In February 1942 work began on a three-barrelled mortar eventually named Squid. It had a fixed elevation of 45°, but could be tilted to 15° either side to compensate for the ship's roll. The three barrels were slightly staggered in the vertical plane to provide a better spread of explosions.

The bomb provided was fitted with fins and a ballistic cap to ensure that it sank rapidly to its preset depth. The payload was about 45 kg (100 lb) of Torpex, and the whole 1.75 m (5 ft 9 in) long projectile weighed 181 kg (400 lb). The triple mortar swung down to the horizontal to allow the bombs to be muzzle-loaded. Squid was used with the Type 144Q depth-finding Asdic set, but its effectiveness was greatly improved by use with the later Type 147 set, which passed depths automatically and had its beam tilted in steps.

As the Squid and its loading system occupied a lot of space and weight it could not be fitted easily in older escorts, although one or two Western Approaches destroyers had two in A position. Two could be provided in B position in the new 'Loch' Class frigates of 1943, but only one in the same position in the 'Castle' Class corvettes. The first ship to receive Squid was the corvette *Hadleigh Castle* in August 1943, but the first kill recorded was by the frigate *Loch Killin* which sank *U 736* in August 1944.

From 1948 Squid was fitted to modernized destroyers and frigates, starting with the *Barfleur* and *Daring* Classes, Type 15 frigates and *Caesar* Class, and has since been fitted to a number of foreign warships. Although still in service in the late 1970s it had become obsolescent more on account of its primitive fire control than for any shortcomings in its ability to sink submarines.

SR-71, Lockheed US strategic reconnaissance aircraft See **Blackbird**

SRAAM, Hawker Siddeley Dynamics

British air-to-air missile. SRAAM (short-range air-to-air missile), previously known as Taildog, was intended to be a simple and

Naval ratings loading a Squid ASW mortar on HMS *Daring*. Squid fired a bomb containing 45 kg (100 lb) of Torpex explosive. It scored its first kill with *U 736* in August 1944

inexpensive weapon which could be installed on a wide range of aircraft with the minimum of modification. HSD received a predevelopment contract in 1970, followed by a project-definition award in early 1972, but in January 1974 the project was downgraded to a technology-demonstration programme and plans to deploy SRAAM as an operational weapon were abandoned.

The missile was of extremely simple appearance: it had no wings, relying on the fuselage to produce lift, and six small fins mounted on a freely spinning ring provided longitudinal stability. Steering was by thrust-vector control, four tabs being deflected into the motor exhaust to manoeuvre the weapon. This method of control allowed SRAAM to undergo violent manoeuvring without the risk of stalling aerodynamic surfaces, but it had the disadvantage that the missile became impossible to control once the motor burnt out.

SRAAM, also known as SRAAM 75 or QC434, was intended to be fired from an arrangement of two launch tubes, one either side of a central beam containing the associated electronics. An infrared seeker was fitted, and a small number of company-financed firings took place from a Hunter trials aircraft. The Royal Air Force has since ordered US AIM-9L Sidewinders in place of SRAAM.

Length: 2.73 m (8 ft 11 in) *Diameter:* 16.8 cm (6.5 in) *Range:* 8 km (5 miles) approx

SRAM, Boeing

US strategic air-to-surface missile. The AGM-69A SRAM (short-range attack missile), also known as Weapon System 140A, originated in privately financed work which Boeing began in December 1963 with the aim

of extending the effective life of B-52G/H Stratofortress strategic bombers. By July 1965 the United States Air Force had drawn up an official requirement for such a weapon, and in October of the following year Boeing was selected as winner of a five-company competition to meet this requirement. The first launch of a powered SRAM took place from a B-52 in July 1969 and was followed by a further 18 from the same type. An additional 19 firings from the FB-111, the last taking place in July 1971, completed the initial trials programme. Boeing had already received a production contract in January of that year and delivered its first operational round in March 1972. The 1500th and last SRAM was handed over to the USAF in July 1975.

The AGM-69A arms the B-52Gs and Hs operated by 17 wings of Strategic Air Command and also equips two wings of FB-111s. The B-52 can carry 12 rounds in triple under-wing clusters plus eight on a rotating launcher in the weapons bay, leaving room for four Mk 28 free-fall thermonuclear bombs. The FB-111 can be armed with four SRAM rounds on swivelling underwing pylons and two in the central bay.

SRAM is intended for suppressing defences in the path of the bombers as well as for attacking primary targets themselves. Four types of mission profile are possible: semiballistic; terrain-following under the control of a radar altimeter; all-inertial; and a combination of inertial and terrain-following. The weapon's on-board Singer Kearfott KT-70 inertial navigator is fed with information from the mother aircraft before launch.

SRAM is powered by a Lockheed SR75-LP-1 (LPC-415) solid-propellant rocket motor which has two burning pulses; the interval between the end of the boost pulse and the start of the sustain pulse can be preset for any time from 1.5 to 80 seconds, depending on the desired range and the type of mission to be flown.

The proposed AGM-69B SRAM-B, 1224 examples of which were to have been bought to arm the Rockwell B-1 bomber (24 rounds per aircraft), was abandoned following the cancellation of its parent aircraft in the summer of 1977. SRAM-B would have been powered by a Thiokol motor and was to have been fitted with a radiation-hardened W80 warhead in place of SRAM-A's W69. Existing missiles are, however, being upgraded with longer-life motors and improved guidance.

Length: 4.27 m (14 ft) *Diameter:* 44 cm (17.5 in) *Weight:* 1000 kg (2200 lb) *Range:* variable 60-160 km (37-100 miles) *Speed:* Mach 3 *Warhead:* 200-kiloton thermonuclear

---

SS-1 Soviet ballistic missile See **Scunner**

SS-1 Soviet battlefield support missile See **Scud**

SS-2 Soviet ballistic missile See **Sibling**

SS-3 Soviet ballistic missile See **Shyster**

SS-4 Soviet intermediate-range ballistic missile See **Sandal**

SS-5 Soviet intermediate-range ballistic missile See **Skean**

SS-6 Soviet intercontinental ballistic missile See **Sapwood**

SS-7 Soviet intercontinental ballistic missile See **Saddler**

SS-8 Soviet intercontinental ballistic missile See **Sasin**

SS-9 Soviet intercontinental ballistic missile See **Scarp**

SS-10 Soviet intercontinental ballistic missile See **Scrag**

SS.10, Nord

French antitank missile. In 1945 Nord-Aviation set up its Arsenal de l'Aéronautique, which formed the nucleus of a missile department and developed the Nord 5203, later designated SS.10, as a contemporary of the similar Entac. The SS.10, which entered service in 1956, was one of the first postwar guided missiles to see service, and was operated by the Israeli army during the invasion of Suez in that year. Nord, later Aérospatiale, built 29 845 examples of the weapon and sold over 60% of its production (18 030 rounds) to a total of nine countries including the United States. The missile also led on to the equally successful SS.11.

SS.10 was widely deployed by the French army as a three-round installation mounted on Jeeps or operated by infantry from portable launchers. An SS.10 platoon comprised a headquarters section, three missile sections (each with two sets of control equipment), a supply section and 75 rounds. Other instal-

lations included trailers carrying six launchers, and armoured personnel carriers with either four missiles on launchers and four in reserve or seven missiles which were mounted and ready for firing.

An SS.10 operator sighted his target with the aid of a pair of ×8-magnification binoculars. The missile was accelerated from its simple launcher by the booster section of a two-stage solid-propellant rocket motor, reaching 80 m/sec (262 ft/sec) at burnout. The cruciform wings spun the round throughout flight and carried trailing-edge spoilers which steered the weapon in response to commands initiated by the operator's joystick and transmitted down a trailing wire. A flare on the missile allowed the operator to keep it in sight until impact. US observers of French army trials put the hit probability at 80%, although 65% is more realistic as an average figure; the hollow-charge warhead could penetrate 42 cm (16.5 in) of armour plating. A dual-purpose armour-piercing/fragmentation charge for use against personnel could also be fitted to the missile.

Length: 86 cm (33.9 in) *Span:* 75 cm (29.5 in) *Diameter:* 16.5 cm (6.5 in) *Weight:* 15 kg (33 lb) *Speed:* 80 m/sec (262 ft/sec) *Minimum/maximum range:* 300/1600 m (330/1750 yards) *Warhead:* 5 kg (11 lb)

SS-11 Soviet intercontinental ballistic missile See **Sego**

SS.11, Aérospatiale

French antitank missile. Aérospatiale (which incorporated Nord-Aviation) developed SS.11 as a successor to its first-generation SS.10 and Entac weapons, and had sold more than 160 000 rounds by the time the production line closed in the late 1970s. The missile was built under licence in the United States (50 000 rounds), Germany and India and was developed into the Harpon, using semiautomatic command to line-of-sight guidance. In 1962 the SS.11B1 variant, employing transistorized fire-control equipment, became the standard production model.

SS.11 is larger than SS.10 and is normally fired from vehicles, although it can also be launched from the ground. The operator sights his target visually and fires a round, guiding it by a joystick which initiates steering commands for transmission down trailing wires. The missile is powered by two SNPE solid-propellant rocket motors: Simplet, which burns for 1.2 seconds to boost the round from its launcher; and Sophie, which has a 20-second burn time during the sustain phase. Deflectors in the sustainer motor exhaust are used to steer the missile. SS.11 and the AS.11 air-launched counterpart are operated by more than 30 countries, although the French army is replacing them with Hot.

Length: 1.21 m (4 ft) *Span:* 50 cm (19.7 in) *Diameter:* 16.4 cm (6.5 in) *Weight:* 30.4 kg (67 lb) *Range:* 3000 m (3300 yards) *Speed:* 540 km/h (335 mph) average *Warhead:* 3 interchangeable types, 2.6 kg (5 lb 12 oz) typical weight

---

SS-12 Soviet short-range ballistic missile See **Scaleboard**

SS.12, Aérospatiale

French antitank and antiship missile. A scaled-up version of SS.11, the Aérospatiale (originally Nord-Aviation) SS.12 packs a punch equivalent to a 175-mm (6.9-in) shell and can be used against a wide variety of targets such as tanks, fortifications or ships. The weapon may be fired from launchers on ground vehicles, but the AS.12 air-to-surface version is the most widely deployed. An antiship variant, SS.12M, was first demonstrated in 1966 and has since been fitted in FPBs operated by at least six countries.

The operator tracks a target in his optical sight, which is stabilized for airborne and naval applications, and steers the missile with a joystick. The later AS.12/SS.12 systems incorporate semiautomatic command to line-of-sight guidance, so the operator has only to track the target; an infrared sensor in the sight detects flares on the missile, allowing a small computer to calculate steering corrections to bring the round back on to the sightline. SS.12 is powered by two solid-propellant rocket motors: an SNPE/Aérospatiale Achille booster, which burns for 1.15 seconds; and the same manufacturers' Hermione sustainer. The sustainer motor exhausts through lateral nozzles which can deflect the gas stream to steer the missile.

Length: 187 cm (73.6 in) *Span:* 65 cm (25.6 in) *Diameter:* 21 cm (8.3 in) *Weight:* 75 kg (165 lb) *Range:* 6000 m (6560 yards) *Speed:* 935 km/h (580 mph) at end of flight *Warhead:* 28.6 kg (63 lb), 3 interchangeable types

---

SS-13 Soviet intercontinental ballistic missile See **Savage**

SS-14 Soviet intermediate-range ballistic missile See **Scamp/Scapegoat**

SS-15 Soviet mobile ballistic missile See **Scrooge**

SS-16

Soviet intercontinental ballistic missile. The SS-16 is a third-generation replacement for the SS-13 Savage, which seems not to have lived up to expectations and was deployed in only 60 silos. SS-16 is slightly smaller than SS-13 but has twice the throw weight of its predecessor for the same range and is more accurate. It may be fired from mobile launchers as well as from silos. SS-16 has three stages, each powered by solid-propellant rocket motors, and carries a computer-controlled dispensing bus which can be fitted with MIRVs. The first SS-16s to enter service carried only a single warhead, however, although a version with three re-entry vehicles has been reported.

(Estimated data) Length: 20 m (65 ft 8 in) *Diameter:* 2.1 m (6 ft 11 in) *Range:* 9000 km (5600 miles)

SS-17

Soviet intercontinental ballistic missile. SS-17 is one of two third-generation ICBMs which are replacing the SS-11 Sego, the other being the SS-19. The new weapon may incorporate technology based on that employed in its predecessor and it is thought to be encased in a sleeve which allows it to be cold-launched (ie ejected from the silo before its rocket motors fire) from existing SS-11 silos. The missile was first tested in the second half of 1974, and the Mod 1 version with four independently targeted re-entry vehicles entered service the following year. The rate of conversion of SS-11 silos to accommodate SS-17 has been slower than was anticipated by the US Department of Defense, however, and by 1978 only about 60 examples of the new type were operational. The Mod 1's re-entry vehicles each carry a thermonuclear warhead with a yield of about one megaton and the circular error probable may be as low as 500 m (1600 ft). A Mod 2 version, with a single warhead, has also entered service. Both variants are likely to be capable of attacking hard targets.

(Estimated data) *Length:* 24 m (78 ft 9 in) *Diameter:* 2.5 m (8 ft 2 in) *Range:* over 10 000 km (6250 miles)

SS-18

Soviet intercontinental ballistic missile. SS-18, powered by rocket motors burning storable liquid propellants, is the world's largest operational missile and was developed to replace the SS-9 Scarp. The weapon is cold-launched (ie ejected from its silo before the first-stage engines ignite) and can carry about 30% greater payload than its predecessor. Three versions have been identified. Mod 1 may have entered service as early as 1974, although it is reported to have suffered from persistent technical problems even after it was declared operational; a single re-entry vehicle containing a thermonuclear warhead with a theoretical yield of up to 50 megatons is fitted. Mod 2, which has been deployed since 1976, carries eight to ten re-entry vehicles with warheads of at least one megaton each; the RVs can be aimed against individual targets, allowing a single SS-18 to attack a large number of ICBM silos. Mod 3, which also entered service in 1976, has a longer range than the first two models and is thought to be more accurate than Mod 1.

SS-18's performance has been improved since the weapon entered service, although some of the impressive results obtained during flight trials may not be representative of operational missiles. Test rounds have supposedly demonstrated a circular error probably of better than 180 m (600 ft), which would allow SS-18s to destroy US Minuteman silos. This improvement may have been achieved using experimental equipment being developed for the fifth generation of Soviet ICBMs, but other aspects of SS-18 itself have been upgraded since the type entered service. A new design of dispensing bus which spins the individual re-entry vehicles before they are ejected, thereby increasing their accuracy, has been perfected and the guidance software has also been improved. In addition, the inertial-guidance system used in the booster has been modified to give a better performance. More than 100 SS-18s had been deployed by 1978.

(Estimated data) *Length:* 36 m (118 ft) *Diameter:* 3 m (9 ft 10 in) *Range:* 12 000 km (7500 miles)

SS-19

Soviet intercontinental ballistic missile. SS-19 was, like SS-17, developed as a replacement for SS-11 Sego. It entered service in 1975, a year after flight-testing began, and more than 200 rounds had been deployed by 1978. The Mod 1 version carries up to six independently targeted re-entry vehicles, each containing a thermonuclear warhead with a yield of between 800 kilotons and one megaton, and a Mod 2 variant equipped with a single RV has also been tested.

(Estimated data) *Length:* 27 m (88 ft 7 in) *Diameter:* 2.5 m (8 ft 2 in) *Weight:* 80 000 kg (176 000 lb) *Range:* 10 000 km (6200 miles)

SS-20

Soviet intermediate-range ballistic missile. SS-20 comprises the first two stages of the SS-16 ICBM and is being deployed as a replacement for the first generation of IRBMs and MRBMs. The missile is launched from a tracked vehicle which can rapidly be reloaded; some 300 to 400 such launchers are expected to be deployed, each with about two reload rounds allocated in addition to the one fitted at the outset. The standard payload is thought to comprise three independently targeted re-entry vehicles containing thermonuclear warheads of 500-600 kilotons yield. A single 1.5-megaton warhead might be an alternative, and some reports have mentioned a lightweight warhead of about 150 kg (330 lb) and a yield of at least 50 kilotons. The substitution of this payload for the 1.5-megaton type, which weighs 500 kg (1100 lb), would theoretically allow SS-20's range to be increased from some 5000 km (3100 miles) to 7500 km (4700 miles) and thus convert the weapon into an ICBM at short notice. A more likely ploy, however, would be to add the third stage, thus converting SS-20s into SS-16s, which could either be fired from the mobile launcher or be deployed in silos.

(Estimated data) *Length:* 16 m (52 ft) *Diameter:* 2.1 m (6 ft 11 in)

SSBS, Aérospatiale

French intermediate-range ballistic missile. SSBS (sol-sol balistique stratégique) is France's land-based IRBM, complementing the submarine-launched MSBS and nuclear weapons delivered by aircraft. France's nuclear-weapons programme began in 1955 and was later extended to include ballistic missiles, SEREB (Société pour l'Etude et la Réalisation d'Engins Balistiques) being set up in 1959 to act as prime contractor for their development; the company has since become part of Aérospatiale. The propulsion, control, guidance and re-entry vehicle expertise needed for IRBMs was built up from 1960 to 1967 with the aid of the Saphir, Agate, Topaze and Emeraude test vehicles, and this stage proceeded so smoothly that in May 1963 the French government authorized simultaneous development of both SSBS and MSBS.

Initial trials of SSBS systems took place from 1965 to 1967 at the Centre d'Essais des Landes on France's Atlantic coast and used the S-112 vehicle with a live motor in the first stage and a dummy second stage. The main objectives of these first trials were to examine the vehicle's performance at high altitude and to check stage separation, as well as to prove the silo design. The first two S-112s were in fact fired from ground-level pads but the remaining five were fired from an experimental silo.

The next series of eight firings took place in 1967 and 1968 using the S-01 vehicle, which had two stages each powered by a P10 solid-propellant rocket motor and was used to develop the guidance and re-entry systems. The final series of trials which followed employed the S-02 vehicle with a P16 first stage and a P10 second stage; this model closely resembled the operational S2 missile, the original S1 design—which had two P10 stages—having been abandoned.

SSBS is operated by the Armée de l'Air's 1ᵉʳ Groupement des Missiles Stratégiques, formed in July 1968 and declared operational with its first squadron of nine S2 weapons on August 2, 1971. A second nine-round squadron has since joined the force, but plans to deploy a third unit were abandoned to save money. The missiles are mounted in silos spaced between 3 km (1.9 miles) and 8 km (5 miles) apart at the Saint-Christol Air Base on the Plateau d'Albion, Haute Provence. The weapons are operated from underground command posts at Rustrel and Reilhannette.

The S2's P16 first stage is powered by a Type 902 solid-propellant rocket motor which produces 55 000 kg (121 250 lb) of thrust for 76 seconds, using four gimballed nozzles for steering. The P10 second stage (which additionally formed the first stage of the MSBS M1 missile) is powered by a Type 903 motor developing 45 000 kg (100 000 lb) of thrust for about 50 seconds and also employing four gimballed nozzles for steering. SSBS S2 carries a nuclear warhead of 150 kilotons yield.

From 1980 the 18 S2s are being replaced by the improved S3 model, which has a new second stage: the P6 Rita 2, developing 32 000 kg (70 500 lb) of thrust for 52 seconds and already employed in the M2 and M20 variants of MSBS. The S3 has a longer range than S2, is more accurate, carries a one-megaton thermonuclear warhead and incorporates penetration aids to confuse the enemy's defences. The new model is shorter and lighter than its predecessor, so it can be installed in existing silos with the minimum of modification.

(S2) *Length:* 14.8 m (48 ft 7 in) *Diameter:* 1.5 m (4 ft 11 in) *Weight:* 32 000 kg (70 500 lb) *Range:* 3000 km (1860 miles)

(S3) *Length:* 13.7 m (44 ft 11 in) *Diameter:* 1.5 m (4 ft 11 in) *Weight:* 25 800 kg (56 900 lb) *Range:* over 3000 km (1860 miles)

SSC-1 Soviet coastal antiship missile	See **Sepal**
SSC-2 Soviet cruise missile	See **Samlet**
SS-N-1 Soviet antiship missile	See **Scrubber**
SS-N-2 Soviet antiship missile	See **Styx**
SS-N-3 Soviet antiship missile	See **Shaddock**

SS-N-7

SS-N-4 Soviet submarine-launched ballistic missile   See **Sark**

SS-N-5 Soviet submarine-launched ballistic missile   See **Serb**

SS-N-6 Soviet submarine-launched ballistic missile   See **Sawfly**

SS-N-7

Soviet submarine-launched antiship missile. SS-N-7 entered service in about 1968 aboard the 'Charlie' Class nuclear-powered attack submarine, each of which is fitted with eight missile launchers. The Soviet navy now operates some 12 'Charlie Is' and a number of 'Charlie IIs', which are allocated to the Northern Fleet. SS-N-7 is similar in concept to the McDonnell Douglas Sub-Harpoon, although the Soviet weapon is thought to be powered by a solid-propellant rocket motor rather than a turbojet and cruises at supersonic speeds. The weapon is launched from containers in the submarine's foredeck while it is submerged, and probably employs an autopilot or simple inertial navigator working in conjunction with a radio altimeter for mid-course guidance. An active radar seeker is thought to be fitted for terminal homing.

(Estimated data) *Length:* 6.7 m (22 ft) *Span:* 2 m (6 ft 7 in) *Diameter:* 75 cm (29.5 in) *Speed:* Mach 1.5 *Range:* 55 km (35 miles) *Warhead:* high-explosive

SS-N-8

Soviet submarine-launched ballistic missile. In deploying the SS-N-8 in 1973 the Soviet navy closed the gap in performance between its own SLBMs and those of the United States. The missile demonstrated a range of 7750 km (4800 miles) during early flight trials, compared with the maximum of 4600 km (2860 miles) which can be achieved by the Lockheed Poseidon and the 7000 km (4350 miles) or so of the follow-on Trident. Not content with this coup, the USSR went on to fly SS-N-8 a distance of 9200 km (5700 miles), which effectively makes the weapon a submarine-launched intercontinental ballistic missile.

The use of stellar-inertial guidance gives SS-N-8 a circular error probable of about 400 m (1300 ft), which is similar to that achieved by Minuteman. The missile is fired from launchers mounted vertically within the pressure hull of 'Delta I' and 'Delta II' submarines; the former type, of which 18 are operational, carries 12 missiles and the latter, of which eight are in service, holds 16. The enlarged 'Delta III' has tubes for 20 rounds but is expected to carry the SS-N-18 missile. SS-N-8 is operational in at least two versions: Mod 1 carries a single re-entry vehicle containing a thermonuclear warhead with a yield of 1-2 megatons; and Mod 2 is fitted with three RVs of unknown yield; a possible Mod 3 version, also with three re-entry vehicles but able to dispense these to attack different targets which are large distances apart, has been tested.

(Estimated data) *Length:* 17 m (55 ft 9 in) *Diameter:* 2 m (6 ft 7 in) *Weight:* 20 000 kg (44 100 lb)

SS-N-9 Soviet antiship missile   See **Siren**

SS-N-10

Soviet antiship missile. The Soviet navy's 'Kara' and 'Kresta II' cruisers and 'Krivak' destroyers are armed with a missile which was for many years designated SS-N-10 by NATO, but it is now generally accepted that the tubes on these vessels are occupied by the SS-N-14 torpedo-carrying missile for use against both surface vessels and submarines. Why the launchers for this weapon should differ so widely in appearance from one ship class to another has not been satisfactorily explained, and SS-N-10 may yet turn out to be a separate weapon.
See also SS-N-14.

SS-N-11

Soviet antiship missile. SS-N-11 is thought to be a development of the SS-N-2 Styx and is fitted to 'Osa II' fast patrol boats in place of the earlier missile, which equips 'Osa Is'. The weapon is assumed to be very similar in operation to Styx: it is fired from fixed launcher/containers and is thought to use the same propulsion arrangement of a solid-propellant rocket booster and turbojet cruise motor. The method of mid-course guidance is likely to be by an autopilot, probably updated by radio command from the launch ship or other vehicle, with an active-radar or infrared seeker for the attack phase.

'Osa IIs' carry four forward-facing launchers, and the same number of rearward-facing bins have been mounted on the modified 'Kashin' destroyers which were originally armed with the SS-N-1 Scrubber. A further application is the modified 'Nanuchka' corvettes supplied by the USSR to India, which carry four SS-N-11 launchers in place of the six SS-N-9 bins fitted to the Soviet navy's vessels of this class.

(Estimated data) *Length:* 6.4 m (21 ft) *Span:* 2.75 m (9 ft) *Diameter:* 75 cm (29.5 in) *Weight:* 2500 kg (5500 lb) *Range:* 50 km (30 miles) *Speed:* Mach 0.9 *Warhead:* 400 kg (880 lb)

SS-N-12

Soviet antiship missile. The SS-N-12 has been developed to replace the SS-N-3 Shaddock. At one time it was thought in the West that the primary application for such a weapon was the 'Echo II' Class of nuclear-powered attack submarines, replacing Shaddock in the eight launchers carried by each of the 27 vessels of this type; but when the first of the *Kiev* Class antisubmarine cruisers made her appearance it became obvious that she was also intended to carry the new missile. *Kiev* has eight launcher/containers mounted in pairs on the foredeck. They can be elevated for firing and are thought to be reloaded from a magazine between the forward and after rows of missile bins. A Trap Door radar is housed beneath a hatch near the vessel's bows, the antenna being elevated when needed for use with SS-N-12. The purpose of Trap Door is not certain, but it probably tracks the missile at long ranges and transmits updated target information to the round in flight.

Information about the method of operation adopted for SS-N-12 is meagre, but some reports have indicated that the missile cruises at about Mach 2.5 and a height of 10 000 m (33 000 ft) for attacks up to a range of 560 km (350 miles). Alternatively, the weapon is said to be capable of travelling up to 3200 km (2000 miles) at transonic speed and high altitude. The latter figure seems extravagant and unnecessary, however. Some form of air-breathing propulsion is assumed to be employed and a large nuclear warhead is thought to be the normal payload.

No reliable data available.

SS-N-13

Soviet submarine-launched antiship missile. SS-N-13 is thought to have been developed to arm 'Yankee' Class fleet ballistic missile submarines, allowing them to attack high-value seaborne targets such as aircraft carriers and enemy FBM submarines. The weapon is believed to be fired from the launch tubes normally occupied by SS-N-6 Sawfly SLBMs in the 'Yankees', either as a mixture with that weapon or as the sole missile in submarines converted for this specialist role. SS-N-13 is reported to carry a nuclear warhead over a range of 750 km (470 miles) at a speed of Mach 4, and to use target information derived from satellites. Some form of terminal guidance is believed to be fitted, but further data have not been released.

SS-N-14

Soviet antisubmarine missile. SS-N-14 is one of the most enigmatic of Soviet missiles, especially since the official view in the West is now that SS-N-10 does not exist and the weapon which arms 'Kara' and 'Kresta II' cruisers and 'Krivak' destroyers is in fact SS-N-14. The missile is said to be similar in concept to the Australian Ikara or French Malafon, carrying a homing torpedo within a winged body which is jettisoned near the target; a nuclear depth charge may be an alternative payload.

The *Moskva* Class helicopter carriers and *Kiev* Class antisubmarine cruisers each carry a twin-arm launcher for the SUW-N-1 system, which can supposedly fire either SS-N-14 or the FRAS-1 rocket; the vessels which were originally thought to be armed with SS-N-10 are fitted with cylindrical launcher/containers. The 'Kresta II' and 'Kara' cruisers each carry launchers in two

The bow of a 'Krivak' Class destroyer showing the four launching tubes for SS-N-14 antisubmarine missiles. The SS-N-14 is believed to be similar to the Australian Ikara missile

'Yankees' carrying SS-N-13s has been discussed. The former weapon is reported to have an effective range of up to 500 km (310 miles).

SS-N-17

Soviet submarine-launched ballistic missile. The first and second generations of the Soviet navy's fleet ballistic missiles were for a long time assumed to use solid propellants, but it is now generally accepted that they employed liquid propellants and that SS-N-17 is the first to have solid rocket propulsion. One of the 34 'Yankee' Class submarines has been converted for use as a testbed and the other vessels of this type are expected to be armed with SS-N-17 as a replacement for their original SS-N-6 Sawfly weapons. The new missile is similar in size to the SS-N-8 and can carry multiple independently targeted re-entry vehicles; no other data are available.

SS-N-18

Soviet submarine-launched ballistic missile. The liquid-propellant SS-N-18 is intended to replace the SS-N-8 in the Soviet navy's 'Delta' Class submarines and to arm the new 'Typhoon' Class. The new missile has a range of at least 7400 km (4600 miles) and can carry three independently targeted re-entry vehicles using more accurate guidance than in its predecessors.

banks of four, one on each side of the superstructure, while 'Krivak' destroyers are fitted with four launchers on the foredeck. There must still be some doubt as to whether the missiles used aboard these vessels are in fact identical.

(Estimated data) *Length:* 7 m (23 ft) *Span:* 2.1 m (6 ft 11 in) *Diameter:* 80 cm (31.5 in) *Range:* 30 km (19 miles)

SS-N-15

Soviet submarine-launched antisubmarine missile. SS-N-15 is the Soviet navy's approximate equivalent of the Goodyear UUM-44A Subroc and is carried aboard 'Victor'

Class nuclear-powered attack submarines, each of which is fitted with eight standard torpedo tubes also used to fire SS-N-15. After launching, the missile pitches up and flies through the air, probably on a ballistic trajectory, before releasing a nuclear depth charge over the enemy submarine. A solid-propellant rocket motor is assumed to be used, and the maximum range is normally quoted as 40 km (25 miles).

SS-N-16

Soviet cruise missile. SS-N-16 is reported to be a long-range cruise missile which arms the Soviet navy's 'Victor' Class nuclear-powered attack submarines, although evidence to support this assertion is slight. Targeting information is thought to be derived from satellites, and the possibility of collaboration between 'Victors' armed with SS-N-16 and

Staaken R

German heavy bomber series. The V.G.O.I. —named after the Versuchsbau Gotha Ost—(East Gotha experimental works), on whose airfield the Flugzeugwerke Staaken, later Zeppelin Werke Staaken, was originally established in 1915, was the first of a series of experimental heavy bombers. Built on an unprecedented scale for a German aircraft, the V.G.O.I was powered by three 240-hp Maybach Mb.IV engines, one driving a tractor propeller in the nose and the others mounted in nacelles between the wings driving pushers; it weighed 9520 kg (20988 lb) loaded and was big enough to provide accommodation for a gunner in the forward part of each engine nacelle. It was followed by the similar V.G.O.II, while the V.G.O.III had two 160-hp Mercedes D.III engines driving each propeller.

The next prototype adopted the official Riesenflugzeug (giant aeroplane) designation

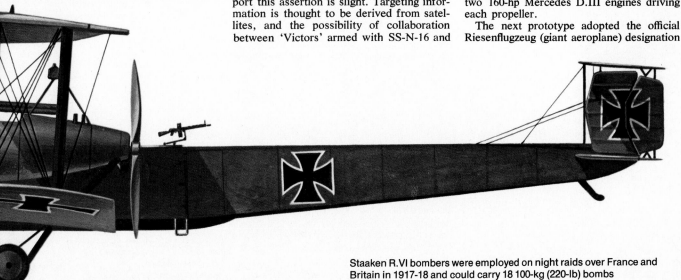

Staaken R.VI bombers were employed on night raids over France and Britain in 1917-18 and could carry 18 100-kg (220-lb) bombs

Standard, General Dynamics

as R.IV, its predecessors being retrospectively designated in the series, and differed from the V.G.O.III mainly in substituting four 220-hp Benz Bz.IV engines in the wing nacelles and nose. By September 1917 the R.V had appeared with three tractor propellers, driven by a single 240-hp Maybach in the nose and two similar engines in each nacelle. The gun positions were moved to the rear of the nacelles, and a new Schwalbenest (swallow's nest) machine-gun post was added above the upper wing centre section.

Only single examples were built of the first five Staaken giants, though all except the first, which crashed during trials, saw operational service on either the Western or Eastern Fronts, but a total of 18 of the next number of the series, the R.VI, were built. The R.VI dispensed with the nose propeller, and had only two tractors, each driven by a pair of 245-hp Maybach or 260-hp Mercedes D.IVa engines. The nacelle gun positions were dispensed with, crew accommodation comprising nose-gunner/bomb-aimer's position in the nose, an enclosed cabin for the two pilots, radio-operator, navigator and mechanic, a dorsal cockpit for two gunners, with access through a tunnel to a ventral gun position, and a cockpit for a flight engineer between the engines in each nacelle. Normal crew carried was seven. A total bombload of 18 100-kg (220-lb) bombs could be carried internally, though larger bombs of up to 1000 kg (2200 lb) were sometimes carried below the fuselage.

The first R.VI entered service in June 1917 and the type equipped two heavy bomber units, RFA 500 and 501, remaining operational until the end of the war. Initially they served on the Eastern Front, but they were soon introduced on the Western Front, and on September 17 they carried out their first raid on England. R.VIs—the largest aircraft to fly over England in either world war—participated in 11 of the total of 52 raids made by German fixed-wing aircraft against England, dropping 27 190 kg (59 944 lb) of bombs, and none was lost. After these raids ended in May 1918 they continued bombing expeditions against Paris, while one made a round trip of 800 km (500 miles) to bomb Le Havre. Later in the war they began to be used against targets in the vicinity of the Allied front lines, where their size and lack of speed made them extremely vulnerable and a number of losses were suffered.

Although the R.VI was the only giant to be built in quantity, development did not stop there. The Type L seaplane was an R.VI mounted on massive floats 13 m (42 ft 8 in) in length. It was destroyed during trials, while the R.VII, an R.VI with a modified tail unit, crashed on its way to the front. The R.XIV, three of which were built in 1918, reinstated the nose propeller and had both tractors and pushers on the wing nacelles, each being driven by a 245-hp Maybach engine, and was followed by a single R.XIVa and three R.XVs, all similar to the R.XIV.

Finally, the R.VI was fitted with one 530-hp and one 220-hp Benz engine in each nacelle driving two tractor and two pusher propellers; one crashed shortly after its completion in October 1918, and another two were still under construction at the time of the Armistice, though one was completed after the war as a civil aircraft and was tested briefly before being broken up.

(R.VI) *Span:* 42.2 m (138 ft 6 in) *Length:* 22.1 m (72 ft 6 in) *Gross weight:* 11 848 kg (26 120 lb) *Maximum speed:* 135 km/h (84 mph)

(R.XV) *Span:* 42.2 m (138 ft 6 in) *Length:* 22.5 m (73 ft 10 in) *Gross weight:* 14 450 kg (31 857 lb) *Maximum speed:* 130 km/h (81 mph)

Standard, General Dynamics

US naval surface-to-air missile. Development of Standard began in December 1964 to replace General Dynamics' earlier Terrier and Tartar naval SAMs. The RIM-66 Standard MR (medium range) is superseding the RIM-24 Tartar, while the RIM-67 Standard ER (extended range) is taking over from the RIM-2 Terrier. Both are known as SM-1 (Standard Missile 1), and by the end of 1978 more than 7000 had been built to equip the United States Navy's cruisers, destroyers and frigates. The missile has also been ordered by at least eight overseas countries.

Standard uses the same shipboard handling and launching equipment as Terrier and Tartar, and only minor changes have to be made to the ship's fire-control system to handle the new weapon, but under the skin an almost complete redesign has taken place. Advances in battery technology have made possible an all-electric missile, and the electronics are solid-state to reduce the warmup time before launching and, thanks to the increased reliability, eliminate the need to check the round on board ship. A larger dual-thrust motor designed for Standard MR has increased the weapon's performance envelope by 50% compared with its predecessor, and the initial design has been successively upgraded to further improve performance and resistance to electronic countermeasures. Additional refinements include the adoption of the new Mk 90 warhead which produces fragments travelling at up to Mach 6 and has a secondary incendiary effect. The new Mk 45 fuze which detonates this warhead is said to be twice as sensitive as its predecessor with respect to target speed and cross-section.

Standard can be interfaced with a variety of fire-control systems and tracking radars, including the Raytheon SPG-51 which is employed with Tartar, the SPG-60 STIR (standard target illuminating radar) used with the Lockheed Mk 86 system, or the Sperry Mk 92 Mod 2 (a licence-built Signaal M28). The radars track the target and illuminate it so that reflected radiation can be detected by the semiactive radar homing head fitted to Standard. The weapon is fired from existing launchers or from the new Northern Ordnance Mk 26; Standard MR is powered by a dual-thrust Aerojet/Hercules Mk 56, while Standard ER has an Atlantic Research Mk 30 boost motor and a US Naval Propellant Plant Mk 12 sustainer.

SM-1 is now being followed by Standard 2, which uses the same airframe and motors as the initial version but incorporates an inertial reference unit for mid-course guidance via a data link. This modification increases the performance envelope of the MR version by 60% compared with SM-1, while that of the ER variant is more than doubled. The SM-2 is being developed as part of the RCA Aegis air-defence system which will be installed in the US Navy's new DDG.47 (modified *Spruance* Class) destroyers, the first of which was ordered in September 1978, and can also replace Terrier in existing vessels. The SPY-1A phased-array radar, which forms part of Aegis, tracks aircraft and transmits mid-course guidance commands for Standard 2, which does not require continuous illumination. As the missile nears its target, the Aegis weapons-control system automatically allocates a Raytheon SPG-62 illuminator, which is included in the Mk 99 fire-control system, to illuminate the aircraft or enemy missile with continuous-wave radiation so that the SM-2's semiactive radar seeker can operate for the last stages of an attack. Aegis trials using SM-1s took place successfully from 1974 to 1976, and the first interception using an SM-2 was made in December 1976.

(SM-1 MR) *Length:* 4.57 m (15 ft) *Span:* 1.07 m (3 ft 6 in) *Diameter:* 35 cm (13.8 in) *Weight:* 590 kg (1300 lb) *Range:* 24 km (15 miles) *Maximum altitude:* over 19 800 m (65 000 ft) *Speed:* Mach 2.8 *Warhead:* high-explosive

(SM-1 ER) *Length:* 8.23 m (27 ft) *Span:* 1.57 m (5 ft 2 in) *Diameter:* 35 cm (13.8 in) *Weight:* 1360 kg (3000 lb) *Range:* 56 km (35 miles) *Maximum altitude:* over 19 800 m (65 000 ft) *Speed:* Mach 2.8 *Warhead:* high-explosive

(SM-2) *Range:* 48 km (30 miles) RIM-66C Standard 2 MR; 97 km (60 miles) RIM-67C Standard 2 ER *(Dimensions* and other performance parameters as SM-1 ER)

A General Dynamics Standard SAM missile launched from a hovercraft during trials

General Dynamics

Standard Active, General Dynamics

US antiship missile. The RGM-66F Standard Active was developed as a back-up to Harpoon, with the aim of providing US Navy surface ships with a 'fire-and-forget' weapon which could engage targets over the radar horizon. The missile used the same airframe, motor, controls and autopilot as the surface-to-air RIM-66A Standard MR but carried a new Raytheon synthetic-aperture coherent-monopulse Doppler radar (CMDR) active seeker. The project was begun in 1971 but was abandoned some three years later when it became obvious that Harpoon would meet its objectives and the back-up programme was unnecessary.

Standard ARM, General Dynamics

US antiradiation missile. Standard ARM was developed from the surface-to-air RIM-66A Standard Missile 1 in a crash programme designed to provide the US Air Force and Navy with a larger, longer-range and more effective complement to the AGM-45 Shrike for use in Vietnam. As much existing equipment as possible was used, including the RIM-66 airframe and solid-propellant rocket motor (with some modifications so that it could be carried at high altitudes for extended periods) together with the Texas Instruments passive radiation seeker employed in Shrike. Development began in 1966, flight trials commenced the following year and the AGM-78A Standard ARM Mod 1 entered service in 1968, arming USAF Wild Weasel F-105F/G Thunderchiefs and US Navy A-6B Intruders.

This Mod 1 version filled the immediate need for a weapon to counter surface-to-air missile defences but had marginal performance. Work therefore proceeded with the Mod 1 series, beginning in 1967 with the AGM-78B in which a new Maxson Electronics seeker replaced the Shrike homing head. The Mod 1 family has since expanded to include the AGM-78C, -78D and -78D2, in which the performance of the missile has steadily been improved while the cost per round has been reduced; in 1978 latest versions were carried by the USN's A-6E Intruders and the USAF's F-4G Wild Weasels.

The US Navy was slow to develop a specialized antiship missile in the form of Harpoon, so in 1970 it launched a programme aimed at adapting existing weapons to provide an immediate counter to missile-armed ships. Both RIM-66 Standard MR and the AGM-78C and -78D versions of Standard ARM were adopted for this role, the antiradiation variants—designated RGM-66D—being fitted in box launcher/containers aboard patrol gunboats. The weapon is also carried by six DDG destroyers and six FFG frigates of the US Navy, using the normal Tartar launcher, and has additionally been fitted to three Iranian destroyers.

Signals from hostile radars to be attacked are processed by a TIAS (target identification and acquisition system) in the launch vehicle, which computes target location and directs the missile's seeker to lock onto the radar's emissions. The IBM 4-Pi computer used in TIAS stores information about the types of radar likely to be encountered and programs the Standard ARM to fly the best trajectory to hit its objective. The missile will follow this flightpath even if the enemy radar stops transmitting, whereas Shrike depends on continuous transmissions for a successful attack.

Length: 4.57 m (15 ft) *Span:* 1.09 m (3 ft 7 in) *Diameter:* 34.3 cm (13.5 in) *Weight:* 635 kg (1400 lb) *Range:* 24 km (15 miles) *Speed:* Mach 2 *Warhead:* high-explosive

Star

Spanish small-arms. The Bonifacio Echeverria company of Eibar, Spain, manufacture small-arms under the tradename Star. The company began operations in 1908, manufacturing an automatic pistol loosely based on the 1901 Mannlicher, a blowback pistol with open-topped slide and external hammer. Its principal difference from the Mannlicher was a less graceful shape and the use of a detachable magazine.

The firm has since produced a vast range of pistols for commercial sale, but the company records were destroyed during the Spanish Civil War, and full details of their models and adoption are not known. In 1921 the firm began producing heavy-calibre locked-breech pistols, copies of the Colt M1911 pattern, in 9-mm (0.354-in) Largo, 9-mm Parabellum, 0.38-in Super (9.65-mm) and 0.45-in (11.4-mm) calibres, and some of these were bought by South American governments at various times during the 1920s and 1930s. One notable model, bought by Nicaragua, was the Model MB, which had a selector switch allowing full-automatic fire and extended magazines for capacities up to 32 shots.

In 1978 the Spanish army and Guarda Civil adopted the Star BM pistol in 9-mm Parabellum calibre as the official sidearm. This is also based on the general outline of the Colt M1911 but with a somewhat shorter slide and barrel. It uses a magazine safety as well as an applied safety, and is manufactured to a high standard of finish and quality.

In 1934 the company began working on the design of submachine-guns and produced four varying models in 1935. The IS34 was a semiautomatic carbine chambered for the Spanish service 9-mm Largo cartridge. It was a simple blowback weapon with finned barrel, and few were made. The SI35, which followed, was capable of full or semiautomatic firing, and also allowed adjustment to fast or slow rates of automatic fire. The RU35 was practically the same weapon, but allowed only the slow rate of fire (300 rds/min), while the TN35 went in the other direction and allowed only the fast rate of fire (700 rds/min). All these weapons were externally almost identical, using perforated barrel jackets, vertical magazines and wooden stocks. Some may be found with muzzle compensators and bayonet bars. A small number of each were used during the Spanish Civil War but, surprisingly, no large-scale manufacture was attempted. In 1940 the TN35 model was offered to the US and British governments under the name Atlantic, via a marketing organization set up in the United States, but after testing it was refused by both countries.

In 1942, by means not entirely clear, the Star factory acquired a set of engineering drawings for the German MP40. The Echeverria engineers made some improvements to this design and, as the Z-45, this went into production in July 1944. It was adopted by the Guarda Civil in 1945 and later by the Spanish air force and army. The principal points of difference in the Z-45, compared to the MP40, are the adoption of a perforated barrel jacket and a muzzle compensator; the shifting of the cocking handle from the left to the right of the receiver; a wooden stock and handguard or a wooden handguard and folding steel stock; and a somewhat lower rate of fire. An unusual feature is the ability to change the barrel quickly by unlocking the muzzle compensator.

The Z-45 was used by the Spanish forces until the mid-1960s, when it was replaced by the Z-62. This was a much simpler design using pressed and welded steel, and plastic mouldings, which generally reflected modern assembly techniques. It has a simple cylindrical receiver, a folding metal stock, jacketed barrel, and an unusual double trigger; pressing the lower section of the trigger gave single shots, while pressing the upper section gave automatic fire. This, unfortunately, was the weak spot of the design, and after considerable trouble it was replaced by a simple trigger with a conventional selector switch on the side of the receiver. In this form, it became the Z-70, and this pattern was issued to replace the Z-62 which was withdrawn.

(Pistol BM) Calibre: 9 mm (0.354 in) *Ammunition:* 9-mm Parabellum *Weight:* 0.88 kg (1 lb 15 oz) *Length:* 185 mm (7.3 in) *Barrel length:* 102 mm (4 in) *Magazine:* 8-round detachable box *Muzzle velocity:* 350 m/sec (1150 ft/sec)

(Submachine-gun Z-45) Calibre: 9 mm *Ammunition:* 9-mm Largo *Weight:* 3.86 kg (8 lb 8 oz) *Length:* 838 mm (33 in) *Barrel length:* 198 mm (7.8 in) *Magazine:* 30-round detachable box *Rate of fire:* 450 rds/min *Muzzle velocity:* 380 m/sec (1250 ft/sec)

(Submachine-gun Z-62) Calibre: 9 mm *Ammunition:* 9-mm Largo or 9-mm Parabellum *Weight:* 2.87 kg (6 lb 5 oz) *Length:* 700 mm (27.6 in) *Barrel length:* 200 mm (7.9 in) *Magazine:* 20- 30- or 40-round box *Rate of fire:* 550 rds/min *Muzzle velocity:* 380 m/sec (1250 ft/sec)

Starfighter, Lockheed F-104

US multirole combat aircraft. One of the most widely flown military aircraft of the 1960s and 1970s, the Starfighter (Lockheed Model 83) was conceived in the closing weeks of 1952 as a short-range, high-speed day intercepter. Subsequently it survived a disappointing career in this role to blossom instead as a multimission tactical-support fighter-bomber and reconnaissance aircraft that became the subject of the largest international collaborative manufacturing programme since the end of the Second World War. Designed by C L ('Kelly') Johnson of Lockheed, the original Starfighter emerged (after computer evaluation of nearly 300 different configurations) as a radical design offering a top speed of Mach 2.2. The engine,

Starfire, Lockheed F-94

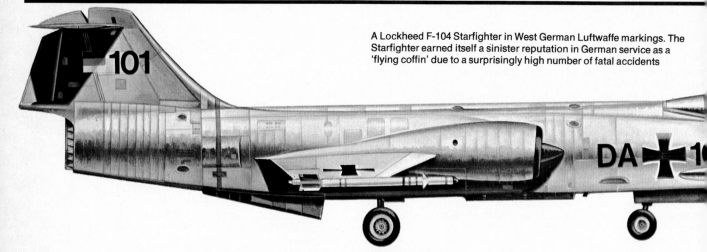

A Lockheed F-104 Starfighter in West German Luftwaffe markings. The Starfighter earned itself a sinister reputation in German service as a 'flying coffin' due to a surprisingly high number of fatal accidents

fuel, landing gear, avionics, armament and pilot were all packed into a long, needle-nosed fuselage. It was supported in flight by tiny, exceptionally thin non-swept wings each measuring only 2.29 m (7 ft 6 in) from root to tip. It was with good reason that Lockheed could publicize its new fighter as 'the missile with a man in it'.

The US Air Force ordered two XF-104 prototypes in March 1953, and the first of these was flown for the first time on February 7, 1954. Each was powered by a single 4536 kg (10 000-lb) st afterburning Wright XJ65-W-6: this was not the intended production powerplant, but it enabled one of the XF-104s to reach a speed of Mach 1.79 during a test flight just over a year later. Johnson's intended engine was the General Electric J79, and Mach 2 became attainable when the 6713-kg (14 800-lb) thrust afterburning YJ79-GE-3 was installed in the 15 YF-104A service-trials aircraft that followed. The first of these flew on February 17, 1956, and Mach 2 was first reached just over two months later. One hundred and fifty-five production F-104As were built; like the YF-104As, they had a longer fuselage to accommodate the bigger engine, and a half-cone body in each intake to generate inclined shock-waves at supersonic speeds. Basic armament comprised a built-in 20-mm (0.79-in) M-61 multibarrel 'Gatling' type cannon in the front of the fuselage, and an AIM-9B Sidewinder air-to-air missile at each wingtip. The short range of these weapons, and the fact that the F-104A's radar and infrared search and tracking gear could not match the speed of the aircraft, were probably among the chief factors limiting the F-104A to a visual day interception role and keeping the initial production run fairly small. Deliveries (to the 83rd Fighter Intercepter Squadron at Hamilton Air Force Base) began in January 1958, but three months later all F-104As were grounded and fitted with J79-GE-3B engines and a ventral stabilizing fin. They were withdrawn from Air Defense Command about 18 months later.

The next four production models also appeared only in small quantities. The F-104B (26 built, first flown on February 7, 1957) was a two-seat operational-trainer version of the A, while the F-104C (77 built) was a single-seat fighter-bomber version for Tactical Air Command. This had a 7167-kg (15 800-lb) st reheat J79-GE-7 engine feeding, blown flaps, in-flight refuelling capability, and could carry (in addition to the wingtip pair of

Sidewinders) two 454-kg (1000-lb) bombs, two rocket pods or two more Sidewinders on underwing pylons. Deliveries of this model began in October 1958, and the F-104C also had its two-seat combat trainer counterpart in the F-104D, of which 21 were completed. After withdrawal from Air Defense Command service, F-104As were supplied to Taiwan (25), Jordan (36) and Pakistan (12); the air self-defence force of Japan received 24 F-104DJs, assembled by Mitsubishi from Lockheed-built components; and Lockheed also produced 30 F-104Fs, basically similar to the D model, for West Germany.

The 279 F-104A/B/C/D models, the only Starfighters built for the USAF, represented only about one-tenth of the production Lockheed had hoped for at the start of the programme. In an effort to promote the Starfighter as a close-support strike fighter for West Germany, Lockheed proposed an extensive internal redesign to strengthen the airframe and upgrade the functional systems. Trailing-edge manoeuvring flaps were to be added, the vertical tail area increased, a North American search and ranging radar (NASARR) inserted into the needle nose, and the old, unpopular downward-ejecting pilot's seat was to be replaced by a more conventional upward-ejecting seat. This paper proposal was accepted by the German government, which gave Lockheed a development go-ahead on March 18, 1959, coupled with plans for the new F-104G to be built under licence in Germany. But by the time that the Lockheed Model 683 prototype was flown on October 5, 1960, Belgium, Italy and the Netherlands had also selected the F-104G, and European coproduction plans were therefore revised. Four production consortia were set up: one all-German, one Dutch/German, one Belgian and one Italian. Between them they built 947 F-104Gs: 604 for the Luftwaffe, 99 for Belgium, 120 for Holland (including camera-carrying FR-104Gs) and 124 for Italy. Lockheed produced a further 96 for Germany, one each for Belgium and Italy, and 192 two-seat TF-104G combat trainers.

At that time Canadair was producing 200 generally similar aircraft designated CF-104 and powered by Orenda-built J79s for the Royal Canadian Air Force. When these were completed the US Defense Department ordered 140 more from Canadair for supply to other NATO countries under the Military Assistance Program: 25 for Denmark, 36 for Greece, 16 for Norway, 25 for Spain and 38 for Turkey. Accompanying them were 28

Lockheed-built TF-104Gs. The other major customer was Japan, whose F-104J is basically an intercepter version of the G. Lockheed supplied three, and 207 more were completed locally by Mitsubishi.

The European F-104G programme ended in the mid-1960s, but in December 1966 Lockheed flew the first of two prototypes of a new model, the F-104S, with an 8120-kg (17 900-lb) thrust J79-GE-19 afterburning engine, updated avionics, and nine external weapon stations for a maximum ordnance load of 3402 kg (7500 lb), including a primary armament of two AIM-7 Sparrow III air-to-air missiles and/or two or four late-model Sidewinders. This version was put into production by the Aeritalia group, initially for the Italian air force (205) and later for Turkey (40), with production completed in late 1978.

The Starfighter has held many records, official and unofficial, during its career, and was the first aircraft to have held simultaneously the world absolute records for speed and height. On October 24, 1977, it acquired perhaps the most remarkable of them all when Darryl Greenamyer (who already held the world piston-engined speed record in an F8F Bearcat) captured also the world record for jets over a 3-km (1.86-mile) 'restricted altitude' course, at hair-raisingly low level, with a speed of 1590.45 km/h (988.26 mph) in the Red Baron Starfighter which he had built himself over a ten-year period from surplus F-104 components gathered from all over the world.

Span: 6.68 m (21 ft 11 in) without tip-tanks *Length:* 16.69 m (54 ft 9 in) *Gross weight:* (F-104C) 10 700 kg (23 590 lb); (F-104G) 13 054 kg (28 780 lb); (F-104S) 14 061 kg (31 000 lb) *Maximum speed:* 2335 km/h (1450 mph)

Starfire, Lockheed F-94

US Air Force fighter aircraft. The first jet-driven all-weather intercepter to be put into service by the US Air Force, the Starfire was the outcome of an urgent requirement in 1948 to evolve a two-seat radar-equipped fighter to bridge the gap until the Northrop F-89 Scorpion was ready for service introduction. Having unexpectedly found that its single-seat F-80 Shooting Star fighter handled even better and flew even faster after conversion into the two-seat T-33A, Lockheed was ideally placed with an aeroplane capable of receiving the new Hughes E-1 (APG-32) radar fire-control system. At the Lockheed

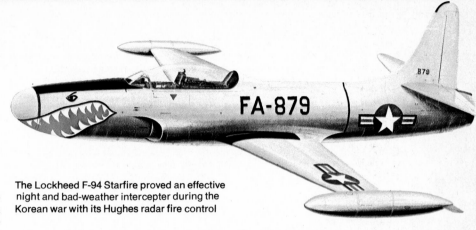

'Skunk Works' (more officially, the Advanced Development Projects section) at Burbank, a team under Russ Daniell began adapting the prototype T-33 to meet the interim fighter requirement. Principal changes involved the selection of the Allison

The Lockheed F-94 Starfire proved an effective night and bad-weather intercepter during the Korean war with its Hughes radar fire control

J33-A-33 turbojet engine, a 2722-kg (6000-lb) st afterburning version of the powerplant in the T-33; the installation of four 0.5-in (12.7-mm) M-3 Browning machine-guns in the nose, and provisions for the radar operator (in the rear seat) and radar equipment. In its new form as the YF-94 the prototype (which had begun life as a TF-80C before becoming the T-33 prototype) made its first flight on April 16, 1949; a second YF-94, also converted from a T-33, was flown on July 1 the same year. These and the early production F-94As, 110 of which were ordered, retained the underslung wingtip auxiliary fuel tanks as carried by the F-80/T-33A: indeed, the first 17 F-94As were aircraft that had been ordered and begun construction as T-33As, but converted into fighters while on the assembly line. Deliveries began at the end of 1949, and the F-94A became operational in June 1950, with the 319th All-Weather Fighter Squadron of Air Defense Command, USAF. With the outbreak, that month, of the Korean war, its presence was more than welcomed by the US, and it soon proved a successful night and bad-weather intercepter.

Development delays with the Scorpion led the air force to order a second Starfire model, the F-94B, for which in 1950 the 19th F-94A served as prototype. Principal improvements were a revised hydraulic system of increased pressure, ILS (instrument landing system), a Sperry Zero Reader in the cockpit, new oxygen system, and larger fuel tanks mounted centrally on the wingtips instead of underneath. Production of the 357 F-94Bs ordered began in 1951, and deliveries were made to Air National Guard squadrons as well as to the USAF. A few ANG aircraft had a lengthened nose, with three 0.5-in guns mounted in the top, above the radome; some had wing leading-edge pods mounting two pairs of 0.5-in guns.

On January 19, 1950, Lockheed had flown the first of two YF-94C prototypes, converted from production B models. This aircraft, converted at company expense after the air force had rejected proposals for an improved version, represented a major redesign effort. A stronger and thinner wing (10% instead of 13% thickness/chord ratio) of greater span, replaced that of the A and B versions; the tailplane was swept back and the vertical tail surfaces enlarged; gun armament was deleted in favour of the Mighty Mouse 2.75-in (70-mm) air-to-air rocket, 24 of which were grouped in an annular cluster around a symmetrically rounded nose; and the elderly J33 engine, which had given the early F-94s a relatively sluggish performance, was replaced by a much more potent powerplant. This was the Pratt & Whitney J48, an afterburning version of the Rolls-Royce

Tay, although an imported Tay was used in the YF-94C. Other new features included a braking parachute, housed in a 'pen-nib' fairing over the longer, fatter rear fuselage, and a Hughes E-5 semiautomatic radar-control system. Performance was much improved—particularly the sea-level rate of climb, which was trebled—and in mid-1950 the USAF placed an initial contract for 110 with the new designation F-79A. In September that year the designation was changed to F-94C, to avoid budget complications, and the eventual total built was the largest so far, 387 in all, before production ended in early 1954. Despite a few teething troubles, the F-94C Starfire successfully entered service, later aircraft being able to carry a further 24 rockets in two 12-round pods on the wing leading edges. The powerplant of the F-94C was the J48-P-5 or -5A (2880-kg [6350-lb] st dry, and 3970-kg [8750-lb] st with afterburning). One F-94C was converted in 1951 into a YF-94D single-seat close-support/long-range escort fighter prototype for the Korean war; a USAF order for 112 was later cancelled.

(F-94A) *Span:* 11.84 m (38 ft 10 in) without tip-tanks *Length:* 12.22 m (40 ft 1 in) *Gross weight:* 7126 kg (15710 lb) *Maximum speed:* 975 km/h (606 mph)

(F-94C) *Span:* 12.93 m (42 ft 5 in) without tip-tanks *Length:* 13.56 m (44 ft 6 in) *Gross weight:* 10977 kg (24200 lb) *Maximum speed:* 1040 km/h (646 mph)

StarLifter, Lockheed C-141

US strategic transport aircraft. Designed to provide the US Air Force's Military Air Transport Service (now Military Airlift Command) with high-speed transportation over very long ranges, the StarLifter gave an early indication of its capabilities when one C-141A airlifted a payload of 22680 kg (50000 lb) in stages over a range of 12070 km (7500 miles) in a flying time of 18½ hours. By contrast, the USAF's other two major transports at that time, the C-130 Hercules and C-124 Globemaster II, would have taken 30½ hours and 41¾ hours respectively to transport a comparable load over the same distance.

Designed in 1960 to meet the USAF's SOR 182 (Specific Operational Requirement 182), the Lockheed Model 300 was the first pure-jet aircraft designed from the outset for military transport duties, and the first of five C-141A development aircraft flew for the first time on December 17, 1963. The flight-test programme was quickly completed, and deliveries (to Tinker Air Force Base) began

The Lockheed C-141A StarLifter, which was the standard US Air Force heavy transport aircraft before the introduction of the Galaxy. StarLifters were used extensively in Vietnam

on October 19, 1964; the StarLifter began its operational service (at Travis AFB, with the 44th and 75th Air Transport squadrons) six months later, on April 23, 1965, and by late 1967 all 285 aircraft ordered had been completed, replacing Boeing C-97 Stratofreighters, C-135 Stratolifters and Globemaster IIs with 14 MAC squadrons. From August 1965 the StarLifters began a regular trans-Pacific supply run between the US and Vietnam, which at its peak was virtually a daily service.

The C-141A carries a flight crew of four, and its capacious, circular-section fuselage has a hold capacity of 247 cu m (8730 cu ft) which can accommodate up to 154 troops, 123 paratroops, 80 stretchers with 16 sitting patients or medical attendants, a 39 104-kg (86 210-lb) Minuteman ICBM in its container, or a 42 638-kg (94 000-lb) cargo payload. Range is 6565 km (4080 miles), cruising at a maximum of 908 km/h (564 mph) on the power of the four 9525-kg (21 000-lb) st Pratt & Whitney TF33-P-7 turbofan engines podded under the high-mounted swept wings; maximum range, with reduced payload, is 9880 km (6140 miles).

After a decade of experience with the C-141A, the USAF found that its hold was frequently filled with bulky cargoes of less than maximum weight; accordingly, in mid-1976 it awarded Lockheed a contract to develop a stretched version which would also be able to refuel in flight. A modified C-141A was flown, as the YC-141B, on March 24, 1977, with a 7.11 m (23 ft 4 in) longer fuselage and other improvements. All 277 surviving C-141As are to be brought up to C-141B standard by 1982, with a 60 cu m (2100 cu ft) increase in cargo hold volume and a maximum payload of 40 439 kg (89 152 lb).

(C-141A) *Span:* 48.74 m (159 ft 11 in) *Length:* 44.2 m (145 ft) *Gross weight:* 136 350 kg (300 600 lb) *Maximum speed:* 919 km/h (571 mph)

Steinbarsch, Steinbutt and Steinwal

German peroxide torpedoes. Steinbarsch was a 50-knot torpedo with a range of 6500 m (7100 yards); about 100 were produced for service. Steinbutt was developed from the Steinfisch, a 45-knot weapon with a range of 7000 m (7650 yards). Using decalin fuel it also ran at 45 knots but had a range of 8000 m (8750 yards). Like Steinbarsch about 100 were produced by May 1945; they fell into British hands and formed the basis of the postwar research which led to the Fancy or Mk 12 HTP torpedo.

Steinwal also used decalin, with helman as a fluid catalyst. (Helman is a 0.05% solution of potassium copper cyanate in 80% hydrazine hydrate/20% ethanol). Combustion was started by mixing the helman and the decalin with hydrogen peroxide in the combustion pot of the torpedo. As soon as it fired, the flow of helman was cut off, leaving the decalin to burn in the hydrogen peroxide at about 2300°C. Helman was difficult to store, and for safety's sake the potassium copper cyanate was added only at the last minute, before the catalyst mixed with the peroxide. If it arrived after the peroxide there was an explosion, so a complex system of cam-operated valves was provided.

It is interesting to note that the Steinwal was the first German torpedo to show any significant improvement in efficiency over the old British Mk 8. Its turbine was the best of all those tried in 1939-45, rated at 500 hp at 30 000 rpm, with blades machined from a solid steel disc. It had a cardan gear on the driving shaft, with an internal toothed flywheel ring, which prevented initial roll on firing. The small amount of exhaust bubbled out through a perforated ring around the engine section, and soon dissolved. It was also claimed that the bubble screen reduced radiated noise. Its ultra-long range allowed it to take advantage of the Lut pattern-running gyroscope.

Sten

British submachine-gun. In 1940 Britain was in grave danger of invasion and every type of weapon was scarce. The only submachine-guns available were US Thompsons, and though a hurried design effort had produced the Lanchester from the German MP 28 this was too expensive in factory effort to make in quantity. There was a desperate need for something simple and effective, and in January 1941 the Design Department of the Royal Small Arms Factory announced that

they had found an answer and had made prototypes. This was a much simplified Lanchester, coupled with some ideas from a captured MP 40; in particular the manufacturing processes of the MP 40 were adapted to the new weapon and stampings and components that could be subcontracted in their entirety were used to the full.

The gun was attractively light and compact and a limited endurance trial of 5000 rounds seemed to prove the soundness of the design. It was named the Sten, the letters being taken from the surnames of the two designers (Major R V Shepherd and Mr H J Turpin, who did most of the detailed work) and the location of the Enfield factory. The overriding requirement for the Sten was simplicity of manufacture and the use of easily available materials. The resulting gun must have horrified the traditional gun makers since it was crude in the extreme; but it worked, though the Mark I had a number of elaborations which soon proved to be of little or no use. There was a folding forehand grip, a conical flash-hider and some wooden furniture.

The basic mechanism set the pattern for the 3 million or so which followed. The blowback system of operation used a heavy bolt and a fairly strong return spring, a combination which gave a rate of fire of about 550

The Sten Mk I with its frame stock, flash-hider and compensator and folding grip

The Sten Mk II was popular with underground forces in Europe and could take a silencer

The simplified Sten Mk III was produced in time to equip the troops landing on D-Day

The airborne forces at Arnhem were armed with the well-made Sten Mk V

rds/min and ensured that the working parts were tolerant of dirt, dust, snow, mud and general neglect. The barrel was short and was held in a tubular metal sleeve, and the body was another similar metal tube. The only machined parts were the bolt and barrel; everything else was stamped or pressed and all joins were by pinning or welding. It was quickly found that manufacture of most of the components could be contracted out to little machine shops and even to large garages around the country. These parts were all gathered in one of the main factories for fitting together, and to be mated with the barrels which had to be made on special machines. The first production models were turned out from BSA in the late summer of 1941 and from then on by both BSA in Birmingham and Enfield in quantity.

The Mark I was soon replaced by the Mark II which was the most famous of the series. It was much simplified, with all unnecessary frills removed. The stock was a single tube with a flat plate on the end for the shoulder, and the woodwork and forehand grip disappeared. The barrel was held in by a screwed jacket and was easily removed. The magazine housing could be rotated to lie in the same plane as the trigger mechanism. The stock was only held by a spring stud, and when taken down to its component parts the Mark II could be carried very easily. It became a favourite of the French Resistance and other underground movements in Europe and in the end more than 2 million were made, a few of which still exist today.

The Mark III was introduced by Lines Brothers, a firm of toy makers, who had a large contract. They made yet more simplifications in the manufacture, building a gun which had a fixed barrel and the body and jacket all in one. It was probably the best version of the Sten, but did not appear in large numbers. In line with the then popular policy of making folding weapons for airborne troops, the Mark IV., IVA and IVB were tried. All followed the same general pattern of turning the gun into a form of automatic pistol with the same mechanism and magazine. This did not work satisfactorily and none of these small versions was ever put into production. A folding or telescoping stock might have achieved a worthwhile result, but for some reason this was never tried.

The Mark II was fitted with a silenced barrel in 1943 and became the first silenced submachine-gun to be accepted into service. Quite large numbers were made and it was a most effective night weapon.

Despite its advantages the Sten was never very popular with the British Army who knew it by a number of uncomplimentary names. The magazine gave some trouble with jams; though it was a perfect copy of that used in the MP 40, it was no comfort to the users to know that the Germans suffered the same sort of jams themselves. The magazine could be neither changed nor improved, so in an effort to convince the troops that a better weapon had been built the Mark V Sten was brought out in 1944. Various small manufacturing improvements were made, and the gun was dressed up with a wooden butt and pistol grip. The Mark V was a good gun, and had it not been saddled with the same magazine it might have been the best submachine-gun of

A Soviet 'Stenka' Class fast patrol boat. The 'Stenkas' are armed as submarine-chasers while their 'Osa' Class sisters mount four SS-N-2 surface-to-surface missiles in angled launchers

US Navy

the whole war. It remained in British Army service until the early 1960s. During the Second World War the Sten was used by all the Allies, and was dropped to underground movements all over the world; it was used on every battlefront and was copied by enemies.

(Mark I) *Calibre:* 9 mm (0.354 in) *Ammunition:* 9-mm Parabellum *Weight:* 3.26 kg (7 lb 3 oz) unloaded *Length:* 895 mm (35.2 in) *Barrel length:* 196 mm (7.7 in) *Magazine:* 32-round detachable box *Rate of fire:* 550 rds/min (cyclic) *Muzzle velocity:* 381 m/sec (1250 ft/sec)

(Mark II) *Calibre:* 9 mm (0.354 in) *Ammunition:* 9-mm Parabellum *Weight:* 2.95 kg (6 lb 8 oz) unloaded *Length:* 762 mm (30 in) *Barrel length:* 196 mm (7.7 in) *Magazine:* 32-round detachable box *Rate of fire:* 550 rds/min (cyclic) *Muzzle velocity:* 381 m/sec (1250 ft/sec)

(Mark II, silenced) *Calibre:* 9 mm (0.354 in) *Ammunition:* 9-mm Parabellum *Weight:* 3.52 kg (7 lb 12 oz) unloaded *Length:* 907 mm (35.7 in) *Barrel length:* 89 mm (3.5 in) *Magazine:* 32-round detachable box *Rate of fire:* 450 rds/min (cyclic) *Muzzle velocity:* 305 m/sec (1000 ft/sec)

(Mark III) *Calibre:* 9 mm (0.354 in) *Ammunition:* 9-mm Parabellum *Weight:* 3.18 kg (7 lb) unloaded *Length:* 762 mm (30 in) *Barrel length:* 196 mm (7.7 in) *Magazine:* 32-round detachable box *Rate of fire:* 550 rds/min (cyclic) *Muzzle velocity:* 381 m/sec (1250 ft/sec)

(Mark V) *Calibre:* 9 mm (0.354 in) *Ammunition:* 9-mm Parabellum *Weight:* 3.86 kg (8 lb 8 oz) unloaded *Length:* 762 mm (30 in) *Barrel length:* 196 mm (7.7 in) *Magazine:* 32-round detachable box *Rate of fire:* 600 rds/min (cyclic) *Muzzle velocity:* 381 m/sec (1250 ft/sec)

'Stenka'/'Osa'

Soviet patrol boats, built during the 1960s. Both classes stem from the same basic design, which was developed to facilitate mass production of the various types of patrol boat needed for operations in coastal waters. The 'Osa' Class guided-missile patrol craft began building in 1959-60, the first being completed in 1961. Series production continued throughout the 1960s resulting in a

total of 200, of which about 100 remained operational with the Soviet navy in 1978. Known names are *Brestsky Komsomolets, Kirovsky Komsomolets, Michurinsky Komsomolets, Tambovsky Komsomolets.* The 'Stenka' Class, which were armed as submarine-chasers, were laid down from 1967 onwards, the first being completed in 1968. A total of 67 boats are thought to have been built, all of which serve in the Soviet navy. No names are known and, like the 'Osa' Class, it is not known in which shipyards they were built.

The steel hulls of the two classes are of identical dimensions, the slightly greater overall length of the 'Stenka' being accounted for by the bulwark added to the bow. Propulsion of both types is by diesel engines on three shafts. Those installed in the 'Stenka' develop only two-thirds of the power of the 'Osa' Class, giving them a speed of 30-32 knots which is sufficient for antisubmarine duties but not for the high-speed strikes demanded of the 36-knot missile boats. The superstructure of both types is similar. The long deckhouse running aft from the bridge contains all equipment for command and control of operations, weapons control, and quarters for the crew. This enables the boats to be 'closed down' in the event of CBW warfare. At either end of the boats is a twin 30-mm (1.18-in) AA mounting, and the prominent Drum Tilt director is carried on a pedestal at the after end of the superstructure.

The 'Osa' Class are equipped with four launchers for SS-N-2 surface-to-surface missiles, a weapon first carried by the 'Komar' Class FPBs on which it did not prove particularly successful owing to the vessels' small size. The launchers on the 'Osa' Class, unlike those fitted to their predecessors, are completely enclosed. The forward launcher is angled upwards at 12°, while the second launcher is angled at 15° and fires above it. Shields behind each launcher deflect the blast outwards. The bulky launchers of the first boats were superseded on later boats by smaller, cylindrical launchers fixed at the same angles. The two types are known as the 'Osa-I' and 'Osa-II' respectively.

The 'Stenka' Class have four single tubes for 40-cm (15.7-in) homing torpedoes angled

Sterling

out alongside the after part of the superstructure. There are also two depth-charge launchers fitted to the stern.

'Osa-I' Class boats have been transferred to Romania (five boats from 1961), East Germany (15 from 1964), China (one in 1965), Yugoslavia (ten in 1965 and 1969), Egypt (ten in 1966), Algeria (three in 1967), North Korea (eight), Sudan (one), Syria (eight), Saudi Arabia (three), Bulgaria (three in 1970-71), India (eight in 1971), Iraq (six in 1972-73), Cuba (five in 1972-74), and Finland (four in 1974). In addition to these, 'Osa-II' Class boats have been transferred to Iraq (four in 1975) and Morocco (six in 1976). Two Syrian and four Egyptian boats were sunk in the 1973 Middle East war.

('Osa' Class) *Displacement:* 165 tons (standard), 205 tons (full load) *Length:* 37.5 m (123 ft) oa *Beam:* 8.5 m (27 ft 11 in) *Draught:* 1.8 m (5 ft 11 in) *Machinery:* 3-shaft diesel, 9900 bhp=36 knots *Armament:* 4 SS-N-2 missile launchers; 4 30-mm (1.18-in) AA mountings (2×2) *Crew:* 39

('Stenka' Class) *Displacement:* 185 tons (standard), 225 tons (full load) *Length:* 38 m (124 ft 8 in) oa *Beam* and *Draught:* as 'Osa' *Machinery:* 3-shaft diesel, 6600 bhp=30-32 knots *Armament:* 4 40-cm (15.7-in) torpedo tubes (4×1); 4 30-mm (1.18-in) AA mountings *Crew:* 40

Sterling

British light automatic rifle. The Sterling company has become well-known through the Patchett-designed submachine-gun which bears its name, and in the late 1960s, while the Patchett was in full production, the company designed a light rifle which used the 5.56-mm (0.219-in) M193 round. After a good deal of effort it seems that the design has been taken by the Singapore government who are intending to build it under licence. The Sterling company has itself taken the manufacturing licence for the Armalite AR 18, which might be called an all-steel version of the AR 15, and has set up a special line to make it.

Production was under way in 1979 and sales had started to some Asian and African countries.

See also Lanchester, Patchett, Stoner.

(Sterling Light Automatic Rifle) *Calibre:* 5.56 mm (0.219 in) *Ammunition:* 5.56-mm×45 *Weight:* 3.4 kg (7 lb 8 oz) unloaded *Length:* 970 mm (38.2 in) *Barrel length:* 457 mm (18 in) *Magazine:* 20-round detachable box *Rate of fire:* 650 rds/min *Muzzle velocity:* 990 m/sec (3250 ft/sec)

Stetchkin

Soviet machine pistol. The Stetchkin pistol is a fully automatic model of conventional appearance, with an external hammer, having a mechanism largely based on that of the Walther Model PP. It is blowback, with an unlocked breech, and is chambered for the 9-mm (0.354-in) Soviet Auto Pistol cartridge (9-mm×18). A selector switch on the left rear of the slide can be set to 'safe' or to give either single shots or automatic fire. A wooden holster-stock is provided, which can be clipped to the rear of the butt grip to use the pistol as a pseudo-submachine-gun.

The foresight with the stock folded forward. The Sterling has a flip aperture rearsight for 90 and 183 m (100 and 200 yards). The foresight can be adjusted for line and elevation to zero the weapon. As a rough rule of thumb it is better to use the smaller aperture when firing the SMG from the shoulder for, though this gives a more restricted sight picture, it is more accurate. With a properly zeroed weapon a firer can get a good group at about 30 m (33 yards)—which defeats the original purpose of an SMG which is to be an area weapon

The Sterling ejecting an empty case. The breech block is moving backwards and the extractor flicking the case to the right. The ejection port on the right makes this SMG almost impossible for left-handed shooters

The breech of the Sterling with a round feeding in from the magazine. Care must be taken when the magazine is inserted into the housing to make sure that it is fully home or rounds will not feed correctly.

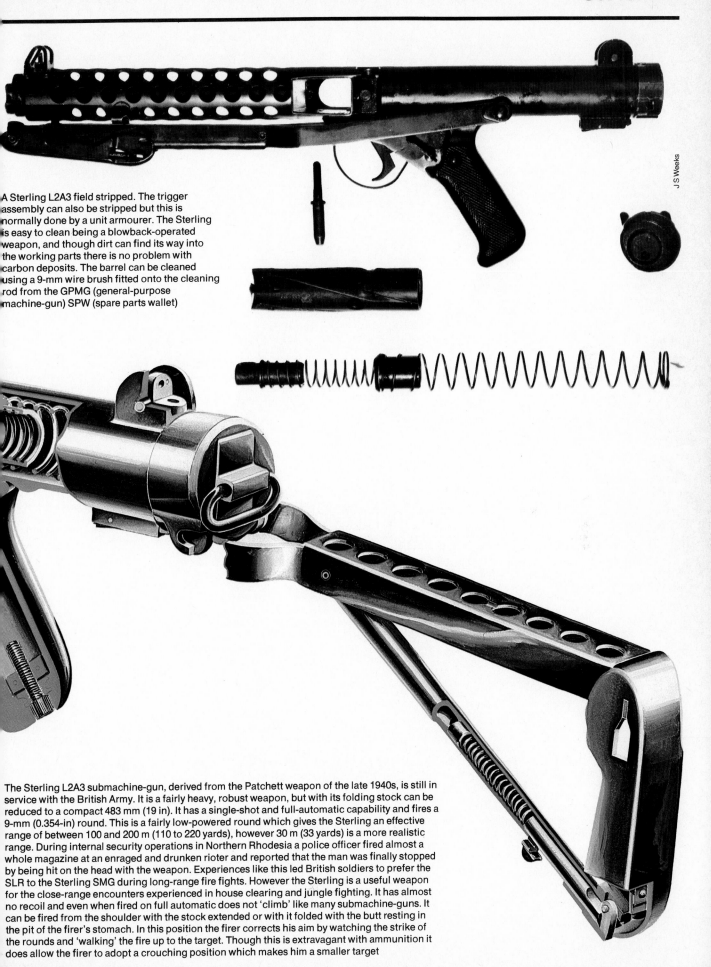

A Sterling L2A3 field stripped. The trigger assembly can also be stripped but this is normally done by a unit armourer. The Sterling is easy to clean being a blowback-operated weapon, and though dirt can find its way into the working parts there is no problem with carbon deposits. The barrel can be cleaned using a 9-mm wire brush fitted onto the cleaning rod from the GPMG (general-purpose machine-gun) SPW (spare parts wallet)

J S Weeks

The Sterling L2A3 submachine-gun, derived from the Patchett weapon of the late 1940s, is still in service with the British Army. It is a fairly heavy, robust weapon, but with its folding stock can be reduced to a compact 483 mm (19 in). It has a single-shot and full-automatic capability and fires a 9-mm (0.354-in) round. This is a fairly low-powered round which gives the Sterling an effective range of between 100 and 200 m (110 to 220 yards), however 30 m (33 yards) is a more realistic range. During internal security operations in Northern Rhodesia a police officer fired almost a whole magazine at an enraged and drunken rioter and reported that the man was finally stopped by being hit on the head with the weapon. Experiences like this led British soldiers to prefer the SLR to the Sterling SMG during long-range fire fights. However the Sterling is a useful weapon for the close-range encounters experienced in house clearing and jungle fighting. It has almost no recoil and even when fired on full automatic does not 'climb' like many submachine-guns. It can be fired from the shoulder with the stock extended or with it folded with the butt resting in the pit of the firer's stomach. In this position the firer corrects his aim by watching the strike of the rounds and 'walking' the fire up to the target. Though this is extravagant with ammunition it does allow the firer to adopt a crouching position which makes him a smaller target

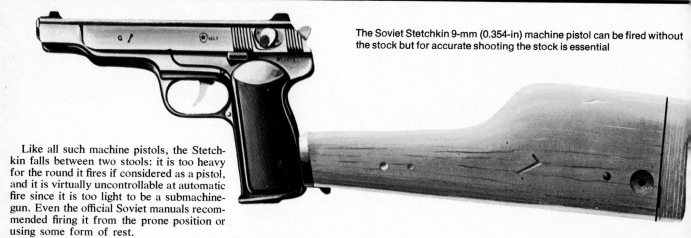

The Soviet Stetchkin 9-mm (0.354-in) machine pistol can be fired without the stock but for accurate shooting the stock is essential

Like all such machine pistols, the Stetchkin falls between two stools: it is too heavy for the round it fires if considered as a pistol, and it is virtually uncontrollable at automatic fire since it is too light to be a submachine-gun. Even the official Soviet manuals recommended firing it from the prone position or using some form of rest.

Calibre: 9 mm (0.354 in) *Ammunition:* 9-mm×18 *Weight:* 1.03 kg (2 lb 4 oz) *Length:* 225 mm (8.9 in) *Barrel length:* 127 mm (5 in) *Magazine:* 20-round detachable box *Rate of fire:* 750 rds/min *Muzzle velocity:* 340 m/sec (1115 ft/sec)

Stettin

German cruiser class, launched 1906-07. Three small cruisers, *Ersatz Blitz, Schiff O* and *Ersatz Wacht* were ordered: *Stettin* was launched on March 7, 1907, by AG Vulcan, *Nürnberg* was launched on August 29, 1906, by Kiel dockyard, and *Stuttgart* was launched on September 29, 1906. They were improved editions of the *Königsberg*, with slightly greater length, reduced draught and more powerful machinery for higher speed. *Stettin* was the only one to have steam turbines, and was a knot faster.

Nürnberg was on foreign service from 1910 and formed part of Admiral von Spee's squadron in the Pacific on the outbreak of war. She took part in the destruction of HMS *Good Hope* and HMS *Monmouth* at the Battle of Coronel but was in turn destroyed by HMS *Kent* at the Battle of the Falklands on December 8, 1914. *Stuttgart* served as a gunnery training ship from 1908, and with her sister *Stettin* fought at the Battle of the Skagerrak (Jutland). She was converted to a seaplane carrier at Wilhelmshaven in 1916-18, with a platform abaft the funnels for handling three aircraft; her armament was reduced to four 10.5-cm (4.1-in) guns and two 8.8-cm (3.5-in) AA. Both she and *Stettin* were stricken in November 1919 and were subsequently allocated to Great Britain for scrapping.

Displacement: 3500 tons (normal), 4000 tons (full load) *Length:* 117.4 m (385 ft 2 in) oa *Beam:* 13.3 m (43 ft 8 in) *Draught:* 5.3 m (17 ft 5 in) max *Machinery:* (*Stettin*) 4-shaft steam turbines, 21 000 shp=25 knots; (*Nürnberg* and *Stuttgart*) 2-shaft reciprocating steam, 12 000 ihp=24 knots *Protection:* 50 mm (2 in) deck *Armament:* 10 10.5-cm (4.1-in) L/40 QF (10×1); 8/10 5.2-cm (2-in) L/55 QF (8/10×1); 2 45-cm (17.7-in) torpedo tubes (submerged, beam) *Crew:* 322

Steyr

Austrian small-arms. In 1863 Josef Werndl, after visiting the US to study the latest methods of manufacture, set up an arms factory in the town of Steyr, Austria, to convert muzzle-loading muskets into breech-loading rifles. In 1869 the company became the Osterreichische Waffenfabrik Gesellschaft and continued to make a wide variety of military arms. After the First World War, it became Steyrwerk AG and diversified into automobiles and heavy engineering. In 1934 it absorbed the Austro-Daimler and Puch companies to become Steyr-Daimler-Puch, and during the late 1930s acted as the production facility for weapons designed by Rheinmetall and developed by Solothurn. After the Second World War the company produced farm machinery and motorcycles, and in the mid-1950s came back into the arms-producing business.

The Steyr factory was primarily the production facility for the designs of Ferdinand Ritter von Mannlicher and produced all the Mannlicher rifles adopted by various countries. Rifles of the Mannlicher type are still manufactured as sporting arms, and the current Austrian army sniping rifle, the SSG, is an up-to-date Mannlicher design. The factory is said to have been designing a submachine-gun in 1918, but nothing is known of this design, and the first Steyr submachine-gun was the Solothurn design, sold as the Steyr-Solothurn MP34. No further submachine-guns were made until the introduction of the Steyr-Daimler-Puch MPi69 in 1970. This is an extremely well designed weapon of robust and simple construction. The receiver is a pressed and welded steel box, fitted to a moulded nylon frame and pistol grip-cum-magazine housing. The barrel screws into an insert in the receiver, and the bolt is of the wrap-around type. A telescoping steel stock is fitted, and a sling; cocking the weapon is done by simply pulling the sling out at right angles to the receiver and then pulling it smartly backwards to cock the bolt. The bolt is provided with three safety slots which prevent accidental firing should the bolt be jarred back or, due to weak ammunition, fail to go back far enough to engage with the trigger mechanism in the proper fashion. One notable feature is that the entire gun can be stripped in 15 seconds and reassembled in the same time.

The most recent introduction by the company is the AUG Universal Weapon, a basic mechanical configuration which can be modified to produce a carbine, an assault rifle or a light machine-gun. The basic concept is a 'bull-pup' rifle, laid out in a straight line, with the plastic magazine inserted behind the pistol grip and alongside the firer's cheek. Much of the receiver is of alloy, while the stock and furniture is plastic; a folding forward grip, flash-hider and unitary optical sight are also fitted. The weapon is chambered for the 5.56-mm (0.219-in) cartridge, though doubtless it could be modified to other calibres. Semi- and full-automatic fire is provided by gas piston action.

In the 1890s Steyr made revolvers of the gas-seal type, more or less based on the Nagant and Pieper patents. They were responsible for making the Schönberger, the first commercially offered automatic pistol, in 1892-93, then went on to make the Mannlicher pistols. In 1907 they produced the Roth-Steyr to Georg Roth's design, and then went on to develop a pistol derived from a design by Karel Krnka, which used a similar rotating barrel breech lock to the earlier Roth model. The Steyr M1912, as this model came to be known, was an enclosed-slide type with external hammer; the barrel was locked to the slide by helical lugs, so that the barrel and slide recoiled locked together, until the barrel had been revolved through 90° to unlock the slide. Like all Krnka's designs, it used an integral magazine which had to be charger-loaded through the top of the open action, and it was chambered for a special cartridge, the 9-mm (0.354-in) Steyr, larger and more powerful than the 9-mm Parabellum.

The M1912 was sold commercially, and was adopted by the Austro-Hungarian army in 1912, although the cavalry retained their Roth-Steyr pistols. It was also adopted by the Romanian army. With this service adoption, almost all production went to military orders, and after 1913 few pistols reached the commercial market. The M1912 Steyr was a reliable and robust pistol and remained in service until 1945; after 1938 most of those in Austrian service were rebarrelled to take the German army's 9-mm Parabellum cartridge. Had it been chambered for this in the first instance, it might have become more successful.

Between 1909 and 1939 Steyr manufactured pocket automatic pistols for commercial sale, basing their product on the Belgian Pieper design. This had a rather unusual form of construction in which the barrel could be hinged down to expose the chamber for cleaning and for loading single shots. It was more novel than practical.

In the late 1950s the company returned to the commercial pistol field with the SP, a 7.65-mm (0.301-in) blowback with double-action lock, roughly comparable with the well-known Walther Model PP. At this time the service sidearm of the Austrian army was the Walther P-1, and these were made by teyr under licence. In 1974 the company announced a 9-mm Parabellum pistol, obviously intended for the military market, called the Pi18. This is a delayed-blowback pistol using gas pressure to provide the delaying orce. The slide fits closely around the barrel, which is shaped so that an annular cylinder is formed between barrel and slide. A vent asses from the chamber into this annulus, so hat, upon firing, gas pressure is built up and esists the rearward movement of the slide. his design gives every appearance of being ound and practical. As well as being available in conventional form, the Pi18 can be rovided with facilities to convert it into a machine pistol; the normal safety catch is eplaced by a selector switch to allow full-utomatic fire, a holster-stock can be clipped o the butt and an extended 36-round magazine is fitted.

SSG Sniping Rifle) *Calibre:* 7.62 mm (0.30 in) *Ammunition:* 7.62-mm NATO *Weight:* 3.83 kg 8 lb 7 oz) *Length:* 113 cm (44.5 in) *Barrel length:* 50 mm (25.6 in) *Magazine:* 5-round rotary, or 0-round box *Muzzle velocity:* 860 m/sec (2820 t/sec)

MPi69 submachine-gun) *Calibre:* 9 mm (0.354 n) *Ammunition:* 9-mm Parabellum *Weight:* 3.12 g (6 lb 14 oz) *Length:* 670 mm (26.4 in) *Barrel ength:* 260 mm (10.2 in) *Magazine:* 25- or 32-ound box *Rate of fire:* 550 rds/min *Muzzle velocity:* 381 m/sec (1250 ft/sec)

AUG Universal Weapon; rifle version) *Calibre:* .56 mm (0.219 in) *Weight:* 3.35 kg (7 lb 6 oz) *Length:* 790 mm (31.1 in) *Barrel length:* 508 mm 20 in) *Magazine:* 30-round box *Rate of fire:* 650 ds/min *Muzzle velocity:* 1000 m/sec (3280 t/sec)

Steyr M1912 pistol) *Calibre:* 9 mm *Ammunition:* -mm Steyr *Weight:* 930 g (2 lb 1 oz) *Length:* 216 nm (8.5 in) *Barrel length:* 127 mm (5 in) *Magazine:* 8-round integral *Muzzle velocity:* 345 n/sec (1130 ft/sec)

Steyr Pi18 pistol) *Calibre:* 9 mm *Ammunition:* -mm Parabellum *Weight:* 950 g (2 lb 2 oz) *Length:* 215 mm (8.5 in) *Barrel length:* 140 mm 5.5 in) *Magazine:* 18-round box *Rate of fire:* 900 ds/min *Muzzle velocity:* 390 m/sec (1280 t/sec)

Stieglitz, Focke-Wulf Fw 44

German training aircraft. Design of the Stieg-tz (goldfinch) in 1931 coincided with Focke-Wulf's amalgamation with the former Alba-os Flugzeugwerke and the arrival in the ompany of the brilliant designer Kurt Tank. t was a single-bay biplane of mixed con-truction, seating two persons in tandem pen cockpits, and was intended for private lying and primary training. The Stieglitz first lew in prototype form in the late summer of 932 as the Fw 44A, with an uncowled 150-hp iemens Sh 14a seven-cylinder radial engine. n its original form it exhibited several highly nsatisfactory characteristics, but after much edesign by Tank the Fw 44B, with a 120-hp Argus As 8 four-cylinder inverted in-line, vent into limited production. Principal ver-ion, however, was the Fw 44C, which rever-ed to the Siemens engine, several thousand of which were built, including some for export

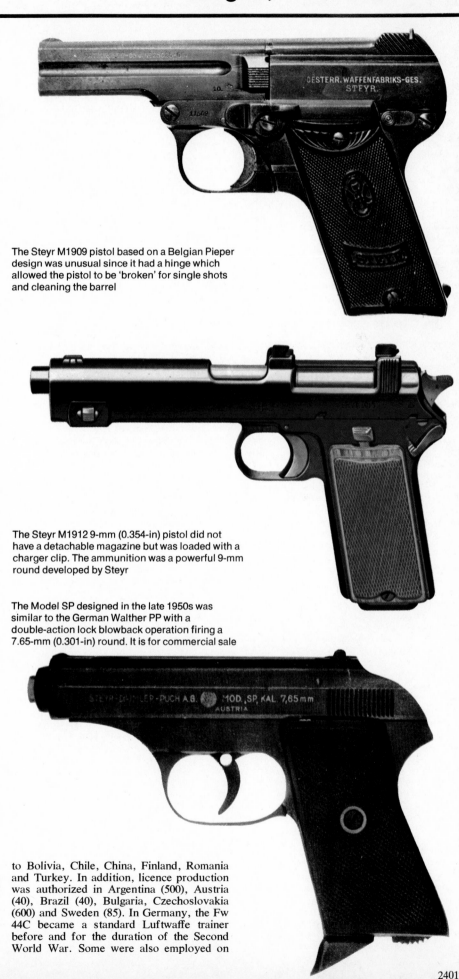

The Steyr M1909 pistol based on a Belgian Pieper design was unusual since it had a hinge which allowed the pistol to be 'broken' for single shots and cleaning the barrel

The Steyr M1912 9-mm (0.354-in) pistol did not have a detachable magazine but was loaded with a charger clip. The ammunition was a powerful 9-mm round developed by Steyr

The Model SP designed in the late 1950s was similar to the German Walther PP with a double-action lock blowback operation firing a 7.65-mm (0.301-in) round. It is for commercial sale

to Bolivia, Chile, China, Finland, Romania and Turkey. In addition, licence production was authorized in Argentina (500), Austria (40), Brazil (40), Bulgaria, Czechoslovakia (600) and Sweden (85). In Germany, the Fw 44C became a standard Luftwaffe trainer before and for the duration of the Second World War. Some were also employed on such additional duties as light reconnaissance and liaison. The normal wheeled landing gear could be replaced by skis on both the main and tail-wheel legs, for operation in winter conditions.

(Fw 44C) *Span:* 9 m (29 ft 6 in) *Length:* 7.28 m (23 ft 11 in) *Gross weight:* 800 kg (1764 lb) *Maximum speed:* 190 km/h (118 mph)

Stier

German auxiliary cruiser. The Atlas Levant Line's *Cairo,* built in 1936, was taken up in 1939 for conversion to *Hilfskreuzer 6,* alias *Schiff 23,* and also known to the British as 'Raider J'. As *Stier* she sailed for the Central and South Atlantic in May 1942, and although attacked by MTBs in the Dover Straits, slipped through the patrols and sank four ships totalling 29406 grt. Her last victim, the US merchantman *Stephen Hopkins,* put up such a stiff fight with her single 4-in (102-mm) gun that the *Stier* caught fire and blew up.

Tonnage: 4778 grt *Length:* 124.4 m (408 ft) wl *Beam:* 17.1 m (56 ft 1 in) *Draught:* 6.4 m (21 ft) *Machinery:* 1-shaft diesel, 3750 bhp=14 knots *Armament:* 6 15-cm (5.9-in)/45-cal (6×1); 2 37-mm (1.46-in) AA (2×1); 4 20-mm (0.79-in) AA (4×1); 2 53-cm (21-in) torpedo tubes (beam, submerged); 2 Ar 231 floatplanes *Crew:* 324 including 3 prize officers

Stinger, General Dynamics

US shoulder-launched surface-to-air missile. The FIM-92 Stinger, originally known as Redeye II, has been developed to replace Redeye itself. The new missile is faster than its predecessor and has a greater maximum range; it can also engage targets from any aspect, whereas Redeye is limited to interceptions from behind the enemy aircraft. An IFF (identification, friend or foe) set is incorporated to reduce the likelihood of friendly aircraft being shot down.

The missile is, like Redeye, fired from a launcher which is supported on the operator's shoulder. The launcher, which includes the sight, is attached to a re-usable gripstock containing the trigger, prelaunch control electronics, IFF interrogator and seeker cooling unit. When the operator receives early warning of an approaching target, or acquires it visually himself, he removes the cover from the front of the launcher tube and rests the launcher/gripstock assembly on his shoulder. He then operates the safety switch, which supplies electrical power to the missile and launcher; pressurized argon gas from the cooling unit is also supplied to the weapon's infrared detector. The gunner looks through his sight and aims at the target aircraft. Once the missile seeker has acquired its objective the operator hears a tone, and he then uncages the missile gyro so that the seeker head can track the target regardless of launcher movement. A continuous tone indicates that the aircraft is being tracked, and the gunner then aims off above and ahead of his objective to compensate for the round's drop during the early stages of flight and to reduce the time of flight against high-speed crossing targets.

When the operator depresses his firing trigger a solid-propellant motor in the launch tube ignites, propelling the missile from its container and spinning it for additional stability. This motor burns out while the round is still in its tube, to protect the gunner from blast, and the first charge of the missile's Atlantic Research dual-thrust solid-propellant rocket motor ignites once the weapon is some 7.6 m (25 ft) from the operator. Once launched, the missile is independent of ground control and homes on to the target's exhaust plume.

By 1978 Stinger had completed engineering development and was ready for full-scale production. Ford Aerospace developed Stinger Alternate, using semiactive laser guidance, as a back-up to Stinger but this is now unlikely to enter production. Work continues, however, on POST (passive optical seeker technology), a programme aimed at providing Stinger with an electro-optical homing head as an alternative to the present infrared seeker.

Length: 1.52 m (5 ft) *Diameter:* 7 cm (2.75 in) *Weight:* 15.1 kg (33 lb 6 oz) *Range:* 5.6 km (3.5 miles) *Speed:* Mach 2.2 *Warhead:* 3 kg (6 lb 8 oz) high-explosive

Sting Ray

British torpedo. Following the cancellation of the Mk 31 torpedo in about 1972 a development contract was given to Marconi Space & Defence Systems to develop a replacement for the US Mk 46, which had been purchased for the Royal Navy as an interim weapon for launching from ships' torpedo tubes and from A/S helicopters. Known for some time as the air-launched lightweight torpedo (ALTT), it was due to come into service in 1980. It is a passive homer which reacts automatically to signals generated by a computerized fire-control system. The closed-circuit control system is made by Sperry Gyroscope, and is built into four pods at the after end of the torpedo. The control surfaces are abaft the propeller and inboard of the pods.

Sting Ray is designed to be compatible with the Mk 44 and Mk 46, and so it can be deduced that it has the same diameter of 32.4 cm (12.75 in) and roughly the same dimensions. However, some differences in the umbilical A link which transfers inputs from the fire-control system before launching make it incompatible with the Plessey STWS-1 shipboard system, and so a new type of triple torpedo tube has been developed. It is believed that this was tested in HMS *Coventry* in 1978, and may be the forerunner of the STWS-2 system known to be under development.

One of the important improvements claimed for Sting Ray is enhanced effectiveness in shallow water. It uses solid-state technology in such areas as hybrid thick-film circuitry and microprocessors. Another improvement is the virtual elimination of testing or maintenance during service.

Stinson US aircraft   See **O-49**

Stirling, Short

British heavy bomber. To the Stirling go the distinctions of being the RAF's first four-engined monoplane bomber to enter service and the first to be used operationally. Designed to Specification B.12/36, it was the first of three heavy strategic bombers initiated by the Air Ministry in 1936, and was designed from the outset for four engines. A half-scale model of the Stirling, designated S.31 by the manufacturers, and powered by four Pobjoy Niagara engines, preceded the full-scale prototype. Flying in 1938, it was a valuable design tool for the S.29 Stirling proper, for both aerodynamics and handling characteristics.

The first prototype Stirling made a disastrous maiden flight on May 14, 1939, crashing on landing and becoming a write-off. A second prototype followed on December 3, 1939, powered by four Bristol Hercules II engines, rated at 1375 hp, and development continued apace.

The Stirling was the first landplane that Shorts had built. It was of stressed-skin all-metal construction, the fuselage being a slab-sided monocoque structure. The bulk of the fuselage was taken up with the bomb bay, which held a maximum load of 6350 kg (14 000 lb), which could be carried over a range of 950 km (590 miles). However, the usefulness of this bomb bay was reduced by being longitudinally sectionalized, and the heaviest single bomb which could be accommodated was only 1814 kg (4000 lb). The aircraft carried a defensive armament of eight 0.303-in (7.7-mm) Browning machine-guns: two in a nose turret, two in a mid-upper turret and four in a tail turret.

One of the limitations of the Stirling's specifications was that it should fit into the standard hangar (span under 30 m [100 ft]). This meant that in order to achieve the required wing area, a longer chord had to be adopted which resulted in a wing of comparatively low aspect ratio. This, in turn, resulted in a low service ceiling, which was to prove a handicap in service. Wing construction consisted of a main-spar torsion box, with leading- and trailing-edge assemblies, in a similar manner to the Sunderland. The same Gouge-type trailing-edge flaps as the Sunderland were fitted with very large chord.

The choice of a shoulder wing position on the Stirling resulted in a tall and extremely complicated main undercarriage, which gave a steep ground angle. Twin tail wheels were fitted. The main undercarriage had a complicated retraction sequence into the inboard nacelles. The Stirling Mk I was powered by 1595-hp Bristol Hercules XI engines.

The first unit of the RAF to operate the Stirling was 7 Squadron, initially based at Leeming when they re-equipped with the type in August 1940, and eventually moving to Oakington. The Stirling's first operational sortie was carried out on the night of February 10-11, 1941, when three aircraft of 7 Squadron dropped 56 227-kg (500-lb) bombs on oil storage tanks at Rotterdam. Stirlings of No 3 Group became the only heavy bombers in the RAF to regularly operate by day and by night. On daylight operations, the three turrets proved an adequate defence against enemy fighters, but Stirlings nevertheless began to get fighter escorts from June 1941. The two German battlecruisers *Scharnhorst* and *Gneisenau,* based at Brest, were the object of the Stirling's attention during 1941. They were attacked by night and day, and on one operation in July against the *Scharn-*

The Short Stirling was the first land aircraft to be built by Shorts of Belfast and the first four-engined monoplane bomber in the RAF

horst, nine 907-kg (2000-lb) armour-piercing bombs were dropped and two out of six defending fighters shot down.

The Stirling enabled Bomber Command to expand its night offensive, visiting Berlin on April 17, 1941, and later reaching targets in northern Italy and Czechoslovakia. In August 1942, Stirlings joined the Pathfinder Force, while a year earlier they pioneered the use of the Oboe blind bombing device during attacks on Brest.

A Mk II powered by Wright Cyclone engines did not see quantity production and the next major variant was the Mk III. It became standard in Bomber Command service during 1943-44, and featured a new type of mid-upper turret (still mounting two guns) and was powered by Hercules XVI engines, rated at 1650 hp.

With the increasing number of Lancaster and Halifax heavy bombers entering service, the Stirling was gradually phased out of the main offensive, to be used on peripheral targets, minelaying and radio counter-measures. The last Stirling bombing mission was carried out on September 8, 1944, and from the beginning of that year the Stirling had assumed a new role with Transport Command as a glider tug and transport aircraft. Designated Mk IV, Transport Command aircraft were converted from Mk IIIs with the nose and mid-upper turrets deleted and glider-towing gear fitted in the fuselage. They towed Horsa gliders on D-Day, and were also used on the Arnhem and Rhine-crossing operations. Additionally they were employed on a variety of transport, para-drops and gasoline delivery tasks.

The final production version of the Stirling was the Mk V which was a specifically developed transport version. All armament was deleted, and a longer streamlined nose was incorporated. It could carry 40 troops or 20 paratroops. The first Stirling V unit was 46 Squadron, which re-equipped with the type in January 1945. It was flown by four other units (48, 158, 242 and 299 Squadrons RAF) and was one of the elements of the long-range transport force, flying the trunk routes from England to India and the Far East. The Stirling V was taken out of service in 1946.

Production of the Stirling finally ceased in November 1945, after 2374 aircraft had been built, of which 618 had been produced by Austin Motors under the 'shadow-factory' scheme. Apart from the two prototypes and two prototype Mk IIs, 756 Mk I, 875 Mk III, 579 MK IV and 160 Mk Vs were built.

A Stirling MK II, powered by Wright Cyclone engines. It was not produced in quantity

Span: 30.2 m (99 ft 1 in) *Length:* 26.6 m (87 ft 3 in) *Gross weight:* 31 750 kg (70 000 lb) *Maximum speed:* 435 km/h (270 mph) at 4420 m (14 500 ft)

Stoner

US rifles. Eugene M Stoner, one of the outstanding weapon designers of this century, joined the design team of the Armalite division of the Fairchild Engine and Airplane corporation shortly after it was set up in 1954. By that time there were already several projects in hand, one of which was the AR 10, a proposed rifle for NATO with a number of new ideas in it.

The AR 10 failed to be accepted by the US Army, and Stoner did some work to correct its defects, including putting in a new barrel. The AR 10 was not a commercial success and was soon dropped, but Stoner meanwhile had been working on a lightweight rifle which he had built around a slightly enlarged version of

the Remington 0.222-in (5.64-mm) hunting cartridge. This gave him a cartridge which propelled a 55-grain bullet at 1005 m/sec (3300 ft/sec) from a suitable barrel. The mechanism and general design were taken from many other rifles, and Stoner's genius lay in welding them all into one properly balanced system. He used the locking system of the AR 10 with seven small lugs on the head of a light bolt which turned to lock into similar recesses in the barrel extension. The general outline was very like the AR 10, being an 'in-line' stock with the backsight set up in the carrying handle. The gas system was much like that of the Swedish Ljungman, in which there is no piston and the gas is piped back to the bolt. Stoner used the gas pressure to move the carrier away from the locked bolt, and so rotate it to unlock by cams and camways. There was extensive use of precision castings, plastics and high-grade metal, both ferrous and non-ferrous. The resulting rifle was designated the AR 15 and Fairchild

The Stoner magazine-fed LMG, one of the weapons developed by Eugene Stoner in the 1960s

tried to interest the US forces in buying it. The latter resisted until 1962, when a small number were taken for Vietnam, but the enthusiasm of the field reports brought steadily increasing orders. In 1967 the AR 15, which by then had become the army's M16A1, was officially adopted for all US forces except those assigned to NATO. The Colt company bought out the manufacturing and marketing rights to the AR 15 in 1959, and by the end of 1976 had produced 3 440 000 M16A1s. Production was licensed in other countries, and by 1979 the total made probably exceeded 4 million.

Stoner joined the Cadillac Gage company in order to develop a small-arms weapon system which could be turned into a variety of weapons using a set of basic assemblies and the 5.56-mm (0.219-in) cartridge. There were 15 main assemblies, and when the system was fully developed these could be used to make up six separate weapons, a rifle, a carbine, two light machine-guns (magazine or belt feed), a medium machine-gun and a vehicle machine-gun. The gas tube arrangement of the AR 15 was not strong enough for the machine-guns, so Stoner reverted to a conventional long-stroke piston which was on top of the barrel in the carbine and rifle, but turned over so as to be underneath for the machine-guns in order to allow enough space for the feed mechanism. All the machine-guns fired from an open bolt, and all used the same bolt locking system as the AR 15.

The concept of the Stoner system was excellent, and at any other time it would probably have been adopted and sold everywhere, but in the early 1960s there were many doubts about the effectiveness of the small bullet, particularly in machine-guns, and Stoner found himself fighting against his own brainchild, the M16, which was fast gaining popularity. Cadillac Gage did manage to license some production to Mauser and NWM in Holland, but very few were ever made and the whole concept was dropped.

Stoner's next venture was a 25-mm (1-in) cannon for the TRW company. This gun has been a candidate for the US Army Bushmaster programme, which is a large and expensive programme to decide on the weapon for the next generation of infantry armoured vehicles. There are certainly some connections between the TRW gun and the designer's previous efforts, particularly in the locking arrangements which still use the familiar rotating bolt and multilugs. But the feed is much more complicated than anything that he has tried before as it can accept two belts with different types of ammunition and switch instantaneously from one to the other. Stoner has also designed the entire family of ammunition to fit the gun. The manufacturing rights have been bought by Oerlikon.

Calibre: 5.56 mm (0.219 in) *Weight:* 2.86 kg (6 lb 5 oz) unloaded *Length:* 990 mm (39 in) *Barrel length:* 508 mm (20 in) *Magazine:* 30-round detachable box *Rate of fire:* 800 rds/min (cyclic) *Muzzle velocity:* 988 m/sec (3240 ft/sec)

Stooge, Fairey

British surface-to-air missile. Stooge was designed during the closing stages of the Second World War as a radio-controlled surface-to-air missile to counter Japanese

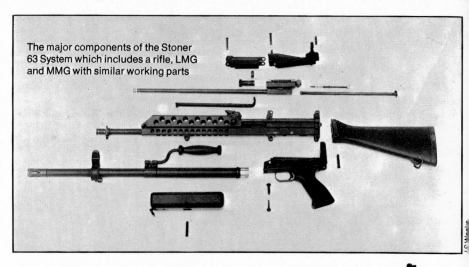

The major components of the Stoner 63 System which includes a rifle, LMG and MMG with similar working parts

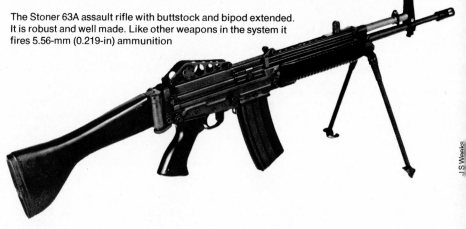

The Stoner 63A assault rifle with buttstock and bipod extended. It is robust and well made. Like other weapons in the system it fires 5.56-mm (0.219-in) ammunition

kamikaze aircraft. It was intended to carry a 100-kg (220-lb) warhead over a range of some 14.4 km (9 miles) but never saw operational service.

After the war the Stooge project became a research programme intended to develop missile technology, particularly radio-command guidance techniques, and trials began in 1947. The vehicle was of aeroplane-type layout, with straight wings carrying ailerons and elevators mounted on the horizontal tailplanes; the fixed vertical fin carried no rudder, turns being made under aileron control alone. Stooge was launched from a 3-m (10-ft) ramp with the aid of four strapped-on 7.6-cm (3-in) antiaircraft rockets which produced a total thrust of 2540 kg (5600 lb) for 1.6 seconds. Cruise propulsion was then taken over by solid-propellant rocket motors built into the rear fuselage; these could be either 12.7-cm (5-in) Swallow rockets, each producing 18.2 kg (40 lb) of thrust for 40 seconds and accelerating the vehicle to 560 km/h (350 mph), or the same number of motors generating 34 kg (75 lb) of thrust each to give a top speed of 800 km/h (500 mph).

Length: 2.3 m (7 ft 6 in) without boosters *Span:* 2.08 m (6 ft 10 in) *Diameter:* 32 cm (12.5 in) *Weight:* 335 kg (738 lb)

Stören

Danish torpedo boat class, built in 1887-88. Two boats, *Stören* and *Sölöven*, of a Thornycroft design similar to the 38-m (125-ft) types

ordered for the Royal Navy, were built at Chiswick. They were followed by a nearly identical pair, *Havhesten* and *Narhvalen*, a year later. All four were reboilered between 1897 and 1905, and towards the end of their lives the torpedo tubes were reduced from four to two. In 1912 they were numbered *T.2-5*, and were stricken in 1919.

Displacement: 110 tons (normal) *Length:* (1st pair) 42 m (137 ft 9 in) oa; (2nd pair) 39.9 m (131 ft) oa *Beam:* 4.3-4.5 m (14 ft 2 in-14 ft 8 in) *Draught:* 2 m (6 ft 8 in) max *Machinery:* 1-shaft reciprocating steam, 1200 ihp=23 knots *Armament:* 2 0.45-in (11.4-mm) Nordenfelt machine-guns; 4 38-cm (15-in) torpedo tubes (2 bow, 2 deck) *Crew:* 20

Storm

Norwegian missile-armed fast strike vessel class, built 1961-71. Under a five-year modernization programme announced in July 1959 the Royal Norwegian Navy planned to build 23 motor gunboats. This was later cut back to 20, but the prototype, *Storm* (P. 960), was completed by Bergens Mekaniska Verksted in May 1963. She was largely experimental and was eventually scrapped after evaluation, and the first series production boat was *Blink* (P.961), from the same yard. She was followed by *Glimt, Skjold, Trygg, Kjekk, Djerv, Skudd, Arg, Steil, Brann, Tross, Hvass, Traust, Brott, Odd, Pil, Brask, Rokk* and *Gnist*, bearing pendant numbers P.961-979. A replacement was also built for *Storm*.

Norwegian *Storm* Class fast patrol boats. They carry a gun and Penguin missile armament

Royal Norwegian Navy

It was given the same number, P.960, and was the last of the class to enter service, being commissioned along with *Gnist* and *Rokk* in 1968.

The original armament of the class was a Bofors 76-mm (3-in) gun in an automatic enclosed turret on the forecastle and a 40-mm (1.57-in) gun aft. The 76-mm L/50 gun weighs 6500 kg (14 330 lb) and uses electro-hydraulic remote control. Although no longer in production it is a useful weapon for small craft. The 40-mm gun is the standard Bofors L/70 single. In 1965 the class was rerated as gunboats, but in 1970 they started to receive the first Penguin surface-to-surface infrared homing missiles, with six launchers aft.

Six repeat editions were ordered from Bätservice at Mandal in 1968, to replace the *Rapp* Class. They had the same hull but carried four 21-in (53-cm) torpedo tubes, a single 40-mm gun forward and four Penguin missiles. Their names are *Snögg* (ex-*Lyr*) (P.980), *Rapp* (P.981), *Snar* (P.982), *Rask* (P.983), *Kvikk* (P.984) and *Kjapp* (P.985). The first of the class came into service in 1970.

Displacement: 100 tons (standard), 125 tons (full load) *Length:* 36.5 m (119 ft 9 in) oa *Beam:* 6.2 m (20 ft 4 in) *Draught:* 1.5 m (4 ft 11 in) *Machinery:* 2-shaft diesel, 7200 bhp=32 knots *Armament:* (*Storm* Group) 1 76-mm (3-in) L/50 Bofors; 1 40-mm (1.57-in) L/70 Bofors; 6 Penguin SSM-launchers; (*Snögg* Group) 1 40-mm L/70 Bofors; 4 53-cm (21-in) torpedo tubes; 4 Penguin SSM-launchers *Crew:* 22

Stösser, Focke-Wulf Fw 56

German single-seat fighter and advanced training aircraft. Widely known before the Second World War as an outstanding aerobatic performer, the Stösser (falcon) owed its great agility to the fact that it was sturdily built and was originally designed (by Kurt Tank) to a 1933 'emergency fighter' specification. Of parasol monoplane configuration, the first of three prototypes made its maiden flight in November 1933, powered by a 240-hp Argus As 10C eight-cylinder inverted-V engine. The second aircraft introduced metal wings and modified landing gear, but the third, which flew for the first time in February 1934, reverted to wooden wings and had further landing gear changes. Other minor modifications appeared on three pre-production Fw 56A-0s, which also were the first to carry armament.

After final trials in mid-1935, series production of the Fw 56A-1 began. This had one or two forward-firing 7.9-mm (0.311-in) MG17 machine-guns above the engine and provision for carrying three 10-kg (22-lb) bombs. The Stösser saw no service in the fighter role, but was used widely by the Jagdfliegerschulen (fighter pilot training school) and also by the NSFK (National Socialist Flying Corps). Between 900 and 1000 are believed to have been built before production ended in 1940, including small batches for Austria and Hungary, and the type served throughout the Second World War. The second prototype was tested before the war as a potential dive-

bomber, but the Stösser was never used as such, though some were used for other experimental work during the war.

(Fw 56A-1) Span: 10.55 m (34 ft 7 in) *Length:* 7.62 m (25 ft) *Gross weight:* 985 kg (2172 lb) *Maximum speed:* 268 km/h (167 mph)

Stranraer, Vickers-Supermarine

British patrol flying boat. Designed by R J Mitchell, who created the Spitfire, the Stranraer was the last of a line of general-purpose reconnaissance flying boats built for the RAF. Originally named Southampton Mk V, it bore little resemblance to the earlier Southamptons from which it was developed, and it was officially renamed Stranraer in August 1935.

Consisting of an all-metal two-step hull constructed of transverse frames and longitudinal stringers, the Stranraer was a biplane with fabric-covered unequal-span metal wings. The two engines were mounted in the centre section of the upper wing close to its underside, supported by splayed-out struts. The ailerons, carried on all wings, were of narrow chord. The prototype Stranraer was powered by two Bristol Pegasus IIIM engines with wooden two-bladed propellers, but production aircraft were fitted with the Pegasus X, rated at 875 hp, driving Fairey-Reed three-bladed metal propellers. Three 0.303-in (7.7-mm) Lewis guns were carried in open bow, mid-upper and tail positions, while a bombload of 454 kg (1000 lb) could be carried.

Built to Specification 17/35, 17 aircraft were ordered in August 1935, with an additional six following in May 1936, production of which was completed in March 1939. Adopted by the Royal Canadian Air Force, a further 40 were built under licence by Canadian Vickers in Montreal. One of these aircraft is now preserved in the RAF Museum at Hendon.

The Stranraer entered RAF service with 228 Squadron of Coastal Command at Pembroke Dock in 1936, and also saw service with 201, 209 and 240 Squadrons, all operating in Home Waters. By the outbreak of war in 1939, some 15 remained in RAF service with 201 and 209 Squadrons which flew them until replaced by Sunderlands and Lerwicks respectively in 1940. The RCAF used Stranraers for coastal reconnaissance until 1943.

Span: 25.91 m (85 ft) *Length:* 16.71 m (54 ft 10 in) *Gross weight:* 8618 kg (19 000 lb) *Maximum speed:* 266 km/h (165 mph) at 1830 m (6000 ft)

Stratofortress, Boeing B-52

US strategic bomber and missile platform. Though officially named Stratofortress, the Boeing type 464 is generally known by its US Air Force designation B-52. For 25 years it has been one of the best known military aircraft, and its history is unique. Planned only as a high-altitude bomber to serve from 1955 until 1960 it has been forced into several totally different roles and is expected to have a front-line active life until the year 2000. By 1979 there was no plan for a successor, though the need for one had become increasingly urgent.

Stratofortress, Boeing B-52

This is the more remarkable when it is remembered that the B-52 was designed at the very start of the jet-bomber era. The original army air force specification for the XB-52 long-range turbine-engined bomber was issued in April 1945. At that time turbojets suffered from high specific fuel consumption—even jet fighters found it hard to fly useful missions—and the long-range jet bomber could be shown on paper to be an impossibility. Boeing's chief studies, with type number 462, centred around the use of four of the largest turboprops, the favoured type being the 5500-hp Wright XT35 Typhoon. The only likely alternative seemed to be the 4000-hp Pratt & Whitney R-4360-VDT compound engine, which Convair also intended to use in an improved model of B-36. Unlike the smaller jet bomber, Model 450, which became the six-jet B-47, there was no point in sweeping back the wings and tail of the XB-52 intercontinental bomber because its speed appeared to be firmly pegged at 644 km/h (400 mph), no faster than the B-50 then forming the mainstay of the newly created Strategic Air Command.

For three years from April 1945 the Boeing project staff sought the best way to build the two XB-52 prototypes for which the company held a contract. Improvements in turbojet engines and in likely fighter defences kept pushing the effort from turboprops towards jets, and with the help of Boeing's Flying Boom flight refuelling a jet XB-52 gradually began to look less impossible. The vital factor that closed the remaining gap in 1948 was the appearance of the Pratt & Whitney JT3 engine, later to receive army/navy designation J57. The first US two-shaft engine, with separate low- and high-pressure compressors, it not only promised 3856 kg (8500 lb) thrust but also substantially better fuel economy. At the start of 1948 Boeing had used four JT3s in a USAF medium-bomber competition which did not lead to any hardware, but when in October 1948 the company project team visited Wright Field to discuss the B-52 they were surprised to find the air force now thinking in terms of a jet. When asked how long it would take to make a submission it was the turn of the air force to be surprised: the men from Seattle said

"We'll be back on Monday" (it was then Thursday evening).

With the help of their experience with the medium bomber the handful of engineers working in their hotel rooms created the greatest bomber of the modern era, working round the clock. They started off by just doubling the figures for the medium bomber: instead of four JT3 pods it had four twin-engined JT3 pods. One of their calculating tools was a three-dimensional block of transparent Plexiglas built up from a stack of carefully plotted graphs of altitude, Mach number and mission radius, with equivalent gross weights. By Saturday night the team drew the detailed three-view of the Model 464, the totally new jet XB-52. The whole package, complete with balsa-wood desk-top model, was delivered first thing Monday.

It led straight to the flight of the YB-52, tail number 49-231, at Boeing Field in the hands of 'Tex' Johnston and Colonel Guy M Townsend on April 15, 1952. The XB-52, with changes, flew the following October 2. Apart from being exceptionally large (though smaller than the rival Convair YB-60) the eight-

The Boeing B-52 Stratofortress has been in service for over 25 years with the USAF and this longevity has prompted the wry joke 'Join the United States Air Force and fly the plane your father flew'. Despite this long service the B-52 airframe has proved robust and versatile, going through a series of modifications and updates that will see it through to 1990. It can carry nuclear or conventional bombs as well as stand-off missiles like Hound Dog and ECM decoys like ADM-20C Quail missiles

engined Stratofortress had other novel features such as a fin 14.6 m (48 ft) high, so tall that it had to fold flat to enter a hangar, and landing gear in the form of four two-wheel trucks which could be steered for crabwise landings in a cross-wind. For lateral stability there were small outrigger wheels under the wingtips, which were high in the air when the tanks were empty but before takeoff on a long mission were pressed hard against the ground by the mass of fuel. Even the first B-52 carried 134 770 litres (29 645 Imp gal) of fuel, about half of it in the wings. The wing was an amazing structure which in static test bent upwards 9.75 m (32 ft) at each tip before breaking. Accessory power was radically new: each twin pod fed stainless-steel bleed pipes ducting high-pressure air to 60 000-rpm turbine power units grouped along the fuselage which drove the alternators, hydraulic pumps and other services. The first engine was the YJ57-P-1 rated at 3946 kg (8700 lb).

In the prototypes the pilots were seated in tandem under a long multipanel greenhouse, but in August 1954 the first B-52A (52-001) introduced side-by-side ejection seats on an airline-style deck. Behind was the navigator, while on the lower deck were the bombardier and radar operator in downward-ejecting seats. Far off in the pressurized tail compartment was a gunner with Arma radar-directed barbette with four 0.5-in (12.7-mm) guns. Engines were J57-9W each rated at 5690 kg (12 500 lb) with water injection, fed from a tank in the rear fuselage. Takeoffs with water injection produced eight impressive streams of black smoke, but the vast flaps, depressed between the jets, soon suffered fatigue cracks from the noise. The Flying Boom receptacle was behind the flight-deck roof, and a non-jettisonable 3787-litre (833-Imp

gal) external tank projected ahead of each outer wing. Normal bombload was four to ten nuclear weapons of four types, or 27 nominal HE bombs of 454 kg (1000 lb).

Of the 13 service-test A-models only three were delivered; the next ten were styled B-52B and had MA-2 Brane (bombing-radar and navigation equipment) filling the lower half of the nose, and many other changes including 19W engines. Altogether there were 50 B-models, 27 of them originally ordered (but not built) as the RB-52B with the bomb bay designed to accept a two-man capsule full of

cameras, other sensors and countermeasures. Service with SAC began on June 29, 1955, when the B-model became operational with 93 Bomb Wing (Heavy) at Castle AFB. Making airfields and men fit the B-52 was a giant task, but at first results were outstanding. In its spare time the 93rd Wing sent three aircraft round the world non-stop, with air refuelling, flying at 853 km/h (530 mph) for 45 hr 19 min (one gunner never left his seat, to claim he had gone round the world backwards), and eight B-models on a non-stop 32-hour mission round North America crossing

Stratofortress, Boeing B-52

the North Pole. In 1956-57 these successes were punctuated by six crashes, caused by air-turbine explosions, hydraulic fires and various other problems.

By this time Boeing was delivering 35 B-52Cs with giant 11 370-litre (2500-Imp gal) external tanks and the injection water moved to the wing roots. Additional production started at Boeing Wichita to let Seattle handle the demand for 20 KC-135 tankers a month, and while Seattle delivered 101 of the D-model, Wichita built 69. The D had the MD-9 rear-defence system, and no provision for a reconnaissance capsule. Next came the B-52E, of which Seattle built 42 and Wichita 58, at a rate of 20 per month, pushing the price down to $6.08 million, cheapest of all versions.

Features of the E were a totally new bomb/nav system, the ASQ-38, with IBM interfaces and displays, Raytheon ASB-4 radar, GPL APN-89 Doppler, Kollsman astro, Kearfott true heading and GE radar camera.

Seattle's last batch comprised 44 B-52Fs, backing up 45 from Wichita. Bulges on the engine pods covered the large shaft-driven hydraulic pumps and a Sundstrand constant-speed drive 40-kVA alternator and cooling system replaced the air-turbine system which, it was now realized, reduced range as well as causing in-flight safety problems. The F introduced the J57-43W engine, rated at 6237 kg (13 750 lb) with water supplied from tanks more logically placed in the wing leading edge. In 1957 the 20-per-month panic eased, and the reduction to 15 per month enabled more to be built of the B-52G, planned to be the final subtype in a run of 603 aircraft to support 11 45-aircraft wings.

The B-52G was almost a new aircraft, and no fewer than 193 were built. The largest change was a completely different integral-tank wing, at that time the largest 'wet wing' ever built, housing an extra 18 150 kg (40 000 lb) of fuel—approximately 26 000 litres (5700 Imp gal)—to a total double that of the B-52A. This was equivalent in mission radius to adding one aerial refuelling by KC-135, and it allowed the external tanks to be cut back to 2650 litres (580 Imp gal). The crew compartment was completely redesigned, to accommodate the pilots, gunner and ECM operator on the top deck and navigator and bombardier below. The tail turret, remotely controlled by an ASG-15 system, was the fourth type used in the B-52. The vertical tail was reduced in height by 2.44 m (8 ft), which limited loading on the rear fuselage and helped increase structure life, while paring weight by 4540 kg (10 000 lb). The tail surfaces became fully powered, and ailerons were at last eliminated. The ADM-20 Quail decoy missile was carried in the bomb bay (usually two, in the forward bay) and wing pylons carried two AGM-28 Hound Dog missiles whose engines assisted on takeoff and whose astro-inertial navigation was

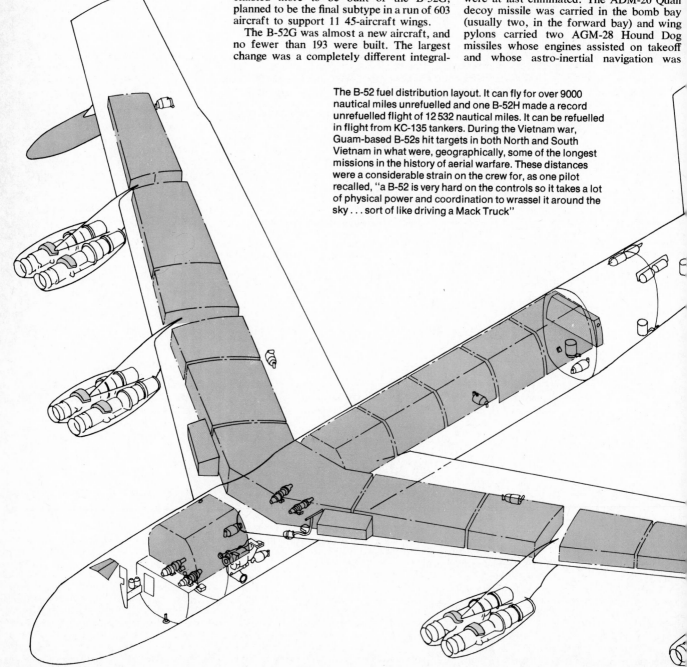

The B-52 fuel distribution layout. It can fly for over 9000 nautical miles unrefuelled and one B-52H made a record unrefuelled flight of 12 532 nautical miles. It can be refuelled in flight from KC-135 tankers. During the Vietnam war, Guam-based B-52s hit targets in both North and South Vietnam in what were, geographically, some of the longest missions in the history of aerial warfare. These distances were a considerable strain on the crew for, as one pilot recalled, "a B-52 is very hard on the controls so it takes a lot of physical power and coordination to wrassel it around the sky . . . sort of like driving a Mack Truck"

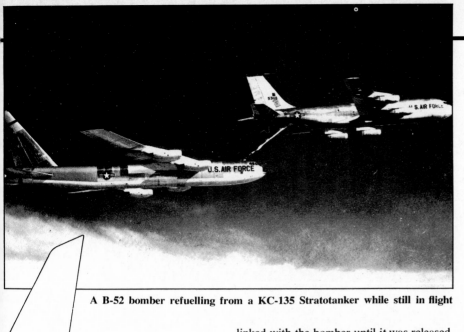

A B-52 bomber refuelling from a KC-135 Stratotanker while still in flight

them for service possibly until the end of the century. The D-models (about 80) have been structurally rebuilt, fitted with MA-6A bombing and A-3A or MD-9 tail defence, and equipped for conventional warfare. The G and H (about 275) were equipped in 1972 to carry the AGM-69A SRAM missile, which has replaced Hound Dog and also fits an eight-round internal dispenser. The ASQ-151 EVS (electro-optical viewing system) has infrared and low-light TV in under-nose bumps, these steerable systems by Hughes and Westinghouse serving large displays on a replanned flight deck and greatly improving low-level navigation and safety. All surviving SAC B-52s are being retrofitted with the Honeywell ASN-131 inertial navigation system, and the G and H are in addition receiving a new offensive-avionics suite including digital nav-attack electronics and a Tercom (terrain-comparison) guidance installation. Electronically steerable aerials are to improve defensive electronics and the ALQ-153 and -154 are alternative new tail-warning systems. No fewer than ten new items are to be included in the Phase VI update including a whole suite of SNOE (smart noise operation equipment), the Afsatcom global satellite nav-communications link and Northrop ALT-28 power-management.

New weapons include the BL77 low-level free-fall nuclear bomb, successfully released from only 46 m (150 ft) at Tonopah range in 1977, and whichever cruise missile is selected from the AGM-86B and AGM-109 fly-off competition in early 1979. Originally the B-52G and H were expected to carry 12 of the shorter AGM-86A externally and eight internally, but capacity for the larger missile (to be chosen in 1980) has not been disclosed. In mid-1978 four B-52Gs were being readied for the fly-off, due to be based at Edwards AFB in May-November 1979. Numerous further proposals exist for spending $1400 million between 1979-83 to update the existing B-52 force to take it through 1990, including a new forward radar, auto terrain-following and new flight controls. It reminds one of the execution axe in The Tower which had a new shaft and a new blade but was still the genuine original.

Span: 56.4 m (185 ft) *Length:* 48 m (157 ft 7 in) *Gross weight:* (A) 188 244 kg (415 000 lb), (C to F) 204 120 kg (450 000 lb), (G) 221 350 kg (488 000 lb), (H) 229 000 kg (505 000 lb) *Maximum speed:* (high altitude) 1014 km/h (630 mph) approximately

Stratofreighter, Boeing C-97

US transport and in-flight refuelling tanker aircraft. A direct derivative of the B-29 Superfortress, the C-97 (Boeing Model 367) did what many contemporary bomber-into-transport adaptations of its period did, and took the bomber's wings, powerplant, tail unit and landing gear, and simply added a new and larger fuselage. 'Simply' is not perhaps the appropriate word in this context, because research into pressurized large structures for high-altitude operation (where cruising was more economical) was still at a fairly rudimentary stage in January 1942, when the three XC-97 prototypes were ordered by the US Army Air Force. Boeing's engineers, deciding that the elliptical fuselage cross-

linked with the bomber until it was released.

Extending the G run to 193 raised total procurement to 642, not including the forthcoming 102 of the B-52H version. Built at Wichita in 1961-2, the B-52H had the 7711-kg (17 000-lb) TF33 turbofan engine, which eliminated water injection (and much of the noise) and extended range by a further 30% to 20 150 km (12 500 miles), just double that of early versions. Yet another new tail barbette was fitted, the ASG-21 system with a T-171 20-mm (0.79-in) 'Gatling' multibarrel cannon. The H was designed to carry four Skybolt ballistic missiles but cancellation of this weapon threw the burden back to Hound Dog. The structure was again redesigned for sustained operations below defensive radars, together with a new suite of defensive electronics.

While all B-52s suffered very severe and prolonged structural problems in the 1960s in their new low-level role, several hundred were assigned to 'temporary duty' operating notably from Andersen AFB, Guam, against targets in South-East Asia, flying at medium levels with conventional bombs. Painted black underneath, the B-52D and F were rebuilt with Hound Dog pylons on which were hung long triple ejector racks for 24 bombs of nominal 340 kg (750 lb), the actual weight being 375 kg (827 lb). The D, in addition, was given the 'big belly' bomb bay equipped to carry 85 bombs of nominal 227 kg (500 lb), actual mass being 263 kg (580 lb). Thus the bombload of the D soared from 12 258 kg (27 024 lb) to 31 750 kg (70 000 lb). The ten-hour bombing missions over Vietnam were at first simply tedious, but before the close of the campaign North Vietnamese defences caused heavy casualties and extra ECM were urgently installed.

Since that time the A, B, C, E and F have been withdrawn, and the remaining 300-odd D, G and H models continually updated to fit

- Fuel tanks
- Water injection tanks
- Engine oil tanks
- Air refuelling point

Stratofreighter, Boeing C-97

section they wanted was not an ideal shape to withstand the stresses of pressurization, came up with an ingenious solution that gave them almost what they wanted: a fuselage built in upper and lower lobes, the latter smaller in diameter than the former, whose circumferences intersected to give a nearly elliptical, but much stronger, cross-section. (Boeing were not the only company to evolve this 'double-bubble' idea, but they have persisted with it more than anyone else, right up to the latest members of the 707 family).

The XC-97 proceeded as a fairly low wartime priority, and the first aircraft did not fly until November 15, 1944. Able to cruise at a typical 616 km/h (383 mph) at 9150 m (30 000 ft), it set a transport aircraft record on January 9, 1945, by flying non-stop the 5348 km (3323 miles) from Seattle to Washington, DC with a 9072-kg (20 000-lb) payload in 6 hours 3 min. In July 1945 the USAAF ordered ten service-trials aircraft in three configurations: six YC-97 cargo transports, three YC-97A troop transports, and one YC-97B personnel transport with airline-type seating for 80 passengers. The six YC-97s were completed with B-29 engines, wings and tail, the first one flying on March 11, 1947. The YC-97A and B introduced the taller fin and rudder and R-4360 engines of the B-50 Superfortress, which became standard on subsequent C-97s.

An initial order for 27 production C-97As was increased to 50 at the end of 1948, and the first of these was delivered to the USAF in October 1949. Earlier that year, one of the three YC-97As had achieved the notable milestone of flying more than 453 592 kg (1 000 000 lb) of freight into Berlin during the airlift, and all three YC-97As were later brought up to C-97A standard, with a 'chin' radome, increased fuel and other improvements. The C-97As saw considerable service during the Korean war, both with the Military Air Transport Service and with Strategic Air Command in support of B-50 bomber units. Also used extensively in Korea was a casualty-evacuation version, the C-97C, of which 14 were built.

In 1950 Boeing flight-tested their Flying Boom in-flight refuelling gear on three C-97As. The USAF ordered 60 similar aircraft in 1951 under the designation KC-97E; deliveries began in July of that year. They carried an additional 27 255 litres (5995 Imp gal) of fuel in the fuselage, but could be stripped of the refuelling installation and used for cargo if required. The KC-97Es were followed from April 1952 by 159 KC-97Fs with 3800-hp Pratt & Whitney R-4360-59B engines instead of the earlier 3500-hp R-4360-35C radials. The last (and most numerous) production version was the KC-97G, similarly powered to the F but with the transferable fuel relocated (some going into underwing tanks), enabling it to operate as a transport with the refuelling gear in place. The last of 592 KC-97Gs was delivered to the air force in November 1956, to complete a grand total of 888 C and KC models.

The Stratofreighter's gradual replacement

The Boeing B-47 Stratojet showing its fuel tank, crew compartments, bomb bay and engine layout. When it was first conceived its design was revolutionary—few US aircraft design teams had considered a swept-wing configuration practical and there were fears that they were too slim to take the strain of jet flight. The first B-47s were delivered in the early 1950s and the last operational aircraft was withdrawn in the mid-1970s. The Stratojet was used for low-level delivery tactics using nuclear weapons. The method was for the bomber to approach the target at around 150 m (500 ft) and then pull up at the start of a loop releasing its bomb when moving in upward climb—this effectively lobbed the bomb into the air ahead of the bomber. The B-47 would then continue through half of the loop, roll out at the top and then break again for low level. These tactics enabled bombers to get in under enemy radar coverage which would confuse them with ground clutter on their screens

from 1957 by the C-135/KC-135 Stratolifter allowed many to be converted or reassigned to other roles. Seven aircraft (one YC-97A, one YC-97B and five C-97As) became passenger-only C-97Ds or VC-97D airborne command posts. A single KC-97H (converted from a J) evaluated a probe-and-drogue alternative refuelling system, the two KC-97Js being turboprop conversions from KC-97Gs with four 5700-ehp YT34-P-5 engines. Twenty-six C-97Ks were KC-97Gs without their extra fuel tankage (but still with their refuelling booms), for passenger-carrying mission-support duties. Remaining Gs became KC-97Ls when, after transfer to the Air National Guard, they were fitted with underwing J47-GE-25A jet pods to improve their compatibility with jet fighters; while 28 others were converted for the USAF's Air Rescue Service and redesignated HC-97G.

(KC-97G) *Span:* 43.05 m (141 ft 3 in) *Length:* 35.79 m (117 ft 5 in) including boom *Gross weight:* 79 379 kg (175 000 lb) *Maximum speed:* 604 km/h (375 mph)

Stratojet, Boeing B-47

US strategic medium bomber and multipurpose reconnaissance aircraft. As the world's first quantity-produced swept-wing jet bomber, the Stratojet has a place in aviation's list of 'firsts', but such a bald statement fails to reveal just how significant a design it was: it has rightly been called one of the world's truly revolutionary aeroplanes. The sharing of preliminary information on the problems and potential of jet propulsion during the early years of the Second World War, and particularly after the first flight in May 1941 of Britain's first Gloster E.28/39, led the US Army Air Force to issue to the US aircraft industry, in late 1943, its first outline requirements for jet-powered bombers and high-flying reconnaissance aircraft. The parameters were kept simple deliberately to allow designers as much flexibility as possible, provided that they could produce an aircraft with a maximum speed of 805 km/h (500 mph) at 12 200 m (40 000 ft) and a range of 3220 km (2000 miles). Prototypes were ordered from four companies: North American (XB-45), Convair (XB-46), Boeing (XB-47) and Martin (XB-48). Of these, only the B-45 Tornado and the B-47 entered production, and the latter was by far the more successful.

Boeing's early designs to meet the original requirement were orthodox straight-winged aircraft, including two proposals (Models 424 and 432) based on the B-29 Superfortress. But all these proposals were scrapped at the end of the war in Europe, when Boeing engineers were among those granted access to German aerodynamic research information. Boeing immediately went for a sweptback wing (the only one of the four competing companies to do so), and submitted a new

Stratojet, Boeing B-47

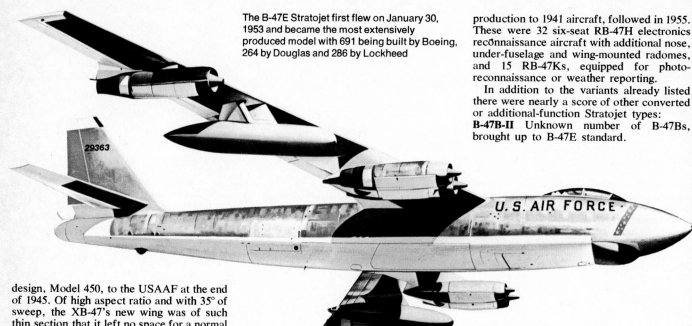

The B-47E Stratojet first flew on January 30, 1953 and became the most extensively produced model with 691 being built by Boeing, 264 by Douglas and 286 by Lockheed

design, Model 450, to the USAAF at the end of 1945. Of high aspect ratio and with 35° of sweep, the XB-47's new wing was of such thin section that it left no space for a normal main landing gear or fuel tankage, both of which had to be housed in the fuselage; at the same time it had to be strong enough to support six podded 1700-kg (3750-lb) st GE TG-180 (J35) jet engines, grouped as one pair and one single engine under each wing. A novel bicycle-type landing gear was designed, with twin-wheel main units forward and aft of the bomb bay, augmented by an outrigger unit for lateral stability retracting into each inboard engine pod. A compartment for 18 454-kg (1000-lb) st JATO solid-fuel rockets was built into the bomber's rear fuselage, while the centre-fuselage weapons bay could accommodate normal and maximum bombloads of 4535 kg (10 000 lb) and 9979 kg (22 000 lb). Above this were tanks for 64 352 litres (14 156 Imp gal), more than treble the fuel load of the B-29. In view of the anticipated speed of the B-47 the only defensive armament considered necessary was a pair of 0.5-in (12.7-mm) machine-guns in the tail, which could be operated either automatically or manually from the cockpit. The crew of three consisted of a pilot and copilot/gunner, in tandem seats under a single fighter-style teardrop canopy, and a navigator/bombardier in the nose behind a transparent hemispherical section.

The first XB-47 flew for the first time on December 17, 1947. Early fears that the thin, narrow wings might twist uncontrollably when the ailerons were used proved to be unfounded, and useful additional lift and wing area stemmed from the use of large Fowler-type trailing-edge flaps, as on the B-29. The second XB-47, powered by 2359-kg (5200-lb) st General Electric J47-GE-3 engines, flew on July 21, 1948, and these engines were later installed also on the first aircraft. The J47-GE-11, at the same rating, was selected for the ten B-47A service-trials aircraft which followed next and were delivered to the air force from December 1950.

Large-scale production, stimulated by the Korean war, began with the B-47B, of which Boeing built 380; Douglas and Lockheed, who were to assume a greater share in subsequent production, built ten and eight respectively. Air force deliveries began, to

the 306th (Medium) Bomb Wing, in mid-1951, all B-47Bs from the 88th onwards having 2631-kg (5800-lb) st J47-GE-23 turbojets. One aircraft was allocated for conversion as a reconnaissance prototype, to be powered by four Allison J71 turbojet engines; but, despite successive redesignation as XB-56, YB-56 and YB-47C, the conversion was never carried out and the proposed production RB-56A was cancelled. One B-47B that did become a testbed, however, was the aircraft which, in 1956, Canadair modified at RCAF request to flight-test the large 9072-kg (20 000-lb) st Orenda Iroquois jet engine. Too big to hang under one wing, the Iroquois was mounted in a separate pod on one side of the rear fuselage, in addition to the normal underwing J47s. Engine testing was also the purpose of two XB-47Ds (again converted Bs), each of which had a single Wright YT49-W-1 turboprop in place of each inboard pair of J47s.

The next production model to appear was thus the B-47E, flown for the first time on January 30, 1953, and eventually built in greater numbers than any other version: 691 by Boeing, 264 by Douglas and 286 by Lockheed. A number of significant improvements were introduced with the B-47E, including increased power in the form of six 2722-kg (6000-lb) st J47-GE-25 engines. The old built-in JATO pack was replaced by a more powerful 33-bottle jettisonable pack; the 0.5-in tail guns were replaced by 20-mm (0.79-in) cannon; standard fuel capacity was reduced to 55 305 litres (12 166 Imp gal), some of it in underwing drop tanks, and an in-flight refuelling receptacle was provided; a new radar bombing system was installed; ejection seats were provided for all three crew members; and, because of the increased operating weights resulting from these changes, the landing gear was strengthened. Boeing also built 240 examples of the RB-47E, a strategic-reconnaissance version with a slightly lengthened nose, built-in JATO, an 11-camera pack in the bomb bay, and 69 670 litres (15 326 Imp gal) fuel capacity. Two other basic models, bringing overall B-47

production to 1941 aircraft, followed in 1955. These were 32 six-seat RB-47H electronics reconnaissance aircraft with additional nose, under-fuselage and wing-mounted radomes, and 15 RB-47Ks, equipped for photo-reconnaissance or weather reporting.

In addition to the variants already listed there were nearly a score of other converted or additional-function Stratojet types:

B-47B-II Unknown number of B-47Bs, brought up to B-47E standard.

DB-47B Four B-47Bs converted as unarmed directors for QB-47E and other remotely controlled targets.

YDB-47B One DB-47B further converted as launcher/director for Bell Rascal guided missile.

RB-47B and **YRB-47B** Twenty-four B-47Bs converted to eight-camera photo-reconnaissance aircraft, chiefly as trainers for RB-47E crews.

TB-47B Sixty-six B-47Bs converted as pilot/navigation trainers, with extra seat for instructor.

WB-47B Unknown number of B-47Bs converted for weather reconnaissance.

DB-47E Two B-47Es converted for service trials with Bell Rascal.

YDB-47E Two B-47Es converted for service trials with Bell Rascal.

ETB-47E Unknown number of B-47Es converted as electronics crew trainers.

QB-47E Fourteen B-47Es converted as radio-controlled target drones.

WB-47E Twenty-four B-47Es converted for weather reconnaissance.

YB-47F One B-47B fitted with probe for in-flight refuelling trials with KB-47G tanker.

KB-47G One B-47B fitted with hose refuelling gear to test probe-and-drogue system with YB-47F.

ERB-47H Three B-47Es converted to RB-47H standard but with only five seats.

YB-47J One B-47E testbed for MA-2 radar bombing/navigation system.

EB-47L Thirty-five B-47Es converted as electronic communications relay aircraft.

The Stratojet entered service with the USAF Strategic Air Command in 1951 and reached its peak in 1957 of 1800 in the inventory with 28 SAC bomb wings. It began training for a low-level penetration role in 1959, and was withdrawn from bomber units in 1966. One version which remained in regular service until 1969 was the WB-47E, though some of the testbed and drone versions soldiered on into the 1970s.

(B-47E) *Span:* 35.36 m (116 ft) *Length:* 33.48 m (109 ft 10 in) *Gross weight:* 93 758 kg (206 700 lb) *Maximum speed:* 975 km/h (606 mph)

Stratolifter/Stratotanker, Boeing C-135/KC-135

US jet transport and in-flight refuelling tanker aircraft. Once Boeing moved into the jet age with the Stratojet and Stratofortress it was virtually inevitable that sooner or later a transport aircraft to a similar configuration would emerge. The company instigated several design studies in 1950, after completing production of the Model 377 Stratocruiser (civil equivalent of the C-97 Stratofreighter), to evolve a jet or turboprop-powered successor for the airlines. Among these studies was the Model 367-74 project, combining a Stratofreighter-type fuselage with moderately swept wings and two pylon-mounted pairs of J57 turbojet engines. Various changes were introduced over the next two years, until the design was finalized in 1952 as the Model 367-80 with a new fuselage and singly podded engines. On May 20 that year the company allocated funds for a prototype to be built, and this was rolled out two years later. The prototype made its first flight on July 15, 1954.

The new jet transport, retitled Boeing 707, appeared at a time when most major airlines had only just bought the latest stretched versions of the piston-engined Constellation and DC-7, and consequently there was little immediate enthusiasm from the potential customers. But Boeing had kept one eye on the potential military market as well, and managed to get the 367-80 prototype evaluated by the US Air Force. An order followed in October 1954 for 29 KC-135A tanker/transport aircraft, which received the Boeing model number 717. The KC-135A was fitted with a streamlined new Boeing Flying Boom, and carried 118 105 litres (25 980 Imp gal) of transferable fuel. Powerplant was four 6237-kg (13 750-lb) st Pratt & Whitney J57-P-59W jet engines. The original contract for 29 was succeeded by others, and 732 KC-135As were eventually built, deliveries to Strategic Air Command taking place between June 1957 and January 1965. These were retrospectively fitted with a taller tail fin and a powered rudder, and the boom nozzle was redesigned to be compatible with aircraft equipped with a probe-and-drogue refuelling system. Four aircraft similar to the KC-135A were built for the USAF Military Air Command (or Military Air Transport Service as it was then) Air Photographic and Charting Service. These differed in having the refuelling boom omitted and cameras installed, and were designated RC-135A (Boeing Model 739).

The MATS was also the customer for the next basic model, the purely transport C-135 Stratolifter. Fifteen were built as C-135As, with similar powerplants to the KC-135A, and 30 more were completed as C-135Bs, with wider-span tailplanes and 8165-kg (18 000-lb) thrust Pratt & Whitney TF33-P-5 turbofans. All had accommodation for up to 126 troops or 40 370 kg (89 000 lb) of cargo, and provision for conversion to tanker use if required. They were preceded by three 'partial' C-135As (first flight May 19, 1961), converted from short-tailed early-production KC-135As.

The designation KC-135B (later changed to EC-135C) was applied to 17 fan-engined aircraft built for SAC as airborne command-post aircraft, with a flight crew of five plus a general officer and a staff of ten; these were equipped with receptacles to receive fuel in flight from other tankers. France ordered 12 C-135Fs, with probe-and-drogue-compatible refuelling booms, as tanker support for its Mirage IVA strategic bomber force. Finally, ten other Boeing 739s (but with TF33 engines) were built as RC-135Bs for electronics reconnaissance, to bring the total number of C-135/KC-135s manufactured to 820 aircraft by the time that production ended in 1966.

More than 20 other known designations have been applied to variants converted for special functions or subjected to equipment or structural change. Six of these, with the numbers concerned shown in brackets, were converted from KC-135As for airborne command-post and/or communications relay duties with various USAF home and overseas commands; these were designated EC-135A (six), EC-135G (four), EC-135H (five), EC-135K (one), EC-135L (three) and EC-135P (five). Eight EC-135Ns were converted from C-135As, as radio/telemetry relay aircraft for use during the Apollo space programme, and three EC-135Js were converted from fan-engined EC-135Cs. Other conversions from KC-135As included the special-test JC-135A, JKC-135A, NC-135A and NKC-135A (numbers unknown); the electronics reconnaissance RC-135D (four); the KC-135Q (number unknown), a special JP-7 fuel tanker for the SR-71 Blackbird; and the special-reconnaissance KC-135R (number unknown). Conversions from fan-engined C-135B models included the VC-135B (11 as VIP transports); the WC-135B (ten for weather reconnaissance); the RC-135C (ten for electronics reconnaissance, from RC-135Bs); the RC-135E (one for electronics reconnaissance); and RC-135M (number unknown, for 'special missions'). Two 'conversions of conversions' are the RC-135S (from RC-135D) and the KC-135T, an elint (electronic intelligence) gatherer, modified from the KC-135R.

(KC-135A) *Span:* 39.88 m (130 ft 10 in) *Length:* 41.53 m (136 ft 3 in) *Gross weight:* 134 717 kg (297 000 lb) *Maximum speed:* 941 km/h (585 mph)

Strela Soviet antiship missile   See **Scrubber**

Strella Soviet surface-to-air missile   See **Grail**

The Swedish Stridsvagn or S Tank sacrifices a turret in favour of a low silhouette

Stridsvagn

Swedish main battle tank. This unorthodox armoured fighting vehicle is in some ways akin to a self-propelled gun, since the main gun is fixed in a low hull and not in a turret, and requires complex steering and suspension to allow the whole vehicle to turn quickly and elevate on its chassis. It has an automatic loader, three-man crew, duplicated gun and driving controls and a considerably smaller height and volume than conventional tanks. It has both a gas-turbine and a diesel engine, each of which can power the tracks separately but which are both needed to slew the vehicle to lay the gun. They give equal facility for forward or reverse driving.

Work began based on a proposal by the Chief Engineer of the Vehicle Division of the Swedish army ordnance in 1956. Two prototypes were built following feasibility studies in 1958 and trials with ten preproduction models in 1963. Full production of the STRV 103 Stridsvagn or S Tank began in 1967, and it entered service with the Swedish army. There have been no export orders.

The Stridsvagn has several advantages over the conventional tank, but cannot operate from a hull-down or dug-in position: its advocates would say that its low silhouette precludes any need to use the cover of a hull-down position. The Swedish army has begun development of a new MBT to replace its S Tank and Centurions and it will be interesting to see if it stays turretless.

Weight: 39 tons *Length:* 9.8 m (32 ft 2 in) with gun *Width:* 3.6 m (11 ft 10 in) *Height:* 2.14 m (7 ft) *Armament:* 105-mm (4.13-in) L7A1; 2 7.62-mm (0.30-in) machine-guns; 1 7.62-mm AA machine-gun *Powerplant:* 1 6-cylinder Rolls-Royce K60 multifuel, 240 bhp at 3750 rpm; 1 Boeing 553 gas turbine, 490 bhp at 38 000 rpm *Speed:* 50 km/h (31 mph) road *Range:* 390 km (240 miles) *Crew:* 3

Strikemaster, British Aerospace (BAC)

British armament trainer and close-support aircraft. Known originally as the British Aircraft Corporation BAC 167, the Strikemaster is the ultimate development of an armed version of the Hunting Jet Provost jet trainer. An interim model, the BAC 145, flew for the first time on February 28, 1967. This retained the 1134-kg (2500-lb) st Rolls-Royce Viper Mk 202 turbojet engine which powered the Royal Air Force's Jet Provost T Mk 4 trainer, but enclosed it in a completely new-design fuselage of shorter overall length, embodying a pressurized cockpit with improved all-round view. Other modifications included additional fuel tankage in the wings, and resulted in a much-improved overall performance. After conversion of the last two Jet Provost T.4s as prototypes, manufacture of 110 BAC 145s began for the Royal Air Force, by whom they are known as the Jet Provost T Mk 5. Deliveries of these took place between September 1969 and October 1972.

The RAF aircraft were unarmed, but five examples of a slightly heavier armed version were built for the Sudanese air force, and these are known as Strikemaster Mk 55s. The mainstream version of the Strikemaster, however, is the BAC 167, which utilizes the

Strim, Luchaire

A British Aerospace Strikemaster of the Kuwait air force, armed with two general-purpose bombs for ground-attack work

same basic airframe as the BAC 145 but with a more powerful 1547-kg (3410-lb) st Viper Mk 535 turbojet, enabling it to carry up to 1360 kg (3000 lb) of assorted external weapons and other stores on four underwing hardpoints. Accommodation is provided for two occupants, seated side by side, and both provided with ejection seats. Typical weapon loads can include four 65-, 125-, 250- or 500-kg (143-, 276-, 551- or 1213-lb) conventional bombs, four 245-kg (540-lb) ballistic or retarded bombs, or 24 practice bombs; various combinations of 6.8-cm (2.7-in), 8-cm (3.1-in) or other air-to-surface rockets and their launchers; napalm; auxiliary fuel in drop tanks; various 7.62-mm (0.30-in) or 20-mm (0.79-in) gun packs with their ammunition; or a five-camera reconnaissance pod. With a pilot and full internal fuel (including tip-tanks), the maximum external load is 1200 kg (2650 lb). In addition, the Strikemaster has a built-in armament comprising a 7.62-mm FN machine-gun in the lip of each engine air intake, each with 550 rounds of ammunition. A BAC 167 prototype flew for the first time on October 26, 1967, and a total of 145 were ordered subsequently, including the five Sudanese BAC 145s. The others were for sale to Saudi Arabia (45 Mk 80/80A), Republic of South Yemen (four Mk 81), Oman (24 Mk 82/82A), Kuwait (12 Mk 83), Singapore (16 Mk 84), Kenya (six Mk 87), New Zealand (16 Mk 88), and Ecuador (16 Mk 89). All are basically similar, differing principally in their internal equipment. With most user air forces, they double in the roles of armed trainer and light strike aircraft, and most customers' totals include repeat orders; in 1978, BAC/British Aerospace had built a further ten in anticipation of further sales.

(Mk 88) *Span:* 11.23 m (36 ft 10 in) over tip-tanks *Length:* 10.26 m (33 ft 8 in) *Gross weight:* 5216 kg (11 500 lb) *Maximum speed:* 774 km/h (481 mph)

Strim, Luchaire

French antitank rocket launcher. Strim entered service with the French army in 1969 as the LRAC model F1, replacing the M20A1 rocket launcher. It has also been exported. The weapon is designed mainly for use by infantry and consists of a lightweight launcher tube with adjustable shoulder-piece and fore grip, and a detachable telescopic sight. The round itself is normally carried in a sealed container which is mated to form part of the launcher before firing, all electrical connections being made automatically during this loading process. The round's rapid-burning propellant charge gives a high muzzle velocity, flat trajectory and smokeless exhaust; it is stabilized in flight by nine fins which unfold after launching.

Calibre: 89 mm (3.5 in) *Weight:* 8.2 kg (18 lb 1 oz) loaded *Length:* 1.6 m (5 ft 3 in) ready to fire *Weight of round:* 2.2 kg (4 lb 14 oz) *Muzzle velocity:* 290 m/sec (950 ft/sec) *Range:* 400 m (440 yards) *Warhead:* 0.56-kg (1 lb 4-oz) hollow-charge

Stuart

British name for US light tanks M2A4, M3 and M5. The development of this series of tanks began in Rock Island arsenal in the early 1930s, the starting model being the T2. This was designed with speed and light guns taking precedence over armour protection, and it mounted two 0.30-in (7.62-mm) and one 0.5-in (12.7-mm) machine-guns. In order to produce the desired performance, a Continental air-cooled radial aircraft engine of 250 bhp was adopted so as to avoid the expense of having to develop a special tank engine, and this adaptation was one of the most important decisions ever taken by the US Ordnance Department. The only drawback was that, due to the engine's height, it was necessary to make the rear end of the tank higher and thus raise the general height so as to give the turret the desired command.

After trials of the T2, Rock Island built a fresh design as the T2E1. This introduced their second significant contribution to tank design, the vertical volute spring suspension which used bogies of two road wheels, sprung by a vertical volute spring inside the suspension pillar. (A vertical volute spring can be likened to a steel leaf which is coiled and then has the inner end poked up; the effect is that of an exceptionally stiff coil spring, well suited to the weight of tanks.) The T2E1 had a fixed turret, the full width of the hull, and in 1935 it was standardized as the Light Tank M2A1; 19 were made at Rock Island.

At this period only infantry were given tanks in the US Army; the cavalry were only allowed 'combat cars'. But the cavalry wanted tracked vehicles and, moreover, they wanted a revolving turret. So a revolving-turret version of the M2 tank, known as the Combat Car M1, was developed. Other variants appeared, and by 1939 Rock Island felt that they had the right answer in the Light Tank M2A4, a revolving-turret model mounting a 37-mm (1.46-in) gun with a coaxial 0.30-in machine-gun, two 0.30-in machine-guns fixed in mounts on each side and firing forward, and a ball-mounted 0.30-in machine-gun loosely mounted in the bow.

Just as the M2A4 completed its trials war broke out in Europe, and the US decided to begin building up her forces. The M2A4 was selected for immediate production and the contract was given to the American Car & Foundry company, who delivered the first production tank in April 1940. A total of 375 were eventually built, and the M2A4 saw combat with the British Army in Egypt in small numbers; it was also used by the US Army and Marine Corps in the Pacific theatre in 1942. It served mostly as a training tank, a role which it filled excellently, and it was also the US Army's major combat vehicle for a large part of 1940-42 until medium tank production got under way.

Once production of the M2A4 had started, the Ordnance Department began an improved design, based on what could be gained from press reports of the campaigns in Europe. The most obvious requirement was greater armour protection, and the armour thickness was doubled. To carry the excess weight the suspension was altered by placing the rear idler wheel on the ground, a change which also improved the stability of the tank. The engine covers were thickened to defend against air attack, and several minor improvements were made; armament remained the same as the M2A4.

The first M3 models came from the production line in April 1941 and were of riveted construction. Shortly afterwards the design was changed to a welded turret, and later to a welded and cast turret; finally came all-welded hulls. In August 1941 the M3A1 appeared, which had a power-operated turret with turret basket to carry the crew. It omitted the side-mounted fixed machine-guns; and the cupola was omitted from the turret to lower the silhouette. An M3A2 design was then approved, this being the M3A1 with a welded hull. It was never put into production. The M3A3 of August 1942 had a welded hull with angled sides and a new turret with a 'bustle' at the back to carry the radio set. More fuel and ammunition could be carried and several small improvements were made, based on reports from British units using the tanks in the Western Desert.

The M3 series used either Continental gasoline or Guiberson diesel engines; the Guiberson was a radial aircraft engine converted to diesel, and fitted into the same space as the Continental with little modification. But both these engines were complicated and expensive, and the expanding aircraft industry was beginning to demand the same engines. The Cadillac division of General Motors suggested that it might be possible to put two Cadillac V-8 engines into the M3, side by side, and couple them to a common Hydramatic transmission. Automatic transmissions were still something of a novelty in 1941, and the Ordnance Department doubted that such transmission could be used in a tank, but Cadillac converted an M3 tank to their design and then drove it 800 km (500 miles) from the factory to a proving ground without trouble. This convinced the sceptics, and Cadillac were told to go ahead. Minor changes were made in the M3 in order

to accommodate the new engines, more armour was added, and in February 1942 the Cadillac design was standardized as the Light Tank M5. It was followed in September by the M5A1 which used the improved turret developed for the M3A3 and various other small improvements. Production of this class of tanks finally ceased in July 1944, a total of 13 859 M3 models and 8884 M5 models having been made.

The name General Stuart was applied by British troops to the first M2A4 tanks which arrived in Egypt in 1941. Since the later M3 and M5 models were substantially the same, they were also given the same name, but with British Mark numbers to distinguish the various models as follows: Stuart (M2A4); Stuart Mk 1 (M3); Stuart Mk 2 (M3 diesel); Stuart Mk 3 (M3A1); Stuart Mk 4 (M3A1 diesel); Stuart Mk 5 (M3A3); Stuart Mk 6 (M5); Stuart Mk 6 (M5A1).

Although replaced as a battle tank by the later Grant and Sherman models, the Stuarts were retained in use by the British Army as reconnaissance vehicles in north-west Europe, and were extensively employed in Burma until the end of the war. When removed from combat service as tanks, they were frequently modified by removing the turrets to become armoured infantry carriers and were used for towing antitank guns until the early 1950s.

(M3A3) *Weight:* 14.4 tonnes *Length:* 5.03 m (16 ft 6 in) *Width:* 2.51 m (8 ft 3 in) *Height:* 2.29 m (7 ft 6 in) *Armour thickness:* 37-12 mm (1.5-0.5 in) *Armament:* 1 37-mm (1.46-in) gun; 2 0.30-in

(7.62-mm) machine-guns *Powerplant:* Continental 7-cylinder gasoline radial, 250 bhp at 2400 rpm; or Guiberson 9-cylinder diesel, 220 bhp at 2200 rpm *Speed:* 58 km/h (36 mph) *Range:* 112 km (70 miles) *Crew:* 4

(M5A1) *Weight:* 15.38 tonnes *Length:* 4.83 m (15 ft 10 in) *Width:* 2.29 m (7 ft 6 in) *Height:* 2.39 m (7 ft 10 in) *Armour thickness:* 64-12 mm (2.5-0.5 in) *Armament:* 1 37-mm (1.46-in) machine-gun *Powerplant:* Dual Cadillac V-8 gasoline, 220 bhp at 4000 rpm *Speed:* 58 km/h (36 mph) *Range:* 160 km (100 miles) *Crew:* 4

StuG 44 German assault rifle   See **Haenel**

Sturgeon

US nuclear-powered submarine class, built 1963-75. In 1962 Congress authorized the construction of the first three of a new class of nuclear-powered attack submarines. *Sturgeon* and her sisters were based on the earlier *Thresher* Class, the more visible changes being that they were slightly longer, with a taller sail and forward diving planes on the sail fitted lower down to improve control at periscope depth. The forward hydroplanes could be rotated to a vertical position to assist in surfacing through the Arctic ice. As with the *Thresher* Class, the four torpedo tubes were fitted amidships and were capable of firing the Subroc antisubmarine missile. The last nine boats, commencing with *Archerfish*, were modified to allow for fitting an improved type of sonar, which increased

The USS *Queenfish*, a *Sturgeon* Class nuclear-powered submarine, surfaced at the North Pole on August 5, 1970. Built at Newport News, she is capable of firing the Subroc antisubmarine missile. Her forward hydroplanes can be rotated to the vertical for surfacing through ice

No and name	laid down	launched	completed	builder
SSN.637 *Sturgeon*	10/63	2/66	3/67	General Dynamics (Electric Boat)
SSN.638 *Whale*	5/64	10/66	10/68	General Dynamics, Quincey
SSN.639 *Tautog*	1/64	4/67	8/68	Ingalls
SSN.646 *Grayling*	5/64	6/67	10/69	Portsmouth navy yard
SSN.647 *Pogy*	5/64	6/67	5/71	Ingalls
SSN.648 *Aspro*	10/64	11/67	2/69	Ingalls
SSN.649 *Sunfish*	1/65	10/66	3/69	General Dynamics, Quincy
SSN.650 *Pargo*	6/64	9/66	1/68	General Dynamics (Electric Boat)
SSN.651 *Queenfish*	5/65	2/66	12/66	Newport News shipbuilding
SSN.652 *Puffer*	2/65	3/68	8/69	Ingalls
SSN.653 *Ray*	4/65	6/66	4/67	Newport News shipbuilding
SSN.660 *Sand Lance*	1/65	11/69	9/71	Portsmouth navy yard
SSN.661 *Lapon*	7/65	12/66	12/67	Newport News shipbuilding
SSN.662 *Gurnard*	12/64	5/67	12/68	Mare Island navy yard
SSN.663 *Hammerhead*	11/65	4/67	6/68	Newport News shipbuilding
SSN.664 *Sea Devil*	4/66	10/67	1/69	Newport News shipbuilding
SSN.665 *Guitarro*	12/65	7/68	9/72	Mare Island navy yard
SSN.666 *Hawkbill*	9/66	4/69	2/71	Mare Island navy yard
SSN.667 *Bergall*	4/66	2/68	6/69	General Dynamics (Electric Boat)
SSN.668 *Spadefish*	12/66	5/68	8/69	Newport News shipbuilding
SSN.669 *Seahorse*	8/66	6/68	9/69	General Dynamics (Electric Boat)
SSN.670 *Finback*	6/67	12/68	2/70	Newport News shipbuilding
SSN.672 *Pintado*	10/67	8/69	9/71	Mare Island navy yard
SSN.673 *Flying Fish*	6/67	5/69	4/70	General Dynamics (Electric Boat)
SSN.674 *Trepang*	10/67	9/69	8/70	General Dynamics (Electric Boat)
SSN.675 *Bluefish*	3/68	1/70	1/71	General Dynamics (Electric Boat)

the length of these boats by 3 m (10 ft).

Later submarines of the class participated in the trials of the new antiship missile Sub-Harpoon. *Hawkbill* has been modified as mother ship for a deep submergence rescue vessel (DSRV), a small submarine 15.2 m (50 ft) long which she carries on the after deck. The DSRV is designed to rescue the crew of other submarines in difficulties in water too deep for the usual submarine rescue methods.

While in the fitting-out basin *Guitarro* sank in 11 m (35 ft) of water as a result of errors by the shipyard. This accident delayed her completion by over two years and cost some $25 million.

Displacement: 3860/4630 tons (surfaced/submerged) *Length:* 89.2 m (292 ft 6 in) oa *Beam:* 9.7 m (31 ft 8 in) *Draught:* 9 m (29 ft 5 in) *Machinery:* nuclear reactor, 1-shaft steam turbine, 15 000 shp≈20/30 knots (surfaced/submerged) *Armament:* 4 21-in (53-cm) torpedo tubes *Crew:* 120

Sturgeon, Short

British naval reconnaissance-bomber and target tug aircraft. The Sturgeon was the first twin-engined aircraft specifically designed for British carrier operations to enter service with the Fleet Air Arm. It was originally designed to Specification S.11/43 which called for a reconnaissance-bomber for service aboard *Ark Royal* and *Hermes* Class aircraft carriers. The prototype Sturgeon first flew in 1946.

With a change in operational requirements after the Second World War the Sturgeon was redesigned as a target tug to meet the new Specification Q.1/46. The new version was known as the Short SA.2 Sturgeon TT.2, and it first flew on September 1, 1949. Of conventional all-metal stressed-skin construction, this mid-wing monoplane was fully equipped for deck landing on carriers. It featured power-folding wings and a lengthened nose to accommodate photographic equipment. It had a crew of two, and was powered by two 1660-hp Rolls-Royce Merlin 140S engines.

The first of 23 production Sturgeons flew on June 8, 1950; 19 of these aircraft were later modified for shore-based duties, with the short nose of the original Sturgeon, manual wing folding and with the deck-landing gear removed. The last of these aircraft, known as the Short SB.9 Sturgeon TT.3, was delivered in May 1957.

Most Sturgeons were flown by 728 Squadron FAA, a fleet requirements unit operating from RNAS Hal Far, Malta. They were used for fleet gunnery practice, radar calibration and air-to-air firing practice. Sturgeons were finally superseded by Meteor TT.20s in the late 1950s.

(TT.2) Span: 18.2 m (59 ft 9 in) *Length:* 14.88 m (48 ft 10 in) *Gross weight:* 10 138 kg (22 350 lb) *Maximum speed:* 573 km/h (356 mph) at 7380 m (24 200 ft)

Sturmgeschütz

German self-propelled guns. The Sturmgeschütz series of vehicles arose from an army demand in late 1936 for an armoured

SSN.676 *Billfish*	9/68	5/70	3/71	General Dynamics (Electric Boat)
SSN.677 *Drum*	8/68	5/70	4/72	Mare Island navy yard
SSN.678 *Archerfish*	6/69	1/71	12/71	General Dynamics (Electric Boat)
SSN.679 *Silversides*	10/69	6/71	5/72	General Dynamics (Electric Boat)
SSN.680 *William H Bates*	8/69	12/71	5/73	Ingalls
SSN.681 *Batfish*	2/70	10/71	9/72	General Dynamics (Electric Boat)
SSN.682 *Tunny*	5/70	6/72	1/74	Ingalls
SSN.683 *Parche*	12/70	1/73	8/74	Ingalls
SSN.684 *Cavalla*	6/70	2/72	2/73	General Dynamics (Electric Boat)
SSN.686 *L Mendel Rivers*	6/71	6/72	2/75	Newport News shipbuilding
SSN.687 *Richard B Russell*	10/71	1/74	8/75	Newport News shipbuilding

infantry-support vehicle mounting a gun of at least 75-mm (2.95-in) calibre. In order to simplify manufacture and keep the weapon compact, no turret was to be used and the gun was to be mounted in the hull front. The design was based on the hull and running gear of the PzKpfw III tank, the hull being sloped in at the sides and roofed over so as to form a crew compartment, with the 75-mm/24-cal gun in the front plate. The design was approved, and production began in January 1940, the first vehicles being used in the latter stages of the campaign in France.

The first model was known as the Ausf A and 30 were built; it was followed by B, C and D models, 520 equipments in all, which differed in having improved transmission and engine units, and minor changes to the superstructure. Ausf E appeared in late 1941, a redesign giving more stowage space, and 272 were built. It had been intended to build 500 of these, but by that time it was apparent that

the 75-mm gun was no longer sufficiently powerful, and design work began on a new model to mount the 43- or 48-calibre 75-mm gun and also improve the armour protection. This resulted in the Ausf F model, production of which began in March 1942; 350 were built. The gun was longer and more powerful, but the additional armour was not added until about half-way through the production run.

By the late summer of 1942 the design of the basic PzKpfw III tank had gone through several improvements, and the next Strumgeschütz, the Ausf F/8, reflected this in having a new pattern of hull. The rear deck was extended and the basic armour improved, while additional armour was bolted to the front surfaces. Fitted with the 75-mm/48-cal gun, 334 of these were built.

In December 1942 the final model, Ausf G appeared. This had some improvements to the hull shape, a better gun mantlet, a new cupola with periscopes for the commander, and other small improvements. This model stayed in production until the end of the war, 7720 being produced.

In 1943 the Alkett factory, which was the principal producer of the StuG III models, was bombed and much production was lost. In an endeavour to compensate, the Krupp production plant working on PzKpfw IV tanks was switched to making Sturmgeschütz, using the PzKpfw IV chassis and hull as the basis. It used the same gun and superstructure design as the StuG III and was generally the same except for the running gear. It remained in production until March 1945, 1139 being built.

The Sturmgeschütz were originally intended to be issued to special Sturmartillerie batteries, but they proved so useful that by the end of the war they could be found in all sorts of formations. Since they were easier, cheaper and quicker to build than

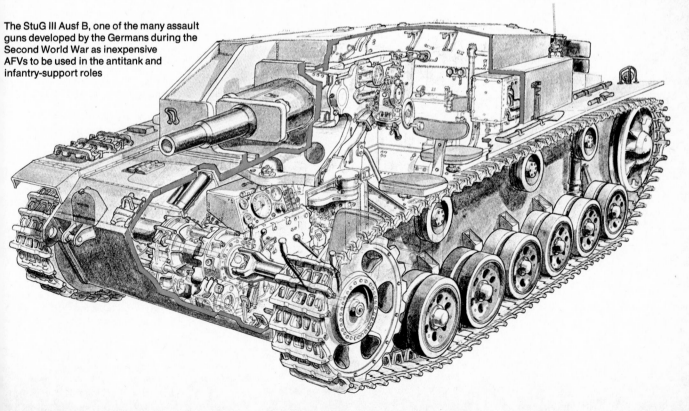

The StuG III Ausf B, one of the many assault guns developed by the Germans during the Second World War as inexpensive AFVs to be used in the antitank and infantry-support roles

Sturmovik, Ilyushin Il-2

tanks, they gradually assumed the major proportion of German armoured vehicle production, to the eventual detriment of tank production. Whilst they were extremely effective vehicles in their designated role, there was a tendency to use them as substitutes for tanks, to which role they were not well suited.

(Sturmgeschütz III Ausf G) *Weight:* 24.3 tonnes *Length:* 6.73 m (22 ft 2 in) *Width:* 2.95 m (9 ft 8 in) *Height:* 2.16 m (7 ft 1 in) *Armour thickness:* 80-15 mm (3.1-0.6 in) *Armament:* 1 7.5-cm (2.95-in) StuK 40 L/48; 3 7.92-mm (0.312-in) machine-gun *Powerplant:* Maybach V-12 gasoline *Speed:* 40 km/h (25 mph) *Range:* 155 km (96 miles)

Sturmovik, Ilyushin Il-2

Soviet ground-attack aircraft. While Sturmovik is a Russian generic term referring to all ground-attack designs, it is universally applied to one of the most remarkable and outstanding aircraft of the Second World War, Sergei Ilyushin's Il-2. By the time it was phased out of production during 1944, no fewer than 36 163 examples of the Il-2 had left the Soviet state factories. By that time it was known to grateful Soviet infantrymen by the affectionate nickname Ilyusha, but to the German tank crews who had lost so many of their comrades to its rockets and cannon it was simply the Black Death.

Throughout the 1930s the Soviet air high command had been seeking an effective ground-attack aircraft, and the Tstentralnoe Kunstruktorskoe Byuro in Moscow evolved a promising prototype in 1938 as the TsKB-55. It was a two-seat low-wing cantilever monoplane with main undercarriage units which retracted backwards into underwing fairings, leaving the wheels partially exposed. The windscreen was of armour-glass. The crew, the 1350-hp AM-35 water-cooled engine, and the water and oil radiators, were protected by what amounted to a 7-mm (0.3-in) armour-plated 'bath'. The armour protection differed from that fitted to most ground-attack aircraft previously built in that it formed an integral part of the fuselage structure. The rear fuselage was a wood monocoque, while wings and tail unit were of duralumin. A second prototype, by then designated BSh-2 (*Bronirovannyi Sturmovik*, armoured ground-attack) flew on December 30, 1939.

It was reported that the third prototype was changed to single-seat configuration at the behest of Stalin. Powered by a 1600-hp AM-38 engine it was designated TsKB-57 and featured a number of other modifications, most important of which were thicker armour plate of 12 mm (0.5 in) and increased fuel capacity. It flew for the first time on October 12, 1940. Tests successfully completed, production was started at the GAZ No 18 (Voronezh), No 22 (Fili, Moscow) and No 38 (also Moscow). Earlier problems of longitudinal stability had been resolved and difficulties about supplies of armour plate settled, and a number of preproduction and early series aircraft were undergoing operational evaluation when Germany launched the invasion of the Soviet Union on June 22, 1941. They gave a good account of themselves, but only 249 had been completed by the end of June and 1293 during the remaining six months of 1941.

The Soviet Ilyushin Il-2 Sturmovik, the 'flying tank' of the Eastern Front, which hit both soft and armoured vehicles and due to its armour protection seemed almost invulnerable to AA fire

The single-seat Il-2s were armed with two 20-mm (0.79-in) ShVak cannon and two 7.62-mm (0.30-in) ShKas machine-guns, all mounted in the wings. These initial production aircraft had a maximum bombload of 400 kg (882 lb) carried internally in bays in the wing centre section, two either side of the fuselage. In addition there were four launching rails under each wing outer section for RS-82 rockets. In the rear fuselage were twin chutes for SAB light bombs.

Il-2s were first committed to combat in quantity during the battle for Moscow. In October 1941 a Sturmovik regiment was joined by two further regiments from the Central Reserve to support the Soviet 5th Army on the Mozhaisk Defence Line. The following month Il-2s of the 65th Regiment were instrumental in halting the German breakthrough near Tula, preparatory to the launching of the first major Soviet counter-offensive in December 1941. Supplies of Il-2s were limited in early 1942 as the aircraft factories evacuated to the east had not yet got into full production. Nevertheless the Sturmoviks wrought considerable havoc on aerodromes in the encircled Demyansk pocket where Junkers Ju 52/3m transports were being hastily unloaded.

During the battle for Stalingrad, which began in August 1942, the Il-2 played an important role. At that stage of the war it was still available in only limited numbers and operated in small groups. Nevertheless it was effective, though proving vulnerable to attack by enemy fighters from the rear and its cannon made only a limited impression against the newest German tanks. The 16th Air Army supporting the Stalingrad Front carried out field conversions of some Sturmoviks to two-seat configuration, recruiting rear gunners from ground staff. Meanwhile there had been conferences early in 1942 which led to the production of the two-seat Il-2m3. As an interim measure, from the spring of 1942 there appeared the Il-2m, with the more powerful 1770-hp AM-38F engine and 23-mm (0.91-in) VYa-23 cannon with greater armour penetration, but retaining the single-seat arrangement. Two-seaters began to reach the ground-attack regiments in November 1942. The gunner was provided with a 12.7-mm (0.5-in) UBT machine-gun on

a flexible mounting and the rear fuselage was of metal instead of wood construction.

Tactical use of the Il-2 had by then been carefully studied, and while some Il-2s continued to operate unescorted in pairs at minimal height, attacking almost horizontally, others operated in groups of eight or ten machines against heavily defended targets, flying at about 2000 m (6600 ft) and then diving at their pinpoint objectives; the large-scale availability of the Il-2m3 enabled attacks to be mounted at regimental strength. To achieve maximum impact, Sturmovik divisions frequently adopted what came to be known as the 'circle of death' technique. The formation crossed the front line some way from the target area, usually flying in a staggered line abreast, reaching a point to the rear of the target and then forming up into a circle nose-to-tail, each machine then diving at a 30° to 40° angle, in turn, to strike with cannon and machine-gun fire, often launching their bombs and rockets when a mere 200 m (660 ft) from the objective. This manoeuvre would be repeated until all ammunition had been expended. It was, however, not until the Battle of Kursk in summer 1943 that this tactic was fully developed. After the initial stages of the fighting, Il-2s became available in greater quantities and were committed in divisional strength. The success of the Il-2m3s led to the destruction of literally hundreds of German tanks in the Kursk salient. On July 7, in one 20-minute period, 70 tanks of the 9th Panzer Division were knocked out.

Early production targets had not been achieved, and Stalin coined the famous phrase "The Il-2 is as vital to our Red Army as air or bread", when he issued a reprimand about poor output on December 23, 1941, to the directors of the factories responsible for building Il-2s. By 1943, however, immense numbers were leaving the production lines and in that year alone over 11 000 Il-2s were delivered to the air force. A number of modifications were incorporated during this period to improve performance. The armoured compartment was extended to include the gunner's position, and the airframe was of all-metal construction. Improved sealing between the armour panels, elimination of gaps in the control surfaces, the addition of a fairing in front of the tail wheel and the location of the oil cooler with the radiator (already protected by armour plate) led to an increase of 35 km/h (22 mph) over the 404 km/h (251 mph) of the original two-seat Ilyusha.

Armament was improved, with 37-mm (1.46-in) cannon firing armour-piercing shells of remarkable potency; an increase in bomb-load to 600 kg (1323 lb), partly carried on external underwing racks; the use on occasion of higher-calibre RS-132 rockets; and the introduction of a load of 200 2.5-kg (5.5-lb) hollow-charge antitank bombs carried in special 'cassette' containers. Some Il-2s utilized DAG 10 grenade launchers in the tail. The grenades were fired into the path of pursuing fighters and were fitted with parachutes. There is no information as to their success rate.

As the Germans retreated to the west, the Ilyusha became a more and more familiar sight to Soviet infantrymen. It played a key role in the reduction of fortress Königsberg, and by the time Berlin was invaded, thousands of Sturmoviks were marshalled through the checkpoints established by the Air Command at the eastern and northern approaches, with the task of reducing enemy strongpoints to rubble and destroying anything that moved in their path. By then they had amply deserved their second popular nickname 'the flying infantryman'.

In addition to enemy armour and transport, the Ilyusha destroyed many enemy aircraft on the ground and quite a number in the air, most while defending itself but quite often, in the later stages of the war, taking the offensive against German bombers and transports, and even fighters, with considerable success. Sturmovik crews gained a high proportion of the awards bestowed upon Soviet fliers during the war, many receiving the gold star of Hero of the Soviet Union, four actually becoming twice HSUs.

After participating in the short sharp campaign by the USSR against Japan in Manchuria in August 1945, the Ilyusha never again fired its guns in anger. It continued to equip some Soviet assault regiments for a short period after 1945, but its most important task was to form initial equipment for the newly created air arms of Poland, Czechoslovakia and most of the countries of southeastern Europe.

Variants of the Il-2 produced included the Il-2T naval torpedo-bomber and the Il-2U trainer, as well as a photo-reconnaissance version.

Built in greater numbers than any other aircraft, the tough and deadly type Il-2 has a firm place in the history of military aviation as the first successful ground-attack aircraft built specially for the task, and the only one to have had a decisive effect on the outcome of the Second World War, due both to the quality of Sergei Ilyushin's unique design and to the quantity of aircraft produced by the Soviet aviation industry in the most difficult conditions imaginable.

A number of other aircraft were developed to the Sturmovik formula. The Ilyushin Il-10 Beast was powered by a 2000-hp AM-42 engine and armed with two 7.62-mm machine-guns and two 23-mm cannon, though some later models had four cannon. The Beast entered service at the beginning of 1945 and, though it did not see much action, it

remained in production in the Soviet Union until 1950, almost 5000 being built, while a further 1200 were built in Czechoslovakia in 1950-54 with the designation B-33. The type remained in Soviet service until 1957, and was also used by Bulgaria, China, Hungary, North Korea and Poland.

The two-seat turboprop Tupolev Tu-91 Boot, produced in the mid-1950s, was abandoned when it was decided to build no more specialized Sturmovik types.

See also Brawny.

(Il-2, single-seater 1940-41) *Span:* 14.6 m (47 ft 11 in) *Length:* 11.58 m (38 ft 1 in) *Gross weight:* 5500 kg (12125 lb) *Maximum speed:* 435 km/h (270 mph) at sea level

(Il-2m3) *Span:* 14.6 m (47 ft 11 in) *Length:* 11.58 m (38 ft 1 in) *Gross weight:* 6360 kg (14021 lb) *Maximum speed:* 439 km/h (273 mph) at sea level

Styx

Soviet antiship missile. The SS-N-2 Styx achieved notoriety in October 1967 when three rounds fired from Egyptian patrol boats struck and sank the Israeli destroyer *Eilat,* demonstrating in no uncertain manner that even small vessels were capable of defeating much larger opponents. Much of the emphasis on antiship missiles in the 1970s stems from this single action. Styx has also taken part in at least three other conflicts: the India-Pakistan war of December 1971, the Middle East war of October 1973 and an engagement between Chinese and South Vietnamese vessels near the Paracel Islands.

SS-N-2 is launched from hangar-type containers fitted on Soviet-built 'Komar' and 'Osa' fast patrol boats; the former carry two rounds and the latter are equipped with four. The missile is of aeroplane-type configuration and is launched with the aid of a solid-propellant boost motor, cruise propulsion then being assumed by a turbojet. Styx flies under the control of an autopilot, probably with the assistance of commands transmitted from the launch vessel, and has some form of terminal seeker: either an active-radar homing head or an infrared sensor; the SS-N-2B version may carry both types.

Styx entered service in 1959 and has been supplied to many countries by the Soviet Union. The 'Osa II' patrol boats carry SS-N-11 in place of SS-N-2, but the earlier weapon is likely to remain in service for many more years.

Length: 6.5 m (21 ft 4 in) approx *Span:* 2.75 m (9 ft) *Diameter:* 75 cm (29.5 in) *Weight:* 3000 kg (6600 lb) approx *Range:* 42 km (26 miles) *Speed:* Mach 0.9 *Warhead:* 360-400 kg (800-880 lb) high-explosive

Su-2, Sukhoi

Soviet light bomber. Pavel Sukhoi's Su-2 is derived from the ANT-51 prototype which flew for the first time on August 25, 1937. Powered by an 830-hp M-62 radial engine, ANT-51 was a low cantilever wing monoplane of mixed construction with a retractable undercarriage. When Sukhoi was allocated his own design bureau in 1938 he developed the ANT-51 into the BB-1 (*blizhnii bombardirovshchik,* short-range bomber). Three prototypes were flown in 1940, differing mainly in powerplant: one had an M-87A, the second an M-87B, both of 950 hp, the third an M-88 of 1000 hp.

The M-88-powered version had a maximum speed of 468 km/h (291 mph), an improvement of 65 km/h (40 mph) over the ANT-51, and an internal bombload of 400 kg (880 lb) as against 200 kg (440 lb). It was placed in production almost immediately as the Su-2, and had a wooden monocoque fuselage and all-metal dihedral wings made up of steel spars with duralumin ribs. The two-man crew was accommodated under a raised glazed canopy which terminated in a ring mounting for a 7.62-mm (0.30-in) ShKas machine-gun under a light Perspex turret. The main undercarriage legs retracted inwards to lie completely within the wing profile, and there was a single curved fin and rudder.

The M-88 engine soon gave way to the M-88B of 1100 hp, which raised top speed to 512 km/h (318 mph) at 7100 m (23 300 ft). A ViSh-23 three-bladed variable-pitch propeller was fitted. The crew was protected in front, below and at the rear by 9-mm (0.354-in) armour plate, and armament was increased,

The Styx Soviet antiship missile has been used in three major conflicts in the Middle and Far East. It made world headlines when three Styx missiles sunk the Israeli destroyer *Eilat* in October 1967

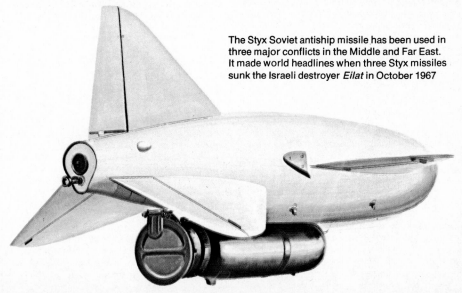

to the detriment of performance. Instead of four fixed ShKas wing guns, six were fitted; bombload was enhanced by external racks for 200 kg (440 lb); ten RS-82 rockets were carried underwing; and twin guns were occasionally installed in the gunner's turret.

During 1941 the powerplant was changed to a 1330-hp M-82 (ASh-82) 14-cylinder radial engine. Additional equipment was fitted and armour protection was increased. Loaded weight rose by 303 kg (668 lb) from the 2970 kg (6548 lb) of the M-88B powered version, but performance was still good. Production continued after the German invasion of June 1940 and it is estimated that some 600 Su-2s, mainly of the ASh-82-powered version, were built. A further 7.62-mm ShKas machine-gun was fitted to an unknown number of Su-2s for ventral protection, firing through a small pair of outward-opening doors in the underside of the fuselage just aft of the wing trailing edge.

A ground-attack development of the Su-2, designated ShB, featured additional crew protection, some aerodynamic refinement and a redesigned undercarriage which retracted backwards into the wing with the wheels turning through 90°. The Su-4 variant, powered by the 1500-hp M-90 radial engine, never overcame its teething troubles and like the ShB did not go into production.

When the Su-2 went into action against the invading German forces it was mainly allocated to Composite Air Divisions and was intended largely for level bombing attacks at medium altitude. As with most inexperienced air arms of that era, it had been assumed that the speed of the light bomber would enable it to operate effectively without fighter escort. Even when it was realized that fighter cover would have cut down the heavy losses being suffered by the Su-2 Regiments, there were not enough fighters available during the first hectic months of conflict. A probable further contributing factor to these losses was the excessive secrecy of the authorities. Many Soviet fighter pilots and antiaircraft crews had not seen recognition material on the Su-2 when war broke out, and air ace Aleksander Pokryshkin has recorded that he nearly shot one down while flying his MiG-3 in the Ukraine during June 1941.

Before production of the Su-2 was phased out at the end of 1942, two or three Su-2s were reportedly attached to each newly formed Stormovik regiment to act as formation leaders and fly reconnaissance missions.

(With M-82 engine) *Span:* 14.3 m (46 ft 11 in) *Length:* 10.46 m (34 ft 4 in) *Gross weight:* 4700 kg (10362 lb) *Maximum speed:* 486 km/h (302 mph at 5850 m (19200 ft)

Su-6, Sukhoi

Soviet ground-attack aircraft. While bearing a superficial resemblance to the Su-2, the Sukhoi design bureau's Su-6, the first prototype of which first flew in December 1940, was in fact an entirely new design. An all-metal low-wing cantilever monoplane, the initial version was of single-seat configuration. The forward section of the circular monocoque fuselage was protected by 12-mm (0.47-in) armour plating and the pilot's enclosed cockpit was faired into the aft fuselage. The wing comprised a centre section and two outer sections, the latter with

The Sukhoi Su-2 without the usual gunner's cupola. It was phased out at the end of 1942

The Su-6-III was the last of the series and may have seen action in the Soviet Far East

considerable dihedral. Leading-edge slots and split flaps were fitted. The great problem was the M-71 powerplant, an 18-cylinder radial engine which delivered an impressive 2000 hp. Its defects were never rectified, although the Su-6 had better performance than the initial production single-seat Il-2, achieving 527 km/h (327 mph) at 2500 m (8200 ft) never went into production.

The undercarriage followed the style of the experimental Su-4, retracting backwards into the wings, the wheels turning through 90° during retraction. The tail wheel was semi-retractable. Armament comprised two 23-mm (0.91-in) VYa cannon and four 7.62-mm (0.30-in) ShKas machine-guns fixed to fire forward. Up to 400 kg (880 lb) of bombs could be carried, partly externally and partly in the fuselage bay and ten RS-82 rockets could be fitted to underwing launching rails.

In parallel with the instructions issued to Ilyushin for a two-seat version of the famed Il-2, Sukhoi was ordered to produce the Su-6-II in early 1942. It employed the M-71F engine of 2200 hp and pilot and gunner (the latter with a 12.7-mm [0.5-in] UBT machine-gun on a free mounting) were housed in an armoured enclosure. Fixed cannon were the very effective 37-mm (1.46-in) 11-P-37. Even after aerodynamic improvements the two-

seat Il-2 M3 reached a maximum of only 480 km/h (298 mph), while Su-6-II reached 514 km/h (319 mph), but development was protracted, and before it was completed (with the engine still causing problems) the Il-2 M3 was in full production.

Sukhoi was still allocated resources, however, as a necessary back-up to the Ilyushin design. The Su-6-III had a 2000-hp AM-42 liquid-cooled engine, with forward armament reduced to two 11-P-37 cannon and two 7.62-mm ShKas machine-guns. The wingtips were more rounded and the area of the wings accordingly increased slightly. Flight testing in 1944 indicated a top speed of 520 km/h (323 mph), but by that time the new Il-10, with generally superior performance, was in production and further Su-6 development was probably abandoned, though there are reports that small batches of the Su-6 were in limited service during 1944-45.

(Su-6-III) *Span:* 13.5 m (44 ft 4 in) *Length:* 9.5 m (31 ft 2 in) *Gross weight:* 6200 kg (13669 lb) *Maximum speed:* 520 km/h (323 mph) at 2500 m (8200 ft)

Su-7, Sukhoi Soviet jet ground-attack fighter **See Fitter**

Su-9/Su-11, **Sukhoi** Soviet jet fighter
aircraft **See Fishpot**

Su-15, **Sukhoi** Soviet jet intercepter
aircraft **See Flagon**

Su-19, **Sukhoi** Soviet attack aircraft
See Fencer

Subroc, Goodyear

US submarine-launched antisubmarine missile. The UUM-44A Subroc is carried by the
US Navy's attack submarines of the *Thresher*
and later classes, primarily for use against
enemy missile-launching submarines. Development began in 1958 at the US Navy Ordnance Laboratory, with Goodyear Aerospace
as prime contractor. The weapon became
operational in 1965 after a series of trials
from the USS *Plunger* in the Pacific. Production ended in mid-1972, but since the retirement in the mid-1970s of the Mk 45 Astor
torpedo the missile has been the US Navy's
sole submarine-launched ASW weapon with
a nuclear warhead.

Targets are acquired by the submarine's
BQQ-2 or BQQ-5 sonar and the relevant
information is fed to Subroc's Singer Kearfott SD-510 inertial-guidance set. The missile
is then launched from a standard torpedo
tube, and the Thiokol TE-260G solid-
propellant rocket motor ignites once the
round is safely clear of the submarine.
Thrust-vectoring nozzles allow the weapon to
steer underwater and pitch it up into the
atmosphere. After a preset distance the
warhead section is separated from its booster
by means of explosive bolts and continues to
fly a ballistic path, using four vanes for
steering under the control of the inertial-
guidance system. A protective cone cushions
the impact with the sea surface, and the
warhead section containing a nuclear depth
charge sinks to a preset depth before detonating.

Length: 6.4 m (21 ft) *Diameter:* 53 cm (21 in)
Weight: 1814 kg (4000 lb) *Range:* 55 km (35
miles) *Speed:* supersonic

US Navy

Subroc breaks the surface during launch trials.
Below: **Loading Subroc into a US submarine.**
The missile became operational in 1965

US Navy

Sudarev

Soviet submachine-gun. In the years before
the outbreak of the Second World War,
Alexei Ivanovich Sudarev was in charge of
mass production at the Leningrad armament
works. He remained in that post during the
German siege of the city, and when weapons
began to run short he headed a design team
which turned out a new submachine-gun in
record time. There is now some doubt as to
whether the team actually designed the gun,
or whether it was an existing design by some
other hand which Sudarev and his colleagues
turned into a practical manufacturing proposition, but whatever the true origin there is
no doubt that the first models were made in
Leningrad in early 1942 and were sent
straight from the factory to the troops man-
ning the defences. The PPS-42, as it was
called, was in many ways a lightened and
simplified version of the PPSh-41. Though
there are no common components between
them many are very similar; the gun is made
up entirely from pressings and stampings and
there is no woodwork in it at all. It only fired
at full automatic, but the rate of fire was low
enough to allow single shots to be snatched
off. The magazine was the curved box which
was an alternative for the PPSh-41, and all
the parts were very crudely finished.

The PPS-42 could not be fired with the
stock folded but a modified version, the PPS-
43, was introduced and issued on a small
scale to the Red Army until 1945. It then went
out of service in USSR, though it remained in
use for some time in China and elsewhere.

(PPS-43) *Calibre:* 7.62 mm (0.30 in) *Ammunition:* 7.62-mm M30 *Weight:* 2.99 kg (6 lb 9 oz)
unloaded *Length:* 889 mm (35 in) *Barrel length:*
272 mm (10.7 in) *Magazine:* 35-round detachable box *Rate of fire:* 600 rds/min (cyclic)
Muzzle velocity: 500 m/sec (1640 ft/sec)

Suffren

French battleship, built 1899-1903. Adhering
to the concept of a 'fleet of samples' at a time
when their chief rivals, the British, were
building homogeneous classes, the French
chose to follow the *Charlemagne* Class and
Iéna with a single ship of enlarged type, with
a deeper armour belt. The design of the
Suffren was closer to British contemporaries
in fighting power, with a fairly orthodox
layout and appearance. Although launched
only six months after being laid down at

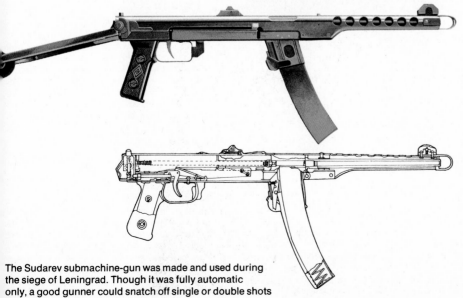

The Sudarev submachine-gun was made and used during
the siege of Leningrad. Though it was fully automatic
only, a good gunner could snatch off single or double shots

Suffren

Brest arsenal she was not completed until 1903, by which time she was outclassed by newer foreign ships. The disposition of intermediate-calibre 164.7-mm (6.5-in) guns in single turrets was years ahead of its time.

An interesting experiment was carried to test the strength of the *Suffren*'s main turrets, with a live firing from the *Massena* at a distance of only 100 m (110 yards). An additional 16-in (406-mm) plate was hung outside the turret, and two uncapped armour-piercing shells were fired at it. Neither shell penetrated the turret, although the outside plate was cracked in half. Some sheep tethered inside the turret showed no distress, and only 1 kW more power was needed to train the turret.

Suffren was the flagship of Admiral Guépratte at the Dardanelles from February 1915, having been in the Complementary or Reserve Division of the Mediterranean Fleet in August 1914. She opened fire on the Kum Kale forts on February 19 and carried out several bombardments. She was slightly damaged by hits from a Turkish battery in March, and during the great bombardment of the narrows on March 18 was hit 14 times and set on fire by a 24-cm (9.4-in) shell. Her forefunnel was almost destroyed, and she had to be repaired at Malta before returning to Toulon with the damaged *Gaulois*. She returned to the Dardanelles in May and served subsequently with the 2nd Division of the 3rd Squadron. On November 29, 1916, while returning to Brest for repairs, she was steaming without escort off Lisbon when she was torpedoed by *U 52*. She was lost with all hands.

Displacement: 12 750 tons (normal) *Length:* 126 m (413 ft 5 in) wl *Beam:* 21.4 m (70 ft 3 in) *Draught:* 8.4 m (27 ft 7 in) *Machinery:* 3-shaft reciprocating steam, 16 000 ihp=18 knots *Protection:* 30 i-229 mm (12-9 in) belt, 76-41 mm (3-1.6 in) decks, 330 mm (13 in) turrets *Armament:* 4 305-mm (12-in)/45-cal Model '96 (2×2); 10 164.7-mm (6.5-in)/45-cal (10×1); 8 100-mm (3.9-in) QF (8×1); 22 3-pdr (47-mm) QF (22×1); 4 45-cm (17.7-in) torpedo tubes (2 above water, 2 submerged, all beam) *Crew:* 730

Suffren

French heavy cruiser class, built 1926-32. Dissatisfaction with the flimsy protection of the *Duquesne* Class led to a redesign, with heavier armour at the expense of extreme speed. Two ships were authorized in 1926, followed by another in 1927 and the fourth in 1929; all were built by Brest arsenal. Although the hull form was standard, there were many differences between the four ships, particularly in armour. The weight of protection started at 951 tonnes with *Suffren*, rose to 1374 tonnes in *Foch* and *Colbert* and again to 1553 tonnes in *Dupleix*. In *Colbert* and *Dupleix* weight was saved by reducing the shell plating from 50-mm (1.97-in) to 20-mm (0.79-in) to allow internal armour of 60-54 mm (2.4-2.1 in) along the machinery spaces. Another difference was that *Suffren* and *Colbert* carried 640 tonnes of coal to give an additional 3200 km (2000 miles) endurance at 11 knots, whereas the later pair had additional oil stowage. The quaintest feature of all was coal protection between the outer plating and the internal antitorpedo bulkhead,

The French battleship *Suffren* was badly damaged at the Dardanelles. She was lost in 1916

The heavy cruiser *Suffren* was interned at Alexandria in 1940 and joined the Allies in 1943

about 2 m (6 ft 6 in) thick abreast of the after boiler rooms and engine rooms.

The first two ships had the same 75-mm (2.95-in) AA guns as the *Duquesne* Class; *Foch* had a new 90-mm (3.54-in) AA gun in eight single mountings, while *Dupleix* had the same gun in four twin mountings. All four were fast: *Suffren* averaged 32.5 knots for four hours, while *Colbert* maintained 31.25 knots for six hours.

All except *Suffren*, which was interned at Alexandria, remained at Toulon after July 1940. In 1941-42 their AA armament was increased by four twin 37-mm (1.46-in) (six singles in *Colbert*), four single 8-mm (0.315-in) machine-guns (seven in *Foch*), and (in *Colbert* only) 20 13.2-mm (0.52-in) machine-guns in four quadruple and two twin mountings. *Suffren* joined the Allies in 1943 and was refitted. Her aircraft and catapult and two triple torpedo tubes were removed and two quadruple 40-mm (1.57-in) Bofors and 20 20-mm (0.79-in) Oerlikon AA guns were added. Even after more than 1600 tons of extra armament and fuel was added in 1943 she could steam at 27 knots continuously at a full load displacement of 14 400 tons.

Colbert, *Foch* and *Dupleix* were all scuttled at Toulon in November 1942. *Suffren* was paid off in December 1962 and was hulked as

an accommodation ship at Toulon, renamed *Océan* in 1964.

Displacement: 11 290 tons (normal), 12 780 tons (full load) *Length:* 194 m (636 ft 6 in) *Beam:* 19.1 m (62 ft 8 in) *Draught:* 6.35 m (20 ft 10 in) *Machinery:* 3-shaft geared steam turbines, 90 000 shp=31 knots *Protection:* 60-51 mm (2.4-2 in) belt, 28-22 mm (1.1-0.9 in) decks, 28 mm (1.1 in) turrets *Armament:* 8 203-mm (8-in)/50-cal Model '24 (4×2); 8 90-mm (3.54-in) AA Model '26/'30 (4×2 or 8×1) (or 8 75-mm [2.95-in] AA Model '22 [8×1]); 8 37-mm (1.46-in) AA (4×2); 12 13.2-mm (0.52-in) AA machine-guns (4×3); 12 55-cm (21.7-in) torpedo tubes (4×3); 1/2 Loire 130 or 2 Gourdon 811 flying boats, 1/2 catapults *Crew:* 752 (wartime)

Suffren

French guided-missile destroyer class, built 1962-64. Under the 1960 Programme two *frégates* were ordered, *Suffren* from Lorient dockyard, and the *Duquesne* from Brest dockyard. They were to be big ocean-going fleet escorts capable of providing area defence, and were the first French ships built from the keel up armed with the Masurca SAM system. Although rated as frigates they carry pendant numbers D.602 and D.603.

The *Duquesne*, a *Suffren* Class guided-missile destroyer, with DRBI-23 three-dimensional radar

A new hull form was adopted, with the forecastle deck carried aft almost to the quarterdeck, a distinctive 'flattened nose' to permit A gun to fire at zero elevation, and a wide shallow transom stern to accommodate a big towed sonar. Other unusual features are the huge 'golf-ball' dome weather-proofing the DRBI-23 three-dimensional radar (which provides air-surveillance and target designation for the SAMs) and a tall mack nearly amidships. The Masurca missiles are launched from a twin-arm launcher aft, with two DRBR-51 fire-control radars on the after superstructure.

A single launcher for the Malafon antisubmarine missile system is positioned abaft the mack, and since 1977 *Suffren* has carried four MM-38 Exocet SSM launchers on the deckhouse immediately abaft this launcher. Her sister completed similar modification in 1978, and both ships surrendered their twin 30-mm (1.18-in) guns to compensate for the weight. The SENIT 1 action data automation system is fitted.

The ships are reported to be exceptionally good seaboats, with little vibration. They have three pairs of gyroscopically controlled non-retractable stabilizers. Accommodation and working spaces are air-conditioned.

Displacement: 5090 tonnes (normal), 6090 tonnes (full load) *Length:* 157.6 m (517 ft 1 in) oa *Beam:* 15.5 m (50 ft 10 in) *Draught:* 6.1 m (20 ft) *Machinery:* 2-shaft geared steam turbines, 72 500 shp=34 knots *Armament:* 2 100-mm (3.9-in)/55-cal DP Model 53 (2×1); 2 20-mm (0.79-in) Oerlikon (2×1); 1 Masurca SAM launcher, 48 Mk 3 Mod 2 and Mod 3 missiles; 1 Malafon launcher, 13 missiles; 4 MM-38 Exocet launchers; 5 L5 A/S torpedo tubes *Crew:* 350

Sumatra

Dutch cruiser class, built 1916-25. Worried by the country's isolation and dependence on food imports the Dutch government authorized the building of three large cruisers in 1916. The design was prepared with German technical assistance, but with the emphasis on overseas operations, and the ship which resulted was some 50% larger than contemporary British and German light cruisers. The machinery was built in Germany.

The armament of ten Krupp 15-cm (5.9-in) Model 6 guns was heavy, and as it was arranged with superfiring guns fore and aft and three on either beam, the broadside was seven guns. By comparison, the best German and British cruisers could only bring five guns to bear, and three end-on as against five in the Dutch design. However, by the time the first ship was ready for trials in 1924 the major navies were building 10 000-ton ships armed with eight or nine 8-in (203-mm) guns, rendering the Dutch ships obsolescent.

Java was laid down in May 1916 by Nederlandse Scheepsbouw, Amsterdam, launched by August 6, 1921, and completed in May 1925. *Sumatra* was launched by K M de Schelde at Flushing on December 29, 1920, and completed in November 1925. The third ship was to be named *Celebes* but she was deferred and finally became *de Ruyter*.

After completion both ships were given two Fairey IIID floatplanes, stowed on deck between the funnels and handled by derricks. In 1934-35 the light pole foremast was replaced by a tubular mast of German type. The original 75-mm (2.95-in) AA guns were replaced by six (*Sumatra*) or eight (*Java*) 40-mm (1.57-in) single Bofors AA guns on the after structure. The bridge wings were extended to the top of the derrick posts, and positions for two 12.7-mm (0.5-in) machine-guns were provided on each.

Java was always the better ship of the two, and *Sumatra* suffered damage from a fire in 1929 and then ran aground in 1931. The two ships were permanently stationed in the East Indies and saw action against the Japanese. *Java* was sunk by torpedoes from the heavy cruisers *Nachi* and *Haguro* 35 nautical miles south-west of Bawean Island on February 27, 1942. *Sumatra* escaped to Australia and later back to England to join the Netherlands forces operating with the RN. She was, however, too worn out to be kept running and in 1944 she was hulked and disarmed to provide new barrels for the gunboats *Flores* and *Soemba*, which were to be used on D-Day. She herself was towed to Normandy and scuttled on June 9, 1944.

Displacement: 6670 tons (standard), 7050 tons (full load) *Length:* 155.3 m (509 ft 6 in) oa *Beam:* 16 m (52 ft 6 in) *Draught:* 5.5 m (18 ft) max *Machinery:* 3-shaft steam turbines, 72 000 shp=31 knots *Protection:* 76-51 mm (3-2 in) belt, 51-25 mm (2-1 in) deck, 102 mm (4 in) gun shields *Armament:* 10 15-cm (5.9-in)/50-cal (10×1); 4 75-mm (2.95-in)/55-cal AA (4×1); 4 12.7-in (0.5-in) machine-guns; 12 mines; 2 Fairey IIID aircraft, replaced by Fokker C XIW *Crew:* 525

Suisei Japanese name for Yokosuka D4Y dive-bomber See **D4Y**

Sukhoi Soviet aircraft See **Su-2,** **Su-6, Fencer, Fishpot, Fitter, Flagon**

Sunderland, Short

British flying boat. With almost 21 complete years' service with the RAF in its original designated role of long-range general recon-

A Short Sunderland takes off. The Sunderland was a remarkably tough aircraft with excellent defensive armament and long endurance

naissance and ASW, the Sunderland can be considered one of the world's finest flying boats. Indeed, it continued to serve a further seven years with the Royal New Zealand Air Force after its withdrawal from RAF service.

Designed to meet Specification R.2/33, which called for a four-engined monoplane flying boat to replace the biplane flying boats which had served the RAF since the latter part of the First World War, the Sunderland was a military derivative of the Short C Class Empire flying boat. The first prototype flew on October 16, 1937, and had a rival contender for the specification in the Saro R.2/33. Following an accident with their prototype, Saro withdrew from the evaluation, and an initial contract for 21 Sunderlands, to be built to Specification 22/36, was placed in March 1936.

Of conventional all-metal construction, the Sunderland featured a two-deck two-step hull constructed of channel-section frames with Z-section stiffeners and a stressed metal skin. The upper deck contained the flight deck and stowage for flares and maintenance equipment; the lower deck contained the mooring compartment in the bow, with access to the upper deck, toilet, wardroom, galley, bomb compartment, crew quarters, and beam gun positions. The bomb aimer's position and nose turret were in the extreme bows and a tail turret in the extreme stern. The rear hull contained the dinghy pack, work bench, various sea markers and flares. The wing was built up of a main-spar torsion box consisting of four extruded T-section members to which the leading- and trailing-edge assemblies (including Gouge-type trailing-edge flaps) were attached. The Sunderland Mk I was powered by four Bristol Pegasus XVIII nine-cylinder radial engines, each rated at 1065 hp.

The Sunderland was the first British flying boat to incorporate power-operated turrets as part of its defensive armament. Two Frazer-Nash turrets, each mounting four 0.303-in (7.7-mm) machine-guns were fitted, one in the bows and one in the tail. The beam armament was a single manually operated 0.303-in Vickers machine-gun on either side of the hull. It could carry a bombload of 907 kg (2000 lb) on racks which slid out from the midships bomb compartment under the inner wing. Various combinations of bombs, depth charges, mines or flares could be carried.

The first Sunderland Is entered RAF service with 210 Squadron at Pembroke Dock and 230 Squadron at Singapore in the summer of 1938, replacing the Singapore III flying boats. At the start of the Second World War, the Sunderland's heavy defensive armament soon proved highly effective, and in April 1940, when a Sunderland operating over the North Sea was attacked by six Junkers Ju 88s, it shot one down in flames, forced a second to land in Norway and drove the remaining four away. On another occasion, during convoy escort duties over the Bay of Biscay, another Sunderland shot down three out of eight attacking Ju 88s. For good reason did the Germans dub the Sunderland the Flying Porcupine.

It was to a Sunderland of 228 Squadron that the first Coastal Command U-Boat kill was credited, when on January 31, 1940, the captain of *U 55* scuttled his vessel on being sighted by the Sunderland. Another less aggressive role of the Sunderland was air-sea

A Sunderland Mk II which entered service in 1941. It had a power-operated mid-upper turret

rescue. In September 1939, two Sunderlands of 204 and 228 Squadrons picked up distress calls from the *Kensington Court*, which had been torpedoed off the Scillies. Landing on a rough sea, one of the Sunderlands took 20 of the 34 survivors on board, and shortly afterwards its partner picked up the remaining 14 crewmen, all of whom were back in England within an hour of being sunk. During the evacuation of Crete in 1941, one Sunderland is reported to have carried 87 people in a single flight. However, it was on convoy escort and antisubmarine patrols that the Sunderland was principally employed throughout the war. It saw service in Home Waters, the Atlantic, the Mediterranean and in the Indian Ocean.

As various refinements were made, the improved Sunderland Mk II entered service during the latter part of 1941, replacing the Mk Is. Later production Mk IIs featured a mid-upper turret mounting two 0.303-in machine-guns in place of the beam positions. This became a standard feature on the Sunderland Mk III, which also introduced an improved planing bottom to the hull, with the forward step being made shallower. The first production Mk III flew on December 15, 1941. The Sunderland Mk IV, powered by four 1800-hp Bristol Hercules 100 engines, first flew in August 1944, and was subsequently renamed the Seaford. The Sunderland Mk V, which appeared in 1943, differed from the Mk III mainly in having four Pratt & Whitney R-1830 Twin Wasp engines, each rated at 1200 hp. It also featured ASV Mk VIc radar under its wingtips, while some Mk IIIs which had been previously modified to carry the ASV Mk III were known as Mk IIIAs.

One of the two Australian units serving with Coastal Command, 10 Squadron, RAAF, introduced a novel additional armament of four fixed forward-firing remotely controlled 0.303-in machine-guns in the bows. Its effectiveness was proved by an aircraft of that unit on January 8, 1944, when it opened fire on a U-Boat from 1100 m (1200 yards) and killed all the gunners before destroying the submarine with its depth charges.

With the cessation of hostilities on May 8, 1945, Coastal Command kept up precautionary patrols for a short period, the last of these being flown by 201 Squadron June 3-4, 1945.

It was not long, however, before the Sunderlands were back in action, carrying freight into Berlin during the airlift of 1948-49, and Sunderlands were the only RAF aircraft to take part in the Korean war. Between them, 88, 205 and 209 Squadrons flew 13 380 operational hours in 1647 sorties. During later British operations in Malaya, Sunderlands were used to drop fragmentation bombs on guerrilla formations. More peaceful employment for the Sunderlands was found in the early 1950s, when aircraft from 201 and 230 Squadrons flew and supported various British expeditions to Greenland.

As land-based maritime reconnaissance aircraft began to enter service with the RAF, the Sunderland was finally phased out. The last home units were disbanded in January 1957, while 205 and 209 Squadrons soldiered on in Singapore until May 15, 1959. Sunderlands supplied to the French Aéronavale after the war continued in service until 1960, and the RNZAF were the final user of the Sunderland, finally retiring their last aircraft in 1967.

In all 739 Sunderlands had been built when production ceased in June 1946, including 240 built by Blackburn at Dumbarton, comprising 90 Mk Is, 43 Mk IIs, 456 Mk IIIs and 150 Mk Vs. Some Mk IIIs were later brought up to Mk V standard.

(Mk V) *Span:* 34.37 m (112 ft 9 in) *Length:* 26 m (85 ft 4 in) *Gross weight:* 29 484 kg (65 000 lb) *Maximum speed:* 343 km/h (213 mph) at 1520 m (5000 ft)

Suomi

Finnish submachine-gun. The first Suomi model was developed in 1926 by Aimo Lahti, a well-respected Finnish firearms designer. It was a wooden-stocked weapon with slotted barrel jacket and a sharply curved box magazine. The construction was somewhat luxurious, with a quick-change barrel, a separate cocking handle beneath the receiver, and a complicated firing system in which an inertia block released the firing pin by way of an intermediate lever. It was chambered for the 7.65-mm (0.301-in) Parabellum cartridge, and only a handful were made.

Having made various changes in his 1926 design, Lahti took out patents in 1930 and in the following year introduced a production model known variously as the M1931 or M1932. It was adopted by the Finnish army in 1931, but the patents were not actually granted until 1932 and this date appears on the weapon. The general shape was the same as the 1926, but the magazine was now a straight box or a drum; the quick-change barrel and separate cocking lever were retained, but the bolt was simplified into a straightforward metal block with fixed firing pin.

The Suomi was built in Finland for both local use and for export. They were also made under licence by Husqvarna of Sweden, Madsen of Denmark and Hispano-Suiza of Switzerland. It was adopted by many other countries, and was tested by the British Army in 1936. The report read, "This is probably the best 'gangster' weapon we have seen" and appears to have been the first official use of the description 'gangster' which was to dog the submachine-gun for several years. In spite of this, the Ordnance Board later declared that the Suomi was the best design they had examined up to the outbreak of war, and when submachine-guns were demanded by the British Army in 1939 the Suomi was selected. Unfortunately, by the time the decision was taken, the Finns were fighting the USSR and had no Suomis to spare for export.

Calibre: 9 mm (0.354 in) *Ammunition:* 9-mm Parabellum *Weight:* 4.68 kg (10 lb 5 oz) *Length:* 870 mm (34.3 in) *Barrel length:* 315 mm (12.4 in) *Magazine:* 50-round box or 71-round drum *Rate of fire:* 900 rds/min *Muzzle velocity:* 400 m/sec (1315 ft/sec)

Super 530, Matra

French air-to-air missile. Super 530 was revealed in 1971 as the successor to Matra's R.530, with twice the range of its predecessor and many other improvements; despite its designation, Super 530 is virtually a brand-new design. Airborne captive trials of Electronique Marcel Dassault's Super AD26 semiactive radar seeker began in September 1972 and flight-testing with inert rounds was carried out in the following year. The initial interception of a target took place in the first half of 1974 and the missile is expected to enter full-scale service in 1980.

Super 530 will be carried by Mirage F.1s and Mirage 2000s, and can snap up or down to intercept high-flying or low-level targets following a launch at medium altitude; when fired at 18 000 m (59 050 ft) it can climb to attack an intruder at 23 000 m (75 450 ft). The missile is powered by a dual-thrust Thomson-Brandt/SNPE Angèle solid-propellant rocket motor which burns for 2 seconds in the boost phase and 4 seconds during the sustain stage. Targets are illuminated by the launch aircraft's fire-control radar, the Super AD26 seeker detecting reflected radiation.

Length: 3.54 m (11 ft 7 in) *Span:* 90 cm (35.4 in) *Diameter:* 26 cm (10 in) *Weight:* 240 kg (529 lb) *Range:* 35 km (22 miles) *Speed:* Mach 4.5 *Warhead:* high-explosive

Super Etendard, Dassault

French single-seat carrier-borne multipurpose fighter. In production to replace the earlier Etendard IV, from which it is devel-

oped, the Super Etendard is intended to fulfil four primary roles with France's Aéronautique Navale: aerial cover for the French fleet; protection of the fleet against surface attack; attacking ground targets; and photographic reconnaissance. The basic changes from the earlier type are a more powerful 5000-kg (11025-lb) st SNECMA Atar 8K-50 turbojet and more modern weapon and navigation systems. The latter include an Agave multimode radar, developed jointly by Thomson-CSF and Electronique Marcel Dassault, for detecting and attacking surface vessels and other targets. A new INS (inertial navigation system) ensures the accurate navigation and pinpoint bombing precision that is essential for an aircraft designed to destroy maritime targets. Armament comprises a pair of built-in 30-mm (1.18-in) DEFA cannon in the base of the engine air-intake trunks, each with 125 rounds, and five external attachment points (two under each wing and one on the fuselage centreline) for weapons and other stores. The fuselage station can carry 250-kg (550-lb) bombs, and the underwing points 400-kg (880-lb) bombs, rocket pods or Magic air-to-air missiles. Alternatively, a single Exocet AM39 air-to-surface missile can be carried under the starboard wing, with an auxiliary fuel tank under the port wing. The engine, which is a non-afterburning version of the Atar 9K-50 in the Mirage F1, has a lower specific fuel consumption than the Atar 8 in the original Etendard IV which, combined with some 10% more thrust, allows a considerable increase in payload/range performance. For example, the high-low-high radius of the Super Etendard on an Exocet-carrying mission against a hostile surface vessel is 650 km (400 miles). The range permissible with the standard internal fuel capacity of 3200 litres (704 Imp gal) can be nearly doubled by carrying a further 2800 litres (616 Imp gal) in external tanks, and the Super Etendard can act as a refuelling tanker for other aircraft.

Two Etendard IV-M aircraft were converted to 'Super' configuration for prototype evaluation, producing a financial problem for Dassault in the process. The original idea of developing the Super Etendard was to save the high cost of an all-new design, and the two types were expected to have 90% commonality of airframes and equipment. In fact, with the changes already noted plus the introduction of performance-improving aerodynamic features (such as double-slotted wing flaps and drooped leading edges) and modern constructional techniques, the outcome is instead, a 90% new aeroplane. The prototypes made their maiden flights on

Above left: Panzerfaust-armed Finnish soldiers, one with a Suomi, walk past the remains of a Soviet heavy tank. *Above:* The Suomi was produced under licence in Sweden and Denmark and in the latter country is still in use with reserve units. It has a staggered 50-round box magazine and fires 9-mm (0.354-in) Parabellum ammunition at 900 rds/min

Superfortress, Boeing B-29/B-50

The Dassault Super Etendard of the French navy has two 30-mm (1.18-in) cannon and five weapons pylons for bombs, rockets or missiles

October 28, 1974, and March 25, 1975, and had between them clocked about 1000 flights by the beginning of 1978 in an extensive test programme which included full shipboard and missile-firing trials. Because of budget limitations, only 71 production aircraft are being built instead of the 100 originally planned. The first of these was flown on November 24, 1977; deliveries to the Aéronavale began at the end of the following June, and are due to be completed by the summer of 1981. They will replace Etendard IV-Ms in three squadrons, Flottilles 11F (based at Landivisiau) and 17F (based at Hyères), and the Landivisiau-based Flottille 14F, previously flying Vought F-8E(FN) Crusaders. When deployed at sea on *Foch* and *Clémenceau* Class ships, the Super Etendards will be these carriers' only fixed-wing aircraft, now that the French navy's ASW and other maritime roles are undertaken by land-based Atlantics and Super Frelon helicopters.

Span: 9.6 m (31 ft 6 in) *Length:* 14.31 m (47 ft) *Gross weight:* 12 000 kg (26 455 lb) *Maximum speed:* 1204 km/h (748 mph)

Super Falcon US air-to-air missile See **Falcon**

Superfortress, Boeing B-29/B-50

US strategic bomber, reconnaissance and in-flight refuelling tanker aircraft. The aeroplane that brought the Second World War to its cataclysmic close originated in March 1938, when Boeing produced for the US Army Air Corps a Model 334 design study for a pressurized, tricycle-gear development of the B-17 Flying Fortress. The army, already having trouble obtaining funds for the B-17 itself, had no specific requirement for such an aircraft, but encouraged Boeing to keep the concept alive. In December 1939 the company built a mockup of what was by then the

Model 334A, but a month later revised the specification in the light of combat reports from the war in Europe. By late August 1940 it had secured funding for two XB-29 prototypes of its revised Model 345 design, and a third prototype was ordered at the end of the year.

The first XB-29 flew on September 21, 1942, but by January 1942 the USAAF had already ordered 14 YB-29s for service trials and 500 production B-29s; a month later it had announced an unprecedented nationwide manufacturing programme involving Bell, North American and the Fisher Body division of General Motors. By the time the XB-29 flew, 1664 B-29s were on order. The B-29 was of conventional all-metal construction, but it was to provide a production and modification problem on a scale unequalled by any other wartime US aircraft. It was the first military aeroplane in the world to have pressurized compartments for all crew members, including the tail gunner, since the guns themselves (ten 0.5-in [12.7-mm] machine-guns and one 20-mm [0.79-in] cannon) were installed in five remotely controlled turrets, sighted and fired from positions within the pressurized areas. Disposal of the bombload in two separate bays necessitated a control gear to release weapons alternately from the front and rear bays, to avoid upsetting the trim. The B-29's tremendous all-up weight also posed an enormous headache, for in 1942 it was the heaviest aircraft in the world to go into production, and its narrow-chord wings (11.5 aspect ratio) produced hair-raising wing-loading figures. For a typical wartime gross weight of 56 245 kg (124 000 lb), the corresponding wing loading was 350.77 kg/sq m (71.88 lb/sq ft), compared to 182.12 kg/sq m (37.32 lb/sq ft) for the B-17E at its maximum overload weight of 24 040 kg (53 000 lb). However, the use of large-area Fowler flaps, adding 20% to the total wing area when extended, minimized risk during takeoff and landing, and Boeing was eventually able to convince the army that the

aircraft could perform both safely and efficiently. The powerplant was the new Wright R-3350 Duplex Cyclone radial engine, fitted with twin turbo-superchargers and developing 2200 hp. The R-3350-13 was installed in the XB-29, changing to the -21 model in the YB-29 and the -23 in the production B-29. One YB-29 was later refitted, as the XB-39, with 2100-hp Allison V-3420 liquid-cooled engines.

First public announcement of the Superfortress in action came after an attack on June 5, 1944, on railway marshalling yards at Bangkok. This was made by aircraft based in India, having arrived via the Atlantic and North Africa in the vain hope of concealing their presence in the Far East from the Japanese. In fact the Japanese already knew of the B-29's existence, and in any case targets in Japan itself were on the receiving end of its bombs only nine days later. From then on a mounting offensive was built up, reaching its peak after US forces recaptured the Marianas Islands, from which 20 bomber groups were eventually able to operate, sending formations of up to 500 Superfortresses in day and night attacks against Japan. Their most effective weapon was the incendiary bomb, against which the flimsy Japanese buildings were virtually defenceless: in the worst B-29 fire raid, against Tokyo, some 84 000 people died. As in Europe, the main objective of the bombing campaign was to destroy the home defences and sources of production as a preliminary to invasion, and it is worth noting that until April 1945 the high-flying B-29s were generally able to operate without benefit of fighter escort. As events were to prove, however, invasion was not necessary. The Superfortress *Enola Gay* was chosen to deliver the first of the new atomic bombs, codenamed Little Boy, on the city of Hiroshima on August 6, 1945; it totally destroyed 12.2 sq km (4.7 sq miles) of the city and killed more than 70 000 people. Three days later a second B-29, *Bockscar*, dropped Fat Boy on Nagasaki, and on August 15,

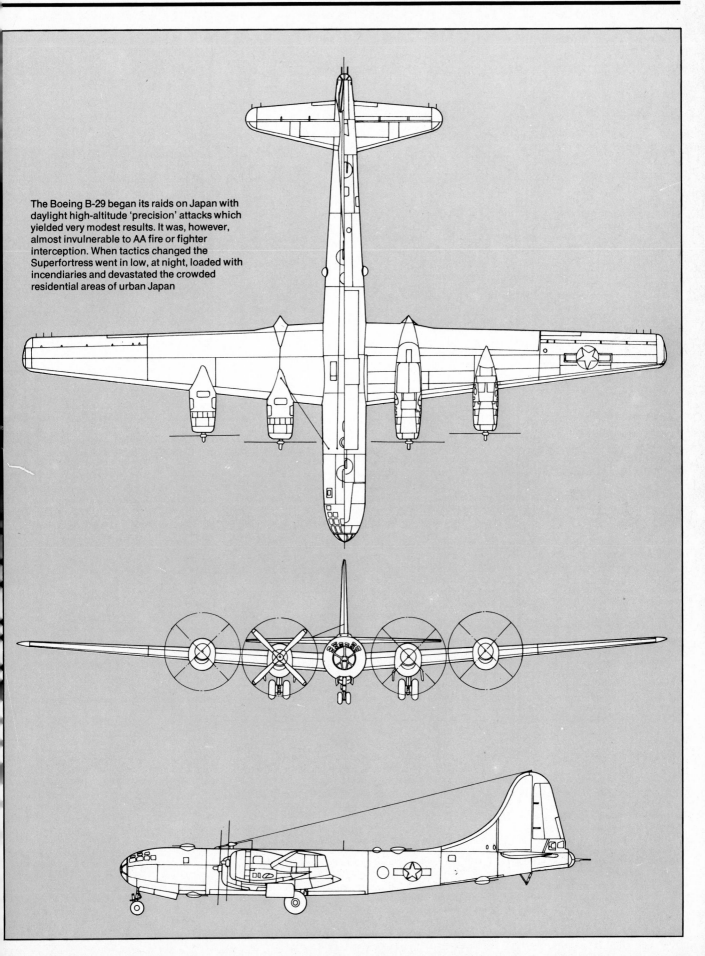

The Boeing B-29 began its raids on Japan with daylight high-altitude 'precision' attacks which yielded very modest results. It was, however, almost invulnerable to AA fire or fighter interception. When tactics changed the Superfortress went in low, at night, loaded with incendiaries and devastated the crowded residential areas of urban Japan

Superfortress, Boeing B-29/B-50

The B-29 with bomb bay doors open. It carried and dropped the first atomic bombs in 1945

1945, Japan was forced to surrender. While operating from China, three returning damaged B-29s diverted to land in the Soviet Union, not then officially at war with Japan, where they were interned. From these aircraft, the Tupolev design bureau produced a copy of the US bomber that became the Tu-4, a standard Red Air Force bomber for many years. Although a blatant piece of design piracy, it was at the same time no mean feat of engineering.

The end of the war in the Pacific inevitably brought large-scale cancellations of all kinds of military equipment on order, including 5092 B-29s. The final total actually built, including test aircraft, was 3960: 2756 by Boeing, 668 by Bell Aircraft corporation, and 536 by the Glenn L Martin company. At its production peak, Boeing was manufacturing 85 of these large and complex aircraft a month.

Towards the end of the war, the lack of fighter opposition over Japan prompted a lightened version of the bomber with all armament except that in the tail deleted, and 311 (all built by Bell) were so modified under the new designation B-29B. During 1945, 118 B-29s and B-29As, retaining their standard armament and bombing capability, were fitted with reconnaissance cameras and re-designated F-13 and F-13A. In 1948 they were again redesignated, to become RB-29 and RB-29A.

All subsequent B-29 variants were conversions or modifications of existing aircraft:

EB-29B One B-29B modified for air launching of the McDonnell XF-85 Goblin parasite fighter.
B-29D Redesigned version, produced as the B-50A.
XB-29E One aircraft converted for fire-control system tests.
B-29F Six aircraft for cold-weather trials with winterization equipment.
XB-29G One aircraft which, while retaining its normal powerplant, was used to flight-test various General Electric jet engines, extended into the airstream from a mounting in the bomb bay.
XB-29H One B-29A converted for armament trials.
YB-29J Approximately six aircraft, originally used to test R-3350-CA-2 fuel-injection engines. Two later converted as YKB-29J hose-refuelling tankers, and others as RB-29J photo-reconnaissance aircraft.
B-29K One B-29 converted as cargo transport.
KB-29M 92 aircraft converted as hose-refuelling tankers.
B-29MR 74 aircraft converted as hose-refuelling receivers.
KB-29P 116 aircraft converted as boom-refuelling tankers.
YKB-29T One KB-29M further converted as

a triple-hose tanker, able to refuel three fighters simultaneously.

The flight-refuelling role was an important one for the Superfortress, initially for its value in extending the range of the bomber itself and later as a support aircraft for the fighters of the US Air Force Tactical Air Command and bombers of Strategic Air Command. Three pairs of KB-29M tankers, placed along the route at appropriate points, refuelled the B-50A *Lucky Lady II* when it made the first-ever non-stop round-the-world flight in 1949. Other postwar episodes in the B-29's career included the transfer of four to the US Navy in 1947, which were employed as P2B-1S long-range over-water search aircraft, and the loan of 88 others to the Royal Air Force (which named them Washington) from 1950-55 pending its receipt of Avro Lincolns. One of the P2B-1S aircraft was modified for use as launch aircraft for the Douglas Skyrocket research aeroplane and, in addition to the XB-29G referred to earlier, other B-29s became flying testbeds for Pratt & Whitney turbojets (including the J42 and J48) and an NACA ramjet engine.

Often neglected in accounts of the B-29's career is its considerable contribution to the US effort in the Korean war of 1950-1953, yet B-29s were in action on all but 26 days of this conflict. During that time they dropped 167 100 tons of bombs in 21 000 sorties, shot down 33 enemy fighters (including 16 MiG-15s) and damaged or destroyed a further 28 'probables'. Total B-29 losses during the war were 34, of which only 20 were attributable to enemy action.

Despite the heavy cancellations of B-29 contracts at the end of the Second World War, plans for an improved version were allowed to proceed. This was to have materialized as the B-29D, built of a stronger and lighter aluminium alloy and powered by four 3500-hp Pratt & Whitney R-4360 Wasp Major 28-cylinder four-row radial engines. A B-29A was allocated to Pratt & Whitney to flight-test the new powerplant, being redesignated XB-44 with this installed. The 200 B-29Ds ordered in July 1945 were, however, cut to 60 after the Japanese surrender. They were redesignated B-50A as a device to encourage approval of funds for a 'new' aircraft which might have been denied to a fresh model of a bomber so recently the subject of large-scale cancellations.

The B-50A, or Boeing Model 345-2, featured several other improvements, the most noticeable external change being an increase of some 1.52 m (5 ft) in the height of the vertical tail surfaces. The first B-50A flew on June 25, 1947, and altogether 371 B-50s were built: 80 B-50As, 45 B-50Bs, 222 B-50Ds (Boeing Model 345-9-6) and 24 TB-50Hs (Model 345-31-26). The new company designation for the D version signified design

changes that included a new one-piece moulded plastic nose cone and provision for underwing auxiliary fuel tanks. For the TB-50H, an unarmed bombing and navigation trainer, it indicated deletion of the in-flight refuelling equipment, the installation of training gear, and three extra crew positions. One of these was the last B-50 delivered, in March 1953.

As with the B-29, there were numerous modified and converted models, as follows:

TB-50A 11 B-50As converted as trainers for B-36 bomber crews; most later became KB-50J tanker aircraft.
EB-50B One B-50B converted for various manufacturer's tests.
RB-50B 44 B-50Bs converted for photo-reconnaissance.
DB-50D One B-50D converted for early drop tests of the Bell Rascal missile.
TB-50D As TB-50A, 11 converted from B-50Ds.
WB-50D and **WB-50H** Unknown number of TB-50Ds and TB-50Hs converted (before they became KB-50s) for weather reconnaissance.
RB-50E 14 RB-50Bs converted for specialized photo-reconnaissance.
RB-50F 14 RB-50Bs converted to have Shoran (short-range navigation) radar.
RB-50G 15 RB-50Bs similar to RB-50F but with additional radar and B-50D-type nose.
KB-50J Total of 112 B-50As and RB-50Bs, converted as triple-hose refuelling tankers for Tactical Air Command; two 2359-kg (5200-lb) st General Electric J47 underwing turbojets in addition to normal powerplant.
KB-50K 24 TB-50Hs converted to a standard similar to the KB-50J.

In addition to the above, other B-50s were used to flight-test Pratt & Whitney J57 and Wright J65 jet engines.

As indicated by the addition of auxiliary jet power to the KB-50 variants during 1957-59, the basic Superfortress design, then 20 years old, had been outpaced both literally and tactically by the postwar generations of jet aircraft in service. Withdrawal of the tanker variants began in 1964, although a few were still operational a year or two later in the early stages of the US war in Vietnam.

(B-29) *Span:* 43.05 m (141 ft 3 in) *Length:* 30.18 m (99 ft) *Gross weight:* 56 246 kg (124 000 lb) *Maximum speed:* 576 km/h (358 mph)

(B-50D) *Span:* 43.05 m (141 ft 3 in) *Length:* 30.18 m (99 ft) *Gross weight:* 78 472 kg (173 000 lb) *Maximum speed:* 612 km/h (380 mph)

(KB-50J) *Span:* 43.05 m (141 ft 3 in) *Length:* 32.03 m (105 ft 1 in) *Gross weight:* 81 420 kg (179 500 lb) *Maximum speed:* 715 km/h (444 mph)

Super Frelon, Aérospatiale

French antisubmarine and transport helicopter. The largest helicopter yet produced in France, the Super Frelon originated with the former Sud-Aviation, which flew the first of two SA 3200 Frelon prototypes on June 10, 1959. Powered by three 750-shp Turboméca Turmo IIIB turboshaft engines, it had a swing-tailed rear fuselage, two large external tanks to carry the fuel, and a cabin with space for up to 28 troops. This was superseded by the SA 3210 (now SA 321) Super Frelon, an altogether larger and more powerful helicopter with an improved transmission system designed with Sikorsky assistance.

The first Super Frelon prototype, flown on December 7, 1962, was powered by three 1320-shp Turmo IIIC₂ turboshafts, and differed from its predecessor in having a watertight boat-type hull and a rear loading ramp instead of the swing tail (though it can fold the extreme tail end and the main rotor blades for stowage). The second prototype was equipped to Aéronavale requirements, with stabilizing floats containing search radar, dipping sonar and other antisubmarine gear, and after four preproduction aircraft Aérospatiale (the successor to Sud-Aviation) built 24 SA 321Gs for antisubmarine duties with the French navy. The first production aircraft flew on November 30, 1965, and deliveries began in early 1966. The French navy's Super Frelons can carry four homing torpedoes or other antisubmarine weapons, two Exocet antisurface-vessel missiles and their launchers, or alternative mission kits for minesweeping, minelaying or ship towing. In service with Flottille 32F, their duties include coastal patrol for France's *Redoutable* Class nuclear submarine bases, and ASW or other operations from the helicopter carrier *Jeanne d'Arc*. Endurance in the antisubmarine role is 4 hours.

The other military version, designated SA 321H (originally SA 321K), is used primarily as a transport helicopter, carrying a flight crew of two (compared with five in the SA 321G) and with accommodation for up to 30 troops, 15 stretchers plus two medical attendants, or 5000 kg (11023 lb) of internal or external cargo. Transport models have been supplied to the air forces or armies of France (one), Iran (16), Iraq (ten), Israel (12), Libya (nine), South Africa (16) and, reportedly, Syria, and also to the Chinese government (five).

(SA 321G) Rotor diameter: 18.9 m (62 ft) *Fuselage length:* 19.4 m (63 ft 8 in) *Gross weight:* 13000 kg (28660 lb) *Maximum speed:* 275 km/h (171 mph)

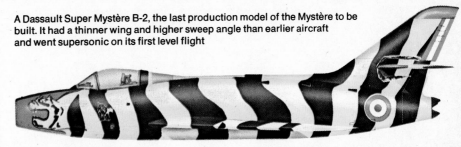

A Dassault Super Mystère B-2, the last production model of the Mystère to be built. It had a thinner wing and higher sweep angle than earlier aircraft and went supersonic on its first level flight

Supermarine British aircraft
See Attacker, Scapa, Scimitar, Seafire, Southampton, Spitfire, Stranraer, Swift, Walrus

Super Mystère B-2, Dassault

French single-seat intercepter and tactical strike fighter. Concurrently with development of the Mystère IVA Dassault evolved the Mystère IVB, which had a Rolls-Royce Avon RA.7R afterburning jet engine and a 'lipped' air intake. This did not go into production in that form, but was developed further (hence the 'B-2' of the designation) into the Super Mystère. This was a quite different aeroplane from the Mystère IV with a brand new wing having more sweepback, a much thinner aerofoil section, and a dogtooth notched leading edge; a flat-oval air intake, similar to that of North American's Super Sabre; a larger-area vertical tail, also with greater sweepback; and improved field of view from the cockpit. The prototype, with an RA.7R engine, flew for the first time on March 2, 1955, and on its fourth test flight exceeded Mach 1 in level flight. A change of powerplant was then made, five preproduction aircraft being completed with SNECMA Atar 101G engines developing 3400 kg (7496 lb) st dry and 4500 kg (9921 lb) st with afterburning. This became the standard engine for the production version, 180 of which were completed by 1959; more were ordered, but later contracts were cut back after the delta-winged Mirage III had exhibited much superior performance. Nevertheless, the Super Mystère became the first European aircraft capable of level supersonic flight to attain production status.

It began to enter service with the Armée de l'Air in 1957, and equipped the 5e, 10e and 12e Escadres de Chasse which formed part of the Commandement 'Air' des Forces de Défense Aérienne. Twenty-four of the total built were supplied to the Israeli defence force/air force, and both air arms continued

to operate the type into the second half of the 1970s, the last of those in French service being replaced by the Mirage F1-C. Dassault flew two prototypes of a Super Mystère B-4 in 1958, with an Atar 9 engine uprated to 6000 kg (13228 lb) st with afterburner, but this did not go into production.

For the intercepter role, the B-2 was equipped with a pair of 30-mm (1.18-in) DEFA cannon and a retractable pack of 55 SNEB Type 22 68-mm (2.7-in) air-to-air rockets under the fuselage; Armée de l'Air aircraft were equipped to carry a Sidewinder air-to-air missile under each wing. The Israeli air force made greater use of the aircraft's potential in the tactical strike role, its two underwing pylons enabling it to carry 12 HVAR (high velocity aerial rockets), two Matra M-116E pods (each with 19 68-mm rockets), two 500-kg (1100-lb) bombs, napalm tanks or drop tanks. One Super Mystère squadron was actively involved during the 1973 Middle East war. Reports emerging some years later suggest that these may have been aircraft modified locally by Israel Aircraft Industries to have a 4218-kg (9300-lb) thrust non-afterburning Pratt & Whitney J52-P-8A turbojet in place of the Atar 101G, resulting in a longer rear fuselage (despite the absence of an afterburner) and able to carry a greater weight and wider variety of underwing stores. Twelve of these modified aircraft were resold by Israel in 1977 to the air force of Honduras.

Span: 10.52 m (34 ft 6 in) *Length:* 14.04 m (46 ft) *Gross weight:* 10000 kg (22046 lb) *Maximum speed:* 1198 km/h (744 mph)

The Aérospatiale SA.321 Super Frelon in its transport role; it can carry up to 30 troops which makes it a highly effective assault helicopter. In its ASW role it has an endurance of up to four hours with four homing torpedoes or A/S weapons

Super Sabre, North American F-100

A flight of USAF F-100 Super Sabres of the Thunderbirds aerial display team over the western seaboard of the United States in the 1960s

Super Sabre, North American F-100

US supersonic fighter, fighter-bomber and combat training aircraft. Entirely by coincidence, the US Air Force's F-for-fighter designations reached the figure 100 with the Super Sabre, which happened to be the world's first production fighter capable of sustained supersonic speed in level flight. This led to the general title Century Series for some half a dozen fighter types (before redesignation started again at F-1 in 1962) which brought a significant new operational capability to the US Air Force.

Design began as early as February 1949, as a private-venture development of the transonic F-86 Sabre, and since the new NA-180 had wings with 45° sweepback (10° more than on the F-86) it was at first known as the Sabre 45. The powerplant was to be a Pratt & Whitney J57 afterburning turbojet. Initial experience of jet-versus-jet combat in the Korean war stimulated air force interest in the NA-180, and two YF-100A prototypes were ordered in November 1951, although North American had already begun engineer-ing work in the previous January. The first YF-100A was flown for the first time on May 25, 1953, followed on October 14 the same year by the second aircraft on its first flight. Construction of the Super Sabre was all-metal, including the first use of heat-resisting titanium in an aircraft, and design features included a one-piece all-moving 'slab' tail-plane, and a flat-oval intake which afforded an excellent forward and downward view from the cockpit.

The initial contract was for 110 F-100As, powered by production J57-P-7 engines developing 6713 kg (14800 lb) st with full afterburner. The first flew on October 29, 1953, and the Super Sabre entered service in the following September with the 479th Fighter Day Wing. Major stability and control problems were exhibited by the early

F-100As, and after about 70 had been delivered an increased-span wing and a taller fin and rudder were introduced—retrospectively on those delivered, and on the assembly line for the remainder of F-100A production, which eventually totalled 203. The last 37 of these had J57-P-39 engines, of similar rating to the P-7. Armament of the F-100A consisted of four 20-mm (0.79-in) M-39E cannon in the underside of the fuselage, each with 200 rounds of ammunition, and two underwing drop tanks cleared to beyond Mach 1; this version was assigned primarily to the air-superiority role.

The F-100B all-weather version, designed in 1953, eventually pursued a separate line of development to emerge as the F-107. The F-100C was a fighter-bomber version, with two additional underwing stations, wings strengthened to carry up to 3402 kg (7500 lb) of stores (compared with 2722 kg [6000 lb] on the F-100A), extra fuel inside the wings, and in-flight refuelling capability. The prototype was a converted F-100A, after which North American manufactured 476 production F-100Cs (first example flown on January 17, 1955) at its Los Angeles and Columbus, Ohio, factories. Most of these had J57-P-21 engines rated at 7257 kg (16000 lb) st with reheat, enabling one F-100C to set a new world air speed record of 1323.098 km/h (822.135 mph) on August 20, 1955, beating the previous record of 1215.295 km/h (755.149 mph) set by a YF-100A on October 29, 1953. Deliveries to Tactical Air Command began in July 1955, the same month in which North American switched production to the improved F-100D, of which it eventually built 1274. This model had larger-area wings, with inboard landing flaps, increased vertical tail area, jettisonable underwing pylons, improved LABS (low altitude bombing system) equipment, and provision for 'buddy' tanker refuelling. Typical weapons of the F-100D included six 340-kg (750-lb) or 454-kg (1000-lb) bombs, or two GAM-83A Bulldog air-to-surface missiles; or, on some aircraft, four Sidewinder air-to-air missiles.

Final production version was the tandem two-seat F-100F combat proficiency trainer, for which a converted F-100C (designated TF-100C) served as prototype, flying for the first time on August 6, 1956. Some 0.91 m (3 ft) longer than the single-seater, it mounted only two 20-mm cannon in the fuselage, but otherwise retained the same weapon-carrying capability. A total of 339 were built, bringing overall Super Sabre manufacture to 2294 (including prototypes) before production ended in October 1959.

The Super Sabre's service career was long and varied, a total of 16 wings of the USAF being equipped with it at one time, four of which were deployed in Vietnam with notable success between 1966-71. It retired from TAC service in 1973, but continued to fly with the Air National Guard. Examples were supplied also to Taiwan (80 F-100As, upgraded to D standard), Denmark (three squadrons of F-100Ds and a small number of F-100Fs), France (two wings of F-100Ds) and Turkey (260 F-100Cs and a few F-100Fs). A number of F-100Fs were converted by the USAF as DF-100F director aircraft for missiles or target drones, and another became the experimental NF-100F, modified for a research programme into low-speed flight by high-performance aircraft and fitted with a bigger airbrake, blown flaps, and a Rohr thrust reverser, in an extended tailpipe, replacing the afterburner.

(F-100A) *Span:* originally 11.15 m (36 ft 7 in) *Length:* 14.07 m (46 ft 2 in) *Gross weight:* 13 109 kg (28 900 lb) *Maximum speed:* 1239 km/h (770 mph)

(F-100D) *Span:* 11.81 m (38 ft 9 in) *Length:* 14.35 m (47 ft 1 in) *Gross weight:* 15 800 kg (34 832 lb) *Maximum speed:* 1390 km/h (864 mph)

Supporter, Saab MFI

Swedish light training and attack aircraft. Derived from a high-wing civil monoplane, designated BA-7 and built in the United States, the Saab Supporter has been developed by its original designer, Bjorn Andreasson, who returned to Sweden to become Special Projects director of Saab-Scania.

Emphasis has been placed on simplicity of construction, the high untapered wing being braced by a single strut either side and a robust fixed cantilever-strut tricycle undercarriage being fitted. Original development of the basic design in Sweden was by Malmö Flygindustri who were taken over by Saab-Scania in March 1968. By that time the civil MFI-9 Junior had been marketed in Scandinavia, and was being sold abroad by the German Bolkow company as the Bö 208. The MFI-9B was intended as a military trainer, but in 1969 five aircraft fitted with rocket pylons were flown against Nigerian airfields on behalf of Biafra during the Nigerian civil war.

The more powerful MFI-15, of which a dozen were built, was intended to replace the Swedish air force Saab Safir trainer and the Swedish army's Piper L-21B liaison aircraft, but was not eventually adopted. The second MFI-15 prototype was modified to take the more powerful 200-hp Lycoming IO-360-A1B6, and its wing was strengthened to take hardpoints for a total weight of 300 kg (660 lb) of underwing stores, to include as alternatives jettisonable containers, rocket pods or antitank missiles. Designated MFI-17, the first three aircraft of this developed type went to Ethiopia where they were used initially for supplying food to isolated villages. In June 1974 Pakistan selected the MFI-17 as its new basic trainer, ordering 45 machines, to be known as Supporters. As the T-17 the type has also been purchased by Denmark, delivery of 32 machines commencing in 1975. Delivery of 20 machines to Zambia began in 1976.

Span: 8.7 m (28 ft 6 in) *Length:* 7 m (23 ft) *Gross weight:* 1100 kg (2425 lb) *Maximum speed:* 257 km/h (160 mph)

Surcouf

French cruiser class, built 1887-91. The six small 3rd Class cruisers, designed to serve as scouts, were sometimes referred to as sloops or *avisos*. They were two-funnelled and had only a light splinterproof deck over the

A North American F-100D Super Sabre. Designed as a fighter the Super Sabre proved a highly effective ground-attack aircraft in Vietnam. With LABS (low altitude bombing system) a typical load comprised six 340-kg (750-lb) or 454-kg (1000-lb) bombs, or two GAM-83A Bulldog air-to-surface missiles. It was deployed against targets in North Vietnam such as road and rail bridges using Bulldog missiles and in the south against Viet Cong and North Vietnamese harbour areas using napalm, fragmentation and low-level retarded bombs. Improved ground-support tactics enabled the F-100s to move the bomb line very close to friendly forces which could be critical if the troops were closely engaged out of range of artillery support

Surcouf

machinery. The armament comprised four 138.6-mm (5.46-in) Model 1887 guns sponsoned in the waist of the ship, with other light guns on the forecastle and the poop and four 36-cm (14-in) torpedo tubes. A feature of the design was the pronounced tumblehome, which reduced topweight. *Surcouf* and most of her sisters had three masts but the centre or mainmast was omitted in *Coëtlogon* and *Forbin*.

Surcouf—built by Cherbourg arsenal
Forbin—built by Rochefort arsenal
Coëtlogon—built by Penhoët, St Nazaire
Cosmao, Lalande, Troude—built by Forges et Chantiers de la Gironde, Bordeaux

After spending most of their time as scouts with the battlefleet the class were downgraded as they were too slow. *Coëtlogon* was scrapped in 1906 followed by *Troude* in 1908 and *Lalande* in 1912. The other three served in the First World War, mostly on patrol work in the Channel or the Mediterranean. In 1917 *Forbin* became a submarine depot ship at Gibraltar, and in 1918 *Surcouf* was disarmed at Brest. *Cosmao* served in the Western Mediterranean and was stricken and scrapped with her sisters in 1921-22.

Displacement: 1848 tonnes (normal) *Length:* 95.1 m (312 ft) oa *Beam:* 9.3 m (30 ft 6 in) *Draught:* 4.3 m (14 ft) *Machinery:* 2-shaft reciprocating steam, 6000 ihp=20 knots *Protection:* 40 mm (1.57 in) deck *Armament:* 4 138.6-mm (5.46-in)/45-cal (4×1); 7 3-pdr (47-mm) QF (7×1); 4 1-pdr (37-mm) QF (4×1); 4 36-cm (14-in) torpedo tubes (beam, above water) *Crew:* 210

Surcouf

French destroyer class. The first group of 12 large destroyers was authorized under the 1949 to 1952 Programmes. Named *Surcouf, Chevalier Paul, Cassard, Bouvet, Du Chayla, Dupetit Thouars, Kersaint, D'Estrées, Maillé Brézé, Vauquelin, Casabianca,* and *Guépratte,* they were laid down 1951-53, launched 1953-54, and completed 1955-57. A further five were authorized in 1953, named *Duperré, La Bourdonnais, Jauréguiberry, Tartu* and *Forbin;* they were laid down in 1954, launched in 1955 and completed 1957-58. The eighteenth ship, *La Galissonnière,* was built to a different design, and was not laid down until 1958, being launched in 1960 and completed in 1962.

In conception the *Surcouf* Class followed on from the large French *contre-torpilleurs* built during the prewar period, except that the experience of the Second World War led to a much-improved capability against aircraft (they were in fact first to be designated antiaircraft escorts). The main armament of the first 17 (as built) comprised a twin 127-mm (5-in) dual-purpose mounting forward and a further two aft. The calibre was chosen to permit them to fire standard US 5-in (127-mm) ammunition, previous ships of this size having been armed with 130-mm (5.1-in) guns. In B position was a twin 57-mm (2.24-in) AA gun, and two other twin mountings were sited side by side just aft of the second funnel. The first 12 ships, designated the T47 type, also had two triple side-mounted torpedo tubes for surface action, and a further pair of triple tubes for antisubmarine homing

The French destroyer *Forbin,* one of the *Surcouf* Class laid down and launched in the mid-1950s

torpedoes. The second group, designated the T53 R type, had only the after sets of tubes, and could fire either sort of torpedo. They were also equipped with additional air-search and height-finding radars for aircraft direction, and a Bofors A/S mortar fitted forward of X mounting.

The final ship of the class, *La Galissonnière,* designated the T56 type, was designed as a squadron escort and flotilla leader, and unlike her sisters was equipped primarily for an antisubmarine mission. When she finally commissioned in 1962 she was the first ship equipped with a missile system of French origin, the antisubmarine Malafon, the launcher for which was mounted aft. She also carried a helicopter aft on a raised flight deck with a collapsible hangar, and bow and towed sonars were fitted. The armament was completed by two of the new single 100-mm (3.9-in) automatic guns forward, and two triple banks of tubes for A/S homing torpedoes. She served for some time as a trials ship for the new ASW weapons and sensors with which she was fitted.

In the early 1960s the remainder of the class began to fragment. *Surcouf, Chevalier Paul,* and *Cassard* were converted to command ships, which involved removal of the forward 57-mm mounting to enable the bridge structure to be extended forward, and removal of the after set of torpedo tubes. *Bouvet, Du Chayla, Dupetit Thouars* and *Kersaint* were then rearmed with the US Tartar surface-to-air missile. The conversion involved the removal of the after 127-mm turrets, which were replaced by a cylindrical magazine topped by a single-arm Mk 13 launcher. Two SPG-51 tracker/illuminators were raised on pedestals just forward of the launcher. The system was completed by a US SPS-39 height-finding radar atop the mainmast, later to be replaced by the planar SPS-52. Only the forward set of torpedo tubes was retained. During 1968-70 *D'Estrées, Maillé Brézé, Vauquelin, Casabianca* and *Guépratte* underwent a major conversion influenced by the success of *La Galissonnière* as an antisubmarine vessel. Malafon was installed aft, but no helicopter was carried, its place being taken by a single 100-mm gun. A second 100-mm mounting replaced A turret, while B position was occupied by a Bofors A/S rocket launcher. As in the other conversions only the forward set of torpedo tubes was retained. A complete new sensor outfit

was installed similar to that of *La Galissonnière.* The final conversion was that of *Duperré* of the T53 type, which after serving as a trials ship from 1967 was converted to an antisubmarine destroyer from 1972-74. The conversion was once again on the lines of *La Galissonnière,* but only a single 100-mm mounting was fitted forward, and she had a 'permanent' hangar with a flight deck extending aft of it in place of Malafon. Four launchers for Exocet surface-to-surface missiles were angled out on either side of the forefunnel, and a new sensor outfit was installed.

Surcouf lost her bow in a collision in the Mediterranean in 1971 and was subsequently scrapped. Of the four unconverted ships of the T53 group, *La Bourdonnais* paid off in 1976, *Jauréguiberry* in 1977 and *Tartu* in 1978. *Forbin* is presently being used as a training ship.

(T47 and T53 types) Displacement: 2750 tons (standard), 3750 tons (full load) *Length:* 128.4 m (421 ft 3 in) oa *Beam:* 13 m (42 ft 8 in) *Draught:* 5.6 m (18 ft 5 in) *Machinery:* 2-shaft steam turbines, 63 000 shp=34 knots *Armament:* 6 127-mm (5-in) DP (3×2); 6 57-mm (2.24-in) AA (3×2); 6 20-mm (0.79-in) AA (6×1); 12 (T53, 6) 55-cm (21.7-in) torpedo tubes (4/2×3) *Crew:* 347

(T56 type) Displacement: as above *Length:* 132.8 m (435 ft 8 in) oa *Beam, Draught* and *Machinery:* as above *Armament:* 2 100-mm (3.9-in) AA (2×1); 1 Malafon A/S missile-launcher; 6 55-cm (21.7-in) torpedo tubes (2×3); 1 A/S helicopter *Crew:* 333

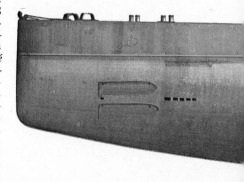

Surcouf

French submarine. *Surcouf* was developed for extended operations as a mercantile raider, a concept the French adopted having studied the German operations with the *U 151* Class during the First World War. She was an exceedingly powerful vessel, and for a long time was the largest submarine in the world. She combined the roles of a submarine and surface raider, carrying heavy guns capable of dealing with any normal convoy escorts which might be encountered.

Surcouf was designed with an endurance of 90 days and had accommodation for 40 prisoners. Initially she carried a large 16-knot boarding launch with a radius of 70 nautical miles, but this was subsequently removed.

Two 203-mm (8-in) cruiser model guns were fitted in an enormous twin watertight turret forward of the conning tower, and a complete fire-control system enabled *Surcouf* to open fire some 2½ minutes after surfacing. The fire-control system included a large and conspicuous stereoscopic rangefinder with a 12-m (39 ft 4-in) arm sited atop the turret housing immediately in front of the conning tower. The magazine for the 203-mm guns held a total of 600 rounds, each weighing 118 kg (260 lb), and the rate of fire was between 2 and 3 rds/min. The range of the guns at 30° elevation was 27 600 m (30 200 yards) and the muzzle velocity was 850 m/sec (2780 ft/sec).

For submerged operations *Surcouf* was armed with eight 55-cm (21.7-in) torpedo tubes sited in two groups of four, one set in the bows and the other set aft on an external trainable mount between the deck casing and pressure hull. In addition four 40-cm (15.7-in) torpedo tubes on a similar mounting were also sited aft. The 40-cm torpedoes were designed in 1926 specifically for use against merchant shipping, and were powered by an air turbine giving a high speed of 44 knots, but a range of only 1400 m (1550 yards). Operational capability was further enhanced by a small Bisson MB-411 aircraft carried in a circular hangar abaft the conning tower. The aircraft had been specially designed for use on *Surcouf* and was carried partially dismantled; it could be assembled in about four minutes, but launching into the water took a further 25 minutes. *Surcouf* carried about 280 tons of fuel and had a radius of action of 10 000 nautical miles at 10 knots surfaced and 60 nautical miles at 5 knots submerged.

Although the design itself was successful, the tactical use of such a large submarine and the conditions and situations under which it could realize its intended role were found to be severely limited in practice. Ordered under the 1926 Programme, a total of three boats was planned, but only the *Surcouf* was ever laid down. When France capitulated in June 1940 *Surcouf* was undergoing a major refit at Brest. She managed to escape and later joined the Free French forces in Britain, carrying out a number of unsuccessful patrols before being accidentally lost in collision with the US cargo ship *Thomson Lykes* in the Gulf of Mexico on February 18, 1942.

Surcouf was laid down at Cherbourg dockyard in December 1927, launched on October 18, 1929 and completed in May 1934.

Displacement: 2880/4304 tons (surfaced/submerged) *Length:* 110 m (361 ft) oa *Beam:* 9 m (29 ft 6 in) *Draught:* 7.25 m (23 ft 9 in) *Machinery:* 2-shaft Sulzer diesels/2 electric motors, 7600 bhp/3400 hp=18/8.5 knots (surfaced/submerged) *Armament:* 2 203-mm (8-in) (1×2); 2 37-mm (1.46-in); 4 13.2-mm (0.52-in); 8 55-cm (21.7-in) torpedo tubes (4 fixed bow, 4 trainable stern), 14 torpedoes; 4 40-cm (15.7-in) (4 stern), 8 torpedoes; 1 seaplane *Crew:* 118

SUW-N-1

Soviet antisubmarine weapon system. SUW-N-1, which is fitted to the Soviet navy's *Moskva* Class helicopter carriers and *Kiev* Class antisubmarine cruisers, comprises a twin-rail launcher together with its associated handling equipment and the weapons fired from it. The latter are thought to comprise both the SS-N-14 torpedo-carrying missile and the FRAS-1 unguided rocket, which is reported to carry a nuclear depth charge or warhead over a range of some 25 km (16 miles). The launcher/containers on several other classes of Soviet ship, which were at one time thought to be loaded with the SS-N-10 antiship missile (now generally believed to be a mythical weapon), have more recently been reported to contain SS-N-14, and the reason for the same missile requiring two

types of launcher remains a mystery. A further riddle is the apparent similarity between SS-N-14 and FRAS-1 in terms of range and payload.

Svea

Swedish coast-defence ship class, built 1884-93. Three small battleships comprise this class. *Svea* was launched on December 12, 1885, by Lindholmensvarv at Gothenburg; *Gota* was launched on September 30, 1889, also by Lindholmensvarv; and *Thule* was launched on March 4, 1893, by Finnbodavarv at Stockholm. They were armed with two single 10-in (25.4-cm) guns and four 6-in (15.2-cm) guns and were the first large steel warships built in Sweden.

The view from the conning tower of *Surcouf*

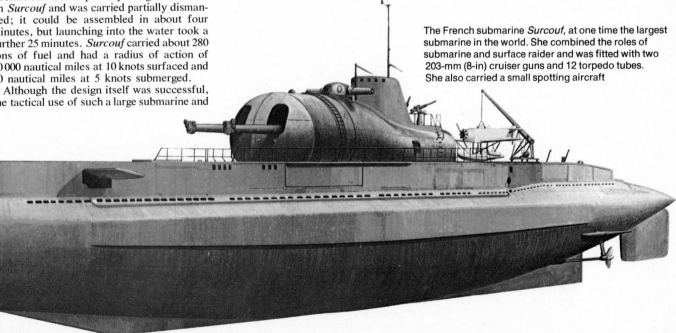

The French submarine *Surcouf*, at one time the largest submarine in the world. She combined the roles of submarine and surface raider and was fitted with two 203-mm (8-in) cruiser guns and 12 torpedo tubes. She also carried a small spotting aircraft

Sverdlov

The Soviet cruiser *Sverdlov*, photographed by a Royal Navy Sea King helicopter in July 1976

In 1897 *Svea* was rebuilt, with 120-mm (4.7-in) quick-firers in place of the 6-in, and 6-pdrs (57-mm) in place of the 1-pdr (37-mm) guns and eight machine-guns. In 1902-04 all three were rebuilt, with the forward guns replaced by a single 21-cm (8.3-in) forward and the after turret replaced by seven 15.2-cm (6-in) guns in shields. In 1921 *Svea* was converted to a depot ship for submarines and disarmed; in this role she served until 1941 and was finally scrapped in 1944. Her sisters served as accommodation hulks (*Gota* 1926-43; *Thule* 1923-28) and were then discarded.

Displacement: 3000 tons (normal) average *Length:* 75.7-79.5 m (248 ft 4 in-260 ft 10 in) wl *Beam:* 14.6-14.8 m (47 ft 11 in-48 ft 7 in) *Draught:* 5.2 m (17 ft 1 in) *Machinery:* 2-shaft reciprocating steam, 4000 ihp approx=14.5-16 knots *Protection:* 293-198 mm (11.5-7.8 in) belt, 49 mm (1.9 in) deck, 293-243 mm (11.5-9.6 in) turrets *Armament:* 2 10-in (25.4-cm)/34-cal (2×1); 4 6-in (15.2-cm)/15-cal (4×1); 2 1-pdr (37-mm) (2×1); 6 machine-guns; 1 38-cm (15-in) torpedo tube (submerged, forward) *Crew:* 232

Sveaska Swedish aircraft   **See Jaktfalk**

Sverdlov

Soviet cruiser class. Of the 24 vessels thought to have been projected, 20 were laid down from 1948 onwards. The class did not find favour with Kruschev, who thought the cruiser an obsolescent type, and only 17 were launched and of these 14 were completed. These ships are thought to have been laid down 1948-53, launched 1951-54 and completed 1952-58, and are named *Sverdlov,*

Molotovsk (later renamed *Oktyabrskaya Revolutsiya*), *Admiral Nakhimov, Admiral Senyavin,   Zhdanov,   Dzerzhinski, Ordzhonikidze, Admiral Lazarev, Admiral Ushakov,   Alexandr   Nevski,   Alexandr Suvorov,   Murmansk,   Mikhail Kutusov, Dmitri Pozharski.* Builders were the Baltic and Marti yards, Leningrad; Yard 402 at Severodvinsk; Nosenko yard, Nikolaiev; and Amur yard, Komsomolsk.

The natural successors to the war-built *Chapaev* Class, the *Sverdlov* Class nevertheless reflected some of the lessons learned in the Second World War, and in particular moved away from the Italian influence of earlier cruiser construction in favour of technology transferred by the Germans under the 1939 agreement or copied from German ships which fell into Soviet hands in 1945. The forecastle deck was extended aft for improved seakeeping, the transom stern (well-suited to minelaying) abandoned, and electric welding introduced.

The main armament comprised the 12 152-mm (6-in) guns in triple mountings introduced by the *Chapaev* Class. Originally intended as the secondary armament of the battleships under construction at the start of the Second World War, it did not become operational until after the war. The gun is not automatic, but thanks to an elevation of about 50° can be used as an AA weapon. German influence can be seen both in the AA armament of the ships and in the hemispherical HA directors which closely resemble those of the German battleships and cruisers. The 100-mm (3.9-in)/60-cal turrets, of which three are mounted on either side of the ship at upper-deck level, closely resemble the C-38 antiaircraft gunhouses of the wartime German navy. The

turret is fully stabilized, allowing it to be tilted 25° about its axis. The AA armament is completed by 32 37-mm (1.46-in) AA in twin mounts, divided equally between the forward and after superstructures. Mine rails with an estimated capacity of 100 mines run the full length of the quarterdeck. *Sverdlov, Ordzhonikidze, Zhdanov, Admiral Ushakov* and *Admiral Nakhimov* were also fitted with two quintuple banks of torpedo tubes amidships. The first three also have a high deckhouse surrounding the forefunnel which distinguishes them from the others.

The steam propulsion plant is a conservative one, the USSR having rejected the high-pressure superheated boilers developed by the Germans because of operating and maintenance problems experienced with their war prizes.

From 1960 to 1962 the Black Sea-built *Dzerzhinski* underwent a major conversion involving the removal of X turret and its replacement by a missile magazine for long-

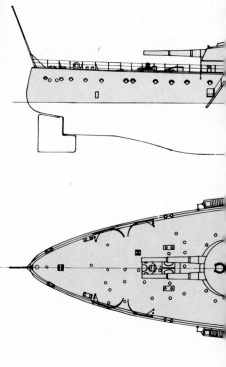

range SA-N-2 surface-to-air missiles with a twin-arm launcher mounted on top of it. Forward of the launcher, a blast deflector extends almost to the deck-edges. The after 37-mm AA guns were also removed and in their place is a large missile-guidance radar mounted on a pedestal. A distinctive height-finding aerial was installed aft of the first funnel, and an air-search radar on the main-mast. The conversion does not seem to have been a success and no further ships were converted.

A conversion of a different nature was undertaken in the early 1970s involving the *Zhdanov* and *Admiral Senyavin.* It began at Nikolaiev in 1970 and was completed 1973-74. *Zhdanov* had X turret replaced by a tall deckhouse containing a bin for the short-range SA-N-4 SAM pop-up launcher. The director for this is mounted on a new lattice

The coast-defence battleship *Sverige* had an unusual origin, the money for her construction being raised by public subscription. As Europe approached the First World War the Swedish opposition blocked funds for the building of new warships. Public funds raised 17 million kroner in three months and this financed the building of the *Sverige* which was launched on May 3, 1915. Further ships followed and although they did not participate in the First World War they were available in the Second World War as guarantors of Sweden's neutrality

Sverige

Swedish coast-defence battleship class, built 1912-22. When it was proposed to build a new class of armoured ships *(pansarskepp)* there was considerable opposition, for the original plan was to build eight ships. When the opposition blocked the programme, a national appeal succeeded in raising over 17 million kroner in three months for the first ship. She was *Sverige*, launched on May 3, 1915, by Gotaverken at Gothenburg. Two more ships were added: *Drottning Victoria*, launched by Gotaverken on September 15, 1917; and *Gustav V*, launched by Kockums at Malmö on January 31, 1918. *Sverige* was

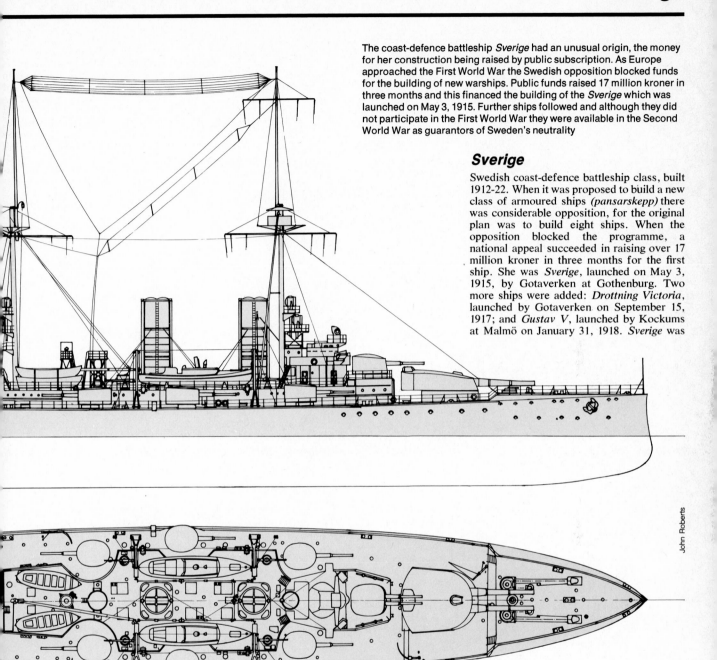

John Roberts

mast which is topped by two V-Cone antennae for long-range communications. The superstructure around the forefunnel was extended to accommodate four twin 30-mm (1.18-in) AA mountings and their directors, and the torpedo tubes were removed. The conversion of *Admiral Senyavin* was similar, except that both her after turrets were removed and replaced by a large hangar which can accommodate two helicopters and on which four extra twin 30-mm mountings with their directors are mounted in addition to the SA-N-4 bin.

Both of these conversions now serve as command cruisers, but the remaining ships of the class have been little altered except for the provision of modern radars. They are presumably retained mainly for shore bombardment, although they are frequently employed as force flagships. *Admiral*

Nakhimov, which was rumoured to have undergone conversion to carry SS-N-1 surface-to-surface missiles about 1960, was discarded in 1969. *Ordzhonikidze* was sold to Indonesia in 1962 and renamed *Irian*. She was discarded in the early 1970s.

Displacement: 15 450 tons (standard), 19 200 tons (full load) *Length:* 210 m (689 ft) oa *Beam:* 20 m (65 ft 7 in) *Draught:* 7 m (23 ft) *Machinery:* 2-shaft steam turbines, 110 000 shp=34 knots *Armament:* 12 (*Dzerzhinski* and *Zhdanov* 9, *Senyavin* 6) 152-mm (6-in) (4/3/2×3); 12 100-mm (3.9-in) AA (6×2); 32 (*Dzerzhinski* 16, *Pozharski* 24) 37-mm (1.46-in) AA (16/8/12×2); 100 mines (unconverted ships only); 2 SA-N-2 launchers (1×2) (*Dzerzhinski* only); 2 SA-N-4 launchers (1×2) (*Zhdanov* and *Senyavin* only); 8 (*Senyavin* 16) 30-mm (1.18-in) AA (4/8×2); 2 helicopters (*Senyavin* only) *Crew:* 1000

completed in 1917 but the others were not completed until 1921-22. All three were similar and resembled small pre-Dreadnoughts with twin turrets forward and aft and light tripod masts.

In 1931-33 *Sverige* was refitted with a heavier tripod foremast, and in 1938-40 was again altered, with the forefunnel trunked back to keep smoke away from the control top, and enhanced AA armament. In this guise she lasted until 1953, and was finally scrapped in 1957.

Drottning Victoria was not so drastically altered, and retained her original funnels, but had her light armament modified and torpedo tubes removed in 1926-27. Her AA armament was considerably augmented in 1940-42, and she was not stricken until 1957. *Gustav V* was reconstructed in 1927-30 with both funnels trunked into one, and was converted from

Sviatoj Georg

Top: The Swedish battleship *Sverige* in 1915. *Above: Sverige* as she appeared in 1925 with a tripod mast and gunnery control station. *Below: Sverige* in 1944. Her funnel has been trunked, AA armament increased and she has an identification stripe on her bow and stern

Statens sjöhistoriska museum, Sweden

coal-firing to oil-firing in 1936-37. She was stricken in 1957 but survived for many years after that as a training hulk.

Displacement: 7100 tons (standard) average *Length:* (*Sverige*) 119.7 m (392 ft 9 in) wl; (others) 120.9 m (396 ft 8 in) wl *Beam:* 18.6 m (61 ft) *Draught:* 6.5 m (21 ft 4 in) *Machinery:* 2-shaft steam turbines 20000 shp=22.5 knots *Protection:* 200 mm (7.9 in) belt, 40 mm (1.6 in) deck, 200 mm turrets, 175 mm (6.9 in) conning tower *Armament:* (As built) 4 28-cm (11-in)/45-cal (2×2); 8 15-cm (5.9-in)/50-cal (8×1); 5 75-mm (2.95-in) QF (6×1); 2 45-cm (17.7-in) torpedo tubes (submerged); (*Gustav V* in 1945) 4 28-cm/45-cal (2×2); 6 15-cm/50-cal (6×1); 4 75-mm AA (4×1); 6 40-mm (1.75-in) AA (6×1); 4 25-mm (1-in) AA (4×1); 3 20-mm (0.79-in) AA (3×1) *Crew:* 450

Sviatoj Georg

Russian submarine. The outbreak of war in 1914 found Russian industry completely incapable of dealing with the demands of a modern war. Plans to expand and modernize the fleet after the disasters of the war of 1904-05 were still only making slow progress; ships were taking a long time to build, and the diesel engines for new submarine construc-

tion had to be obtained from Germany – a source of supply which ended with the outbreak of war. In an attempt to overcome some of these delays an order was placed in 1916 with Ansaldo-San Giorgio, La Spezia, for a Laurenti-type submarine to be called *Sviatoj Georg* (St George). The boat was to be of 260 tons surface displacement, 313 tons dived, and armed with only two 46-cm (18-in) bow torpedo tubes and one 75-mm (2.95-in) deck gun abaft the conning tower. She was to have a designed speed of 13 knots on the surface and 8.5 knots when dived.

Sviatoj Georg was handed over to the Russians in 1917 and arrived in northern waters to join their Northern Ocean Flotilla in September. She saw no action against the Germans and it is doubtful whether she was capable of operations at that time. She was taken over by the Soviets in 1918 and was eventually renamed *Kommunist;* she played no part in the fighting of 1919 and was finally decommissioned in 1925 and scrapped.

Displacement: 260/313 tons (surfaced/submerged) *Length:* 45.15 m (148 ft 2 in) oa *Beam:* 4.2 m (13 ft 9 in) *Draught:* 3 m (9 ft 10 in) *Machinery:* 2-shaft diesel/electric, 700 bhp/450 shp=13.5/8.8 knots (surfaced/submerged) *Armament:* 2 45-cm (17.7-in) torpedo tubes (bow); 1 75-mm (2.95-in)/30-cal AA *Crew:* 24

Swatter

Soviet antitank missile. The AT-2 Swatter is fired from a quadruple launcher which is elevated from the rear body of a BRDM-1 Model B scout car, and may also have been deployed as an interim weapon on the Mi-24 Hind attack helicopter. The missile is powered by a solid-propellant rocket motor exhausting through a pair of lateral ports and employs manual command to line-of-sight guidance during the initial stages of flight. Some form of terminal homing, probably infrared, is also employed, and the small foreplanes may be used for final adjustments of the weapon's trajectory under control of the terminal seeker. Swatter has been replaced by the AT-3 Sagger in the Middle Eastern armies which operated it, and is likely to be obsolescent in the Soviet Union itself, although an improved version with a greater maximum range of 3500 m (3830 yards) has been reported and this may also employ semiautomatic command to line-of-sight guidance for the mid-course phase.

Length: 1.14 m (3 ft 9 in) *Span:* 66 cm (2 ft 2 in) *Diameter:* 13.2 cm (5.2 in) *Weight:* 20 kg (44 lb) *Range:* 2500 m (2730 yards) *Warhead:* hollow-charge, can penetrate 30 cm (12 in) of armour

Swift

British destroyer. Having revolutionized capital-ship construction in 1904-05 by initiating the designs of the battleship *Dreadnought* and the battlecruiser *Invincible,* Admiral Fisher also sought to revolutionize destroyer design by asking for a 36-knot vessel when existing destroyer speeds were around 25 to 30 knots. The Admiral had little time for intermediate types and envisaged a fleet consisting solely of his large Dreadnought battleships and cruisers, and small, lightly armed, high-speed destroyers. The fleet was saved from becoming such an ill-balanced force by Fisher's retirement from his post as First Sea Lord, and although the Dreadnought type was proving highly successful, both the battlecruiser and the super destroyer were expensive and ill-conceived hybrids which the navy could well have done without. Only one super destroyer, the *Swift,* was actually built. She was designed by Cammell Laird to Admiralty specifications, laid down at Birkenhead in 1906 and launched on December 7, 1907. Designed load displacement was 1825 tons, over twice that of a standard destroyer, but additions to the hull and machinery weight during construction increased this figure to 2170 tons. When completed in 1909 she was the largest destroyer in existence and until the construction of the *Afridi* Class in the late 1930s was the largest to be built for the Royal Navy. Everything was subordinated to speed, and she carried a very light armament for her size (a feature that caused much acid comment) while over half her length was occupied by the machinery. The after engine room contained the main turbines, while a similar but smaller set of cruising turbines was installed in the forward room. Steam was supplied by 12 Laird-Yarrow water-tube boilers housed in four boiler rooms, with two boilers in each of those furthest forward and aft and four each in the remaining pair. She carried a single 4-in (102-mm) gun on either side of the forecastle and two more, together with her two 18-in (46-cm) torpedo tubes, on the centreline aft. She had three very large funnels and, unlike most destroyers, had a mainmast as well as a foremast.

On her first trials in March 1909 she failed to reach her designed speed. Her funnels were therefore raised 0.9 m (3 ft) to increase the draught to the boilers, but even after trying her with several different propellers she still did not achieve 36 knots, and was eventually accepted at a little over 35 knots in February 1910. This was a remarkable speed for the time, but though some saw her as being useful as a fleet scout it was soon recognized that she hardly justified her cost which was twice that of a standard destroyer.

During 1910-12 she served with the 1st Destroyer Flotilla of the Home Fleet and in 1913 was reclassified as a destroyer leader; she was the first ship to be so designated as the first purpose-built leaders (the *Lightfoot* Class) were still in the design stage. She served as leader of the 4th Destroyer Flotilla, first with the Home Fleet and then the Grand Fleet, until the end of 1915 when she transferred to the 6th Flotilla at Dover. During July-September 1916 she was refitted at Portsmouth during which time the two 4-in guns on the forecastle were replaced by a single 6-in (152-mm); 6-pdr and 1½-pdr AA guns were added aft and the bridge structure was enlarged. The 6-in gun, a specially modified weapon, was not a success as the motion of the ship made it very difficult to operate and load in even moderate weather.

On the night of April 20-21, 1917, *Swift* was patrolling the Dover Barrage with the leader *Broke* when they encountered the German destroyers *V.71, V.73, V.81, S.53, G.85* and *G.42* which were retiring after bombarding Dover. A confused action followed in which the *G.85* and *G.42* were sunk and several others of the German force damaged while *Broke* received heavy damage bringing her to a standstill, and had to be towed back to Dover. *Swift* received minor damage and both ships were out of action for some weeks. While under repair *Swift* had her 6-in guns removed and the 4-in guns replaced. In April 1918 she covered the raid on Zeebrugge and in November of the same year left Dover to be paid off. She was sold for scrap in November 1921.

Displacement: 2170 tons (load), 2388 tons (full load) *Length:* 107.6 m (353 ft) oa *Beam:* 10.4 m (34 ft 2 in) *Draught:* 6.6 m (21 ft 8 in) *Machinery:* 4-shaft direct-drive steam turbines, 30 000 shp=36 knots *Armament:* 4 4-in (102-mm) (4×1); 2 18-in (46-cm) torpedo tubes (2×1) *Crew:* 126

Swift, Blackburn

British torpedo-bomber. Although only produced in small numbers, the Blackburn T.1 Swift served to improve the design of torpedo-carrying aircraft between the wars. In 1919 the requirement for a Sopwith Cuckoo replacement for carrier-borne operations was re-issued, following the unsuitability of the Short Shirl and the Blackburn Blackbird. Work on the aircraft began in early 1920, and it was shown at the Olympia Aero Show in July, and flew later that year.

The Swift was a single-seat two-bay biplane with folding wings for carrier stowage. It was built around a central nucleus comprising the centre fuselage, upper wing centre section, lower wing roots and undercarriage attachments, all built of steel tubing. A tubular-steel rear fuselage was attached to this unit, as were the two-spar wooden wings and the 450-hp Napier Lion IB engine.

Among its advanced features was a fireproof bulkhead between the engine bay and the self-sealing fuel tank, and also a divided undercarriage to allow the torpedo to be dropped. It was evaluated by the RAF at Martlesham Heath, and early in 1921 a fin modification was implemented. Deck landing trials were carried out on *Argus* later in 1921.

An export version, differing in the nose and tail contours, could carry an 18-in (46-cm) naval torpedo or 680 kg (1500 lb) of bombs. Two aircraft designated Swift F were delivered to the US Navy, and were among five types of torpedo-bomber evaluated between October 1922 and March 1923. Two Swift Mk IIs were among the types sent with the British Aviation Mission to Japan, carrying out landings on the carrier *Hosho* in 1922. A further three Swift Mk IIs were produced for the Spanish government and delivered in 1923 to Prat de Llobregat, where they were based until being struck off charge in 1927.

Although no further versions were built, the aircraft was developed into the Blackburn Dart torpedo-bomber for the Fleet Air Arm. Several other development projects were pursued, and a scheme to deepen the fuselage of the Swift was later used in the Blackburn Blackburd fleet spotter.

Span: 14.78 m (48 ft 6 in) *Length:* 10.82 m (35 ft 6 in) *Gross weight:* 2858 kg (6300 lb) *Maximum speed:* 171 km/h (106 mph)

Swift, Supermarine

British fighter-reconnaissance aircraft. The Swift was the RAF's first British-built swept-wing jet fighter in service. Introduced as an intercepter, it suffered severe aerodynamic problems before serving well in the low-level fighter-reconnaissance role. The Swift was ordered in November 1950 as a failsafe against the Hunter ordered a month previously, and was the less successful of the two. Developed from the Supermarine Type 510 and 535, it was powered by a Rolls-Royce Avon RA.7, rated at 3402 kg (7500 lb) st. The first of two prototype Swifts flew on August 5, 1951, and the initial production order was increased from 100 to 150 aircraft shortly afterwards.

The Swift was a low-wing cantilever monoplane of stressed-skin all-metal construction, designed as a high-altitude intercepter. The ailerons were power-operated and the tricycle undercarriage retracted hydraulically. The Swift F.1 was fitted with two 30-mm (1.18-in) Aden cannon, fixed tailplane and no afterburning, and 20 aircraft were built. The Swift F.2 doubled the firepower to four Aden cannon, and the wing had a cranked leading edge. The Swift F.3, with the Avon 108 and reheat, and F.4 with reheat and a variable-incidence tailplane, were never introduced into service. One of the prototype Swifts was converted to F.4 configuration, and flew on May 27, 1953, but the only other Swifts in this batch to be produced were 16 F.2s. The F.1 to F.4 carried the maker's designation Type 451.

The brief RAF career of the Swift F.2 began in February 1954 when it was issued to 56 Squadron, who also flew examples of the three other versions. It was dogged by ill-

A Supermarine 541/549 Swift makes a low pass during trials in Britain in the early 1950s

Vickers

Swiftsure

luck, which led to its withdrawal in May 1955. The company F.4 prototype did, however, raise the world air speed record to 737.7 mph (1187.2 km/h) on September 25, 1953, in the hands of test pilot Mike Lithgow.

With the failure of the Swift as an intercepter, it was decided to concentrate its development for tactical reconnaissance duties. By the time this had been completed, it was almost a new aircraft; it carried the maker's designation Type 549, and was known as the Swift FR.5 by the RAF. It differed from earlier versions in having a lengthened nose to accommodate three F.95 cameras. One was sited in the extreme nose while the two oblique cameras were placed just forward of the air intakes. The wings were given increased-chord tips, resulting in a dog-tooth leading edge, and a clear-view canopy was fitted. The engine was an Avon 114 rated at 3255 kg (7175 lb) st dry, 4286 kg (9450 lb) st with reheat. The armament was reduced to two 30-mm cannon although there was provision for eight air-to-surface rockets below the wings. The already considerable fuel capacity of 3538 litres (778 Imp gal) could be increased by the addition of a ventral 1000-litre (220-Imp gal) blister tank. The first FR.5s began life as F.4 airframes, while 62 new-build FR.5s were also produced, the first of which flew on May 24, 1955.

In RAF service the Swift FR.5 replaced the Meteor FR.9, and served with the 2nd Tactical Air Force in Germany. The first unit (2 Squadron) took its aircraft early in 1956 and by the end of the year 79 Squadron had also been re-equipped. In 1957, the Swift was winner and runner-up in the NATO reconnaissance competition, and gained first place again in 1959. The Swift FR.5 remained in RAF service until the summer of 1961, when the final Swifts of 2 Squadron were replaced by Hunter FR.10s. The Swift FR.5 was to have been followed by an unarmed PR.6 version for strategic reconnaissance (to replace the Meteor PR.10) but the project was cancelled.

The Swift F.7 was similar to the FR.5 but with an increased wing span and longer fuselage. The prototype flew in April 1956, and 12 production aircraft were built. They entered RAF service with 1 Guided Weapon Squadron, for indoctrination with the Fairey Fireflash beam-riding air-to-air guided missile, at RAF Valley in 1957. Neither the aircraft nor missile saw operational service, but valuable experience was provided in missile-handling and operation.

(FR.5) *Span:* 9.86 m (32 ft 4 in) *Length:* 12.88 m (42 ft 3 in) *Gross weight:* 9707 kg (21 400 lb) *Maximum speed:* 1102 km/h (685 mph) at sea level

Swiftsure

British battleship class, built 1902-03. On February 26, 1902, the Chilean battleships *Constitucion* and *Libertad* were laid down by Armstrongs at Elswick and by Vickers at Barrow respectively. The two ships were designed by Sir Edward Reed, who had been chief constructor at the Admiralty during 1863-70, to a specification requiring comparatively light protection and armament combined with high speed on a limited displacement of 11 000 tons. Both ships were

launched in January 1903 but shortly afterwards the Chilean authorities decided they no longer required them and they were purchased by the British government in December. They were not in fact suitable for RN service and were only purchased to prevent their sale to Russia, which at this time was on the brink of war with Japan. *Constitucion* was renamed *Swiftsure* and *Libertad* was renamed *Triumph*.

They were unusual ships, with quite different hull dimensions from standard British vessels: they were long and narrow with a shallow draught, which helped towards obtaining high speed but was in fact mainly dictated by the available docking facilities in Chile. Although their protection and main armament was comparatively light they carried a heavy secondary battery, unequalled by any other ship in the fleet, and they would no doubt have been useful in countering some of the 2nd Class battleships and the slower armoured cruisers of foreign powers. The final designed displacement was 11 800 tons but this was exceeded by 375 tons in the completed ships. On trials *Triumph* achieved 20.17 knots with 14 105 ihp and *Swiftsure* 20.05 knots with 14 018 ihp which made them the fastest battleships to serve in the Royal Navy until the completion of *Dreadnought*.

Both ships commissioned in June 1904 for the Home Fleet (Channel Fleet from 1906) with which they served until transferred to the Mediterranean in 1909. In 1913 *Triumph* became flagship of the East Indies station and *Swiftsure* transferred to the China station where they remained until March 1915 when

they transferred to the Eastern Mediterranean for the Dardanelles operations. They took part in all the major bombardments of the Dardanelles forts and later provided cover for the Gallipoli landings. On May 25, 1915, *Triumph* was torpedoed and sunk by the submarine *U 21* while providing gunfire support off Gaba Tepe. Shortly after this *Swiftsure* was withdrawn from the beachhead and although she remained in the Eastern Mediterranean until late in 1916 she saw no further action during the war. She was laid up at Chatham during 1917-18 and in 1919 was employed as a target prior to being sold for scrap in 1920.

Displacement: 12 175 tons (load), 13 840 tons (full load) *Length:* 146.2 m (479 ft 9 in) oa *Beam:* 21.6 m (71 ft) *Draught:* 7.7 m (25 ft 4 in) *Machinery:* 2-shaft triple-expansion, 12 500 ihp=19 knots *Protection:* 178 mm (7 in) side, 254 mm (10 in) barbettes, 254-203 mm (10-8 in) turrets, 76-25 mm (3-1 in) decks *Armament:* 4 10-in (254-mm) (2×2); 14 7.5-in (191-mm) (14×1); 14 14-pdr (14×1); 2 12-pdr (2×1); 4 6-pdr (4×1); 2 18-in (46-cm) torpedo tubes (submerged) *Crew:* 802

Swiftsure

British nuclear-powered submarine class. *Swiftsure*, the first of an improved *Valiant* Class of submarine was ordered in November 1967. The *Swiftsure* Class are 4 m (13 ft) shorter than their predecessors and have their diving planes fitted slightly lower on the hull; they are fitted with improved sonar and

No and name	laid down	launched	commissioned
S.104 *Sceptre*	10/73	11/76	1978
S.108 *Sovereign*	9/70	2/73	7/74
S.109 *Superb*	3/72	10/74	11/76
S.111 *Spartan*	1974	—	—
S.112 *Severn*	1976	—	—
S.126 *Swiftsure*	4/69	9/71	4/73

HMS *Superb* leaving Barrow-in-Furness to join the Second Submarine Squadron in 1976. She is a *Swiftsure* Class submarine and the ninth British warship to bear the name *Superb*

other electronic equipment. Armament is reduced from six to five torpedo tubes, but these tubes are capable of firing the new Tigerfish torpedoes as well as the old and well-tried Mark 8**. Power is provided by a Rolls-Royce pressurized water-cooled reactor and English Electric geared turbines. As is usual with all but the very early US nuclear-powered boats there is only one propeller shaft, with a seven-bladed propeller made of special anticavitating alloy. The entire class was built by Vickers, Barrow.

Displacement: 3500/4500 tons (surfaced/submerged) *Length:* 82.9 m (272 ft) *Beam:* 9.8 m (32 ft 3 in) *Draught:* 8.2 m (27 ft) *Machinery:* 1 pressurized water-cooled reactor, 1-shaft geared steam turbine, 15 000 shp=20/30 knots (surfaced/submerged) *Armament:* 5 21-in (53-cm) torpedo tubes (bow), to be fitted with Sub-Harpoon missiles *Crew:* 97

Swingfire, British Aerospace

British antitank missile. Swingfire was conceived at the Royal Armament Research and Development Establishment in 1958 as a command-guided weapon which could outrange all tank guns and disable any armoured vehicle. The missile was to be operated by the Royal Armoured Corps, complementing the infantry's man-portable Vickers Vigilant. In 1959 Fairey Engineering was awarded a contract to develop and test vehicles designed to prove the concept of using jet deflection to maintain control at low air speeds. Like Fairey's cancelled Orange William, the missile was designed to have a low acceleration during the boost phase so that the round could be gathered in a short distance, thus giving as short a minimum range as possible. Since aerodynamic controls would be ineffective at these low speeds, the missile was to be steered by deflecting the exhaust from its solid-propellant rocket motor by means of a device known as a jetavator: hence the name Swingfire. The low initial speed also allowed the weapon to be gathered easily and quickly by a remote operator, as in the Vigilant system.

Fairey fired the first test round in December 1960 and had completed 16 shots by February 1962, when the company was absorbed into the British Aircraft Corporation. BAC carried out a further 12 firings of the original design, completing the programme in September 1963. The project suffered from problems with the jetavator and wire breakages, and BAC's first design proved to be too expensive and difficult to produce. Thirty-three firings were made in this series and the knowledge gleaned from this stage was fed into the 'Build 2' design, which was hand-built to production standards. The first Build 2 missile was test flown in August 1965 and was followed by a further 19 before the end of that year. Evaluation trials started in August 1966, the first firings by the British Army took place towards the end of 1968, and the weapon was declared operational in the following year.

Swingfire was originally intended to arm the Chieftain main battle tank but, by the time the missile design snags had been ironed out, it was too late to incorporate the weapon into the tank. Swingfire was thus fitted instead in the FV438, an antitank version of

A British Aerospace Swingfire antitank missile streaks away from an FV438 during training on the ranges at Hohne, West Germany, in 1974. The FV438 carries a total of 14 missiles

the FV432 armoured personnel carrier, and in the Ferret Mk 5 (FV712) scout car; the former has a two-round launcher, with 12 spare missiles in the hull, while the latter has four launchers and two reload rounds. The weapon has since been introduced in the FV102 Striker, one of the Combat Vehicle Reconnaissance (Tracked) family, operated by the Belgian army and the British forces; in this case there are five missiles ready to fire and five more in reserve.

Striker is fitted with an Avimo No 43 periscopic sight with × 1 magnification in the upper half and × 10 in the lower half; movement in elevation is achieved by an adjusting mirror in the sight head, and adjustment in azimuth is by rotating the cupola on which the sight is mounted. The operator acquires his target in the sight and tracks it manually. He then fires a missile, which is automatically gathered into his field of view by means of a programme generator. The gunner continues to follow the target and steers the round onto his sightline using a joystick. Swingfire contains an autopilot which maintains it on the desired course, although the operator continues to feed in fine adjustments which are transmitted down trailing wires to operate the jetavator for steering.

The sight can be removed from the vehicle if desired, allowing the engagement to be controlled from a distance of up to 100 m (330 ft). This facility permits the operator to control an engagement while the launch vehicle is completely hidden from its target and also affords him greater protection if fire is returned.

A pallet-mounted version, known as Beeswing Mk 2, is operated by the Egyptian army on its Land Rovers, although the British Army has abandoned plans to equip soft-skinned vehicles with such a system. An air-launched derivative, known as Hawkswing or Airstrike Swingfire, was also cancelled in 1974. In the more recent Light Air Transportable Swingfire a four-round launcher is fitted on a lightweight cross-country vehicle such as the Somerton Rayner Saboteur. In this case the missiles are fired with the aid of a small and compact sighting and guidance station, which replaces the standard sepa-

rated sight. LAT Swingfire is being offered for export and may be adopted by the British Army.

Length: 1.07 m (3 ft 6 in) *Span:* 39 cm (15.3 in) *Diameter:* 17 cm (6.7 in) *Weight:* 28 kg (62 lb) *Range:* 4000 m (4370 yards) *Speed:* 185 m/sec (600 ft/sec) *Warhead:* 7-kg (15.4-lb) hollow-charge

Swordfish

British submarine class. Designed during the 1930s as a replacement for the obsolete *H.21-54* Class, the *Swordfish* Class proved exceedingly successful. Production was resumed when war broke out and continued until the end of hostilities. The design developed into three distinct groups, and within each group various vessels displayed a number of differences resulting from various war modifications. These included partial and finally fully welded construction, the addition of radar, a heavier gun armament and external fuel tanks for operations in the Far East. The *Swordfish* Class differed from previous classes in having the main fuel tanks within the pressure hull, and avoided the problems of fuel leaks previously experienced with external tanks. Another innovation which saved many lives during the war was the fitting of an escape hatch in the forward and after compartments of the pressure hull.

The 3-in (76-mm) gun on the first group was carried on a hinged, disappearing mounting on an extension in front of the conning tower. The conning tower was thus a very high structure which spoilt the normally low silhouette of the submarine. Succeeding groups had a much lower conning tower with the gun mounted normally on the foredeck casing. Later vessels which mounted a 4-in (102-mm) gun reverted to the breastwork-type mounting used in the *Rainbow* Class.

The *Swordfish* design was developed principally as a medium-range patrol type with higher surfaced speed and radius of action than the 'H' Class, higher submerged radius of action resulting from increased battery capacity, and a much heavier armament. In spite of the increased size and displacement

Swordfish, Fairey

MOD

HMS *Syrtis*, a *Swordfish* Class submarine lost during the Second World War after striking mines. The *Swordfish* Class were highly successful

they retained the rapid-dive capability and good submerged handling of their predecessors. Group I vessels carried 45 tons of fuel, giving a radius of action of 3690 nautical miles at 10 knots surfaced; Group II vessels carried 40 tons of fuel giving a radius of action of 3800 nautical miles at the same speed. Group III vessels initially carried 48 tons of fuel and had a surfaced radius of action of 6000 nautical miles at 10 knots; bunkerage was later increased to 91 tons.

The *Swordfish* Class was the most numerous submarine class ever built for the Royal Navy. A quantity of units were completed with numbers only and were not named until 1943 (by which time *P.222* had been sunk).

Group I (launched 1931-33)
Seahorse, Starfish, Sturgeon, Swordfish—built by Chatham dockyard

Group II (launched 1934-37)
Salmon, Sealion, Spearfish—built by Cammell Laird
Shark, Snapper, Sterlet, Sunfish—built by Chatham dockyard
Seawolf—built by Scotts

Group III (launched 1941-45)
Safari (ex-*P.211*, ex-*P.61*), *Saga**, *Sahib* (ex-*P.212*, ex-*P.62*), *Sanguine**, *Saracen* (ex-*P.213*, ex-*P.63*), *Scorcher**, *Seadog* (ex-*P.216*, ex-*P.66*), *Sea Nymph* (ex-*P.223*), *Seascout**, *Selene**, *Sibyl* (ex-*P.217*, ex-*P.67*), *Sickle* (ex-*P.224*), *Sidon**, *Simoon* (ex-*P.225*), *Sleuth**, *Solent**, *Spearhead**, *Spirit, Springer**, *Spur**, *Statesman, Stoic* (ex-*P.231*), *Stonehenge* (ex-*P.232*), *Storm* (ex-*P.233*), *Stratagem* (ex-*P.234*), *Stubborn* (ex-*P.238*), *Sturdy, Stygian, Subtle**, *Supreme**, *Surf* (ex-*P.239*), *Syrtis*—built by Cammell Laird.
Satyr (ex-*P.214*, ex-*P.64*), *Sceptre* (ex-*P.215*, ex-*P.65*), *Scotsman**, *Scythian* (ex-*P.237*), *Sea Devil**, *Sea Rover* (ex-*P.218*, ex-*P.67*), *Seneschal**, *Sentinel**, *Sirdar* (ex-*P.226*), *Spark* (ex-*P.236*), *Spiteful* (ex-*P.227*), *Strongbow* (ex-*P.235*)—built by Scotts

Seraph (ex-*P.219*, ex-*P.69*), *Shakespeare* (ex-*P.221*, ex-*P.71*), *P.222*—built by Vickers-Armstrongs, Barrow
Shalimar, Splendid (ex-*P.228*), *Sportsman* (ex-*P.229*)—built by Chatham dockyard
(*signifies later boats with revised armament)

A number of vessels were lost during the Second World War. *Salmon* (July 9, 1940), *Sickle* (June 18, 1944) and *Syrtis* (March 28, 1944) sank after striking mines. *Spearfish* was sunk by the German submarine *U34* on August 2, 1940, and *Simoon* was sunk by *U565* on November 15, 1943. German surface antisubmarine vessels and minesweepers accounted for *Seahorse* (January 7, 1940), *Starfish* (January 9, 1940), *Shark* (July 6, 1940) and *Sterlet* (April 18, 1940), and *Splendid* was sunk by the German destroyer *Hermes* on April 21, 1943. The Italian corvettes *Gabbiano* and *Minerva* sank *Sahib* (April 24, 1943) and *Saracen* (August 18, 1943) respectively, and the Italian destroyer *Fortunale* sank *P.222* on August 24, 1942. *Stratagem* was sunk by Japanese antisubmarine forces, and *Shakespeare* was sunk by Japanese aircraft on January 3, 1945. *Swordfish* (November 1940), *Snapper* (February 1941) and *Stonehenge* (March 1944) were all lost due to unknown causes. *Sunfish* was transferred to the USSR as *B.1*, and was sunk in error by the RAF in July 1944.

Sturgeon was transferred to the Netherlands as *Zeehond* in 1943, but was returned at the end of the war and scrapped. *Satyr, Spiteful, Sportsman* and *Statesman* were transferred to France in 1951-52 as *Saphir, Sirène, Sibylle* and *Sultane*; all except *Sibylle* (*Sportsman*), which was lost, were returned in 1958-61 and subsequently scrapped. Israel received *Springer* (as *Tanin*) and *Sanguine* (as *Rahav*) in 1958 and both survived until scrapped in 1969. Portugal received *Saga, Spearhead* and *Spur* in 1948-49 as *Nautilo* (scrapped 1969), *Neptuno* (scrapped 1968) and *Narval* (scrapped 1969).

Of the ships remaining in RN service, *Sealion, Stubborn* and *Sidon* were expended

as targets. The remainder were scrapped at various times during 1945-66.

(Group I) *Displacement:* 640/935 tons (surfaced/submerged) *Length:* 61.7 m (202 ft 6 in) oa *Beam:* 7.3 m (24 ft) *Draught:* 3.2 m (10 ft 6 in) *Machinery:* 2-shaft diesels/2 electric motors, 1550 bhp/1300 hp=13.75/10 knots (surfaced/submerged) *Armament:* 1 3-in (76-mm); 6 21-in (53-cm) torpedo tubes (bow), 12 torpedoes *Crew:* 36

(Group II) *Displacement:* 670/960 tons (surfaced/submerged) *Length:* 63.6 m (208 ft 9 in) oa *Beam:* 7.3 m (24 ft) *Draught:* 3.2 m (10 ft 6 in) *Machinery:* as Group I (except *Sunfish*, 1900 bhp=15 knots [surfaced]) *Armament:* as Group I *Crew:* 39

(Group III) *Displacement:* 715/990 tons (surfaced/submerged) *Length:* 66.1 m (217 ft) oa *Beam:* 7.3 m (24 ft) *Draught:* 3.4 m (11 ft) *Machinery:* 2-shaft diesels/2 electric motors, 1900 bhp/1300 hp=14.75/9 knots (surfaced/submerged) *Armament:* (Most early boats) 1 3-in; 7 21-in torpedo tubes (6 bow, 1 stern), 13 torpedoes; (Later boats) 1 4-in (102-mm); 7 21-in torpedo tubes; (*Safari, Sahib, Saracen, Satyr, Sceptre* as Group 1) *Crew:* 48

Swordfish, Fairey

British carrier-borne torpedo, spotter and reconnaissance aircraft. Known most affectionately to its pilots and aircrew as the 'Stringbag', the Swordfish was obsolete at the start of the Second World War. Yet during that war it proved not only reliable and resilient, but also operationally very effective. Its slow speed made it uniquely suitable for carrier operations and deck handling, and also for torpedo and dive-bombing attacks. Its flexibility was such that the Swordfish remained in service long after its designed replacement, the Albacore, had been withdrawn (in November 1943). Indeed, nine squadrons of Swordfish were still in service at the end of the war. The origins of this remarkable biplane can be traced to 1933, when Fairey's TSR.I (torpedo, spotter, reconnaissance Mk I) made its maiden flight on March 21. Essentially similar to its successor, it had a shorter fuselage and a higher-aspect-ratio fin and rudder. During its short existence, it was flown with both a Bristol Pegasus and Siddeley Tiger engine. Though promising, the TSR.I was lost in an accident in September 1933. The TSR.II followed, built to Specification S.15/33, incorporating a redesigned fin and rudder and an extra fuselage bay. Flying for the first time on April 17, 1934, the TSR.II was successfully flown and following Air Ministry trials (including a twin-float seaplane conversion) it was adopted for service and named the Swordfish.

A single-bay biplane of almost equal span, the Swordfish was of metal construction with fabric covering. The wings comprised a wide centre section and outer wings, which folded aft to facilitate stowage. A pyramid structure which carried the upper centre section was also used as a hoisting sling. The lower wing roots were braced to the fuselage by V-struts. Handley Page slots were fitted to the upper wings, while all wings were equipped with ailerons. The fuselage was of a rectangular steel tube structure with detachable metal panels covering the nose and fabric covering the rear fuselage, all faired to an oval section. The aircraft was stressed for catapult launches and carried an arrester hook.

The Swordfish could be operated as either a landplane or seaplane, but was mainly used in the former role. The undercarriage was a divided-axle type, with medium pressure tires and pneumatic brakes. Twin metal floats of special design were readily interchangeable with the wheeled undercarriage.

The Swordfish Mk I was powered by a single Bristol Pegasus IIIM3 air-cooled radial engine, rated at 690 hp, driving a Fairey-Reed fixed-pitch metal propeller. It was armed with a single fixed 0.303-in (7.7-mm) Vickers machine-gun, synchronized to fire through the propeller arc, and either a Vickers K or Lewis gun of similar calibre on a Fairey high-speed gun-mounting in the rear cockpit. The fuselage crutch could accommodate an 18-in (46-cm) torpedo of 730 kg (1610 lb) or a 680-kg (1500-lb) mine. Alternatively, 680 kg of bombs could be carried either as three 227-kg (500-lb) bombs or two 227-kg and two 113-kg (250-lb) bombs. A crew of three (pilot, observer and telegraphist/air gunner) was carried. In addition to the TSR.II prototype and three preproduction aircraft, Fairey built 689 and Blackburn 300 Swordfish Mk Is, constructed to Specification S.38/34.

In 1943 the Swordfish Mk II appeared. This version had a strengthened lower mainplane, to enable it to carry and launch eight 27-kg (60-lb) rocket projectiles, which could replace the torpedo or bomb weapon load. Initial batches of Mk IIs were powered by the Pegasus IIIM3, but the Pegasus XXX, rated at 750 hp, was later substituted. Blackburn, who constructed all Swordfish procured after December 1940, built 1080 airframes, and followed on with 320 Mk III. This was basically a Mk II with ASV Mk X radar mounted in a radome between the undercarriage legs. Some Swordfish were also fitted with enclosed cockpits for use in Canada, and these were designated Mk IV. A total of 2393 Swordfish were built, and production ceased in August 1944.

The first Swordfish unit in the Fleet Air Arm was 825 Squadron, who received their aircraft in July 1936, replacing Fairey Seals. By the end of that year, a further three squadrons had re-equipped, and by the outbreak of the Second World War, the Swordfish was the Fleet Air Arm's only torpedo bomber and equipped 13 squadrons.

Although employed mainly on antisubmarine duties, armed with depth charges and later rocket projectiles, Swordfish were active in all theatres. They were used during the second Battle of Narvik in April 1940, spotting for the guns of the task force led by HMS *Warspite*; operations from Malta; the attack on the French fleet in Oran in July 1940; strikes against the *Bismarck* in May 1941; the Battle of the Atlantic and the Soviet convoys.

The highlight of the Swordfish's career, however, must certainly be the raid on Taranto on the night of November 11, 1940, when 21 aircraft, launched in two waves from HMS *Illustrious*, successfully crippled the Italian fleet at anchor in the harbour. The Swordfish, which were fitted with long-range fuel tanks displacing the third crew member, were drawn from 815 and 819 Squadrons, based on the *Illustrious*, and 813 and 824 Squadrons from HMS *Eagle* and temporarily detached for that operation. Despite severe antiaircraft fire, only one aircraft from each wave was lost. Taranto proved once and for all that aircraft were capable of knocking out an enemy fleet, and altering the balance of naval power at sea.

Another famous Swordfish raid was the attack on the German battlecruisers *Scharnhorst*, *Gneisenau* and *Prinz Eugen* as they attempted to slip through the English Channel on the morning of February 12, 1942. Six Swordfish of 825 Squadron, commanded by Lieutenant-Commander Eugene Esmonde, attacked the three vessels through a devastating AA barrage and German fighter screen. All six aircraft were shot down, and only five of the 18 aircrew survived.

The last Swordfish unit to disband was 836 Squadron, which was the operational pool for 19 merchant aircraft carriers. During its service the Swordfish had equipped a total of 26 Fleet Air Arm squadrons and two RAF squadrons. It was a Mk III of 119 Squadron, RAF which attacked a German midget submarine off the Belgian coast only 3½ hours before Germany surrendered. A Swordfish Mk II is retained in flying condition by the Fleet Air Arm at Yeovilton.

(Mk I) *Span:* 13.87 m (45 ft 6 in) *Length:* 10.87 m (35 ft 8 in) *Gross weight:* 4196 kg (9250 lb) *Maximum speed:* 224 km/h (139 mph) at 1450 m (4750 ft)

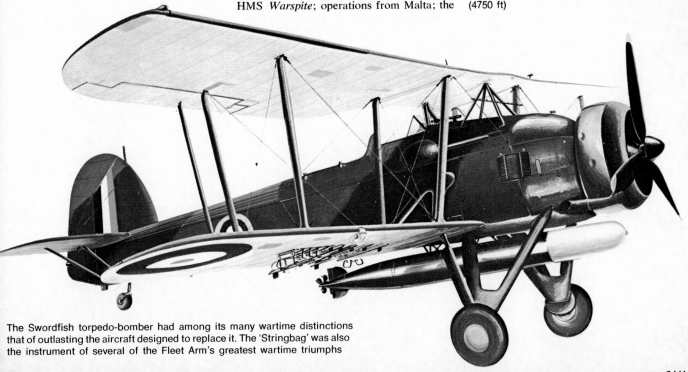

The Swordfish torpedo-bomber had among its many wartime distinctions that of outlasting the aircraft designed to replace it. The 'Stringbag' was also the instrument of several of the Fleet Arm's greatest wartime triumphs

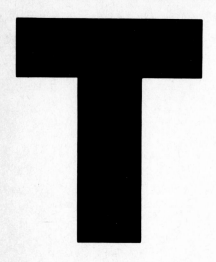

T.1

German torpedo boat class, built 1937-42. In 1935-36 eight torpedo boats were authorized to supplement the destroyer programme. They were diminutives of the *Wolf* Class, with two knots more speed, the same torpedo armament but a much lighter gun armament and lower endurance. In 1937 a further 13 were added to the programme.

T.1-4, T.9, T.10, T.13-21—built by Schichau, Elbing
T.5-8, T.11, T.12—built by AG Weser, Bremen

From *T.13* the fuel stowage was increased by 11 tons and two single 37-mm (1.46-in) AA guns replaced the 20-mm (0.79-in), but in other respects they were identical. The hull was flush-decked with a single funnel. The main gun was mounted aft, with only a light AA gun on the forecastle. These tough little escort destroyers saw much action in the North Sea, English Channel and Baltic, and suffered heavy losses. The AA armament was increased in all, and a clipper stem was added to give them better seakeeping. By the end of the war a 40-mm (1.57-in) Bofors gun had replaced the after torpedo tubes.

T.6 was mined west of the Shetlands on November 7, 1940. *T.3* was sunk by RAF bombs at Le Havre in September 1940 but was salved in 1941; she was finally mined north of Hela on March 14, 1945, with *T.5*. *T.2* and *T.7* were bombed by US aircraft at Bremen on July 29, 1944; they were later salved and scrapped. *T.10* was sunk by bombs at Gdynia on December 18, 1944, and *T.1* at Kiel on April 10, 1945. *T.8* and *T.9* were both scuttled off Kiel on May 3, 1945. *T.15* was sunk at Kiel by US bombers on December 13, 1943. *T.18* was sunk by Soviet aircraft in the Gulf of Finland on September 17, 1944, while *T.13* was bombed in the Kattegat on April 10, 1945. The last casualty was *T.16*, which was decommissioned at Kiel on April 13 after severe damage from bombs.

T.4 and *T.19* were transferred to the US Navy and then to the Royal Danish Navy in 1947; they were stricken in 1951. *T.14* was transferred from the USN to the French as *Dompaire*, while the British transferred *T.11* as *Bir Hacheim* and *T.20* as the *Baccarat*. The remaining USN prize, *T.21*, was badly damaged and had to be scuttled in the Skager-rak in 1946. The remaining pair, *T.12* and *T.17* became the Soviet *Podvischny* and *Porivisty*.

Displacement: 850 tons (standard), 1100 tons (full load) *Length:* (*T.1*) 84 m (275 ft 8 in), (*T.13*) 85 m (278 ft 10 in) oa *Beam:* (*T.1*) 8.6 m (28 ft 3 in), (*T.13*) 8.9 m (29 ft 2 in) *Draught:* (*T.1*) 2.9 m (9 ft 6 in) max, (*T.13*) 3.1 m (10 ft 2 in) max *Machinery:* 2-shaft geared steam turbines, 31 000 shp=35.5 knots *Armament:* 1 105-mm (4.1-in) L/45; 3 20-mm (0.79-in) AA (3×1) or 2 37-mm (1.46-in) AA (2×1); 6 53-cm (21-in) torpedo tubes (2×3) *Crew:* 119

T.1

US submarine class, built 1917-20. In 1914 the first fleet submarine was authorized for the US Navy, to be named *Schley* (SF.1). She was about 21.3 m (70 ft) longer than the previous biggest, *M.1*, and about 30.5 m (100 ft) longer than the standard 'L' Class. The diesel horsepower was more than trebled to achieve 20 knots on the surface but, as the British had found with their 'J' Class, existing diesel engines were not equal to such an increase in power.

In August 1917 *Schley* was renumbered *AA.1*, and although there were misgivings about her design, two more were ordered, *AA.2-3*, also from Bethlehem's Fore River yard. The design was Electric Boat company's EB 63, *AA.1* being built to the A variant and the others to a C variant. Two of the torpedo tubes were mounted in the deck casing abaft the conning tower.

AA.1 was commissioned on January 30, 1920, but was soon renumbered *T.1* and given the hull designation SS.52; *AA.2* and *AA.3* were commissioned in January 1922 and December 1920 respectively as *T.2* (SS.60) and *T.3* (SS.61). The designations SF.1-3 were dropped subsequently.

The three boats were a failure, and it was admitted that they could not operate with the Fleet as designed. The unusual arrangement of four diesels coupled in tandem to twin screws was partly to blame, but they were also difficult to handle, and could not dive below 46 m (150 ft). They were all stricken in 1930 and scrapped.

Displacement: 1107/1482 tons (surfaced/submerged) *Length:* 81.9 m (268 ft 9 in) oa *Beam:* 6.9 m (22 ft 9 in) *Draught:* 4.3 m (14 ft 3 in) *Machinery:* 2-shaft diesel-electric, 4000 bhp/1350 shp=20/10.5 knots (surfaced/submerged) *Armament:* 2 3-in (76-mm) QF (2×1) replaced by 1 4-in (102-mm); 6 21-in (53-cm) torpedo tubes (4 bow, 2 in deck casing, 16 torpedoes carried) *Crew:* 38

T-1, Fuji

Japanese intermediate jet training aircraft. The first jet aircraft designed and built in quantity by Japan after the Second World War, the tandem two-seat T-1 originated as the Fuji T1F1, planned to have a Japanese-designed jet engine. Pending availability of this, Fuji built two T1F2 prototypes with Bristol Orpheus turbojets, the first of these flying on January 19, 1958. The first Japanese-engined T1F1, with a 1200-kg (2645-lb) st Ishikawajima J3 turbojet, made its maiden flight on May 17, 1960. Production batches of both versions followed, totalling 60 aircraft: 40 T1F2s (designated T-1A by the Air Self-Defence Force), with 1814-kg (4000-lb) st Orpheus 805 engines, and 20 T1F1s (JASDF designation T-1B). Deliveries, to replace ageing North American T-6 piston-engined trainers, were completed in 1963. The T-1 has provision for a 0.5-in (12.7-mm) machine-gun in the nose and underwing pylons for up to 680 kg (1500 lb) of bombs, rockets, or two Sidewinder missiles. One prototype was test-flown as a T1F3 (T-1C) in 1965 after installation of a more powerful J3 engine of 1400 kg (3085 lb) thrust, but proposals to refit the T-1Bs with this powerplant did not materialize. Similar plans in late 1973 to substitute a Rolls-Royce/Turboméca Adour turbofan engine were also abandoned.

(T-1A) *Span:* 10.5 m (34 ft 5 in) *Length:* 12.12 m (39 ft 9 in) *Gross weight:* 5000 kg (11 023 lb) *Maximum speed:* 925 km/h (575 mph)

T-2, Rockwell US tactical jet trainer
See **Buckeye**

T2D-1, Douglas

US Navy torpedo-bomber. During the interwar years the US Naval Aircraft Factory at the Philadelphia navy yard engaged in both design and construction of aircraft. In May 1926 the factory completed the XTN-1, a moderately large equal-span two-bay biplane with two uncowled Wright R-1750 radial engines on the lower wings. Construction had been started in May 1925 and two months later the navy had ordered three similar aircraft from Douglas. These appeared in July 1926 and were followed by nine more of the type two years later. Designated T2D-1, they could be distinguished from the XTN-1 by their high balanced rudder. They had open bow and midships gunners' cockpits, each with a single 7.62-mm (0.30-in) machine-gun on a ring mounting. The pilot's cockpit was just in front of the wings with the observer immediately behind him. Offensive load comprised a 734-kg (1618-lb) torpedo carried on racks beneath the fuselage or an equivalent bombload. The T2D-1s were intended either for operation on twin floats or, with a wheeled undercarriage, from aircraft carriers. They had folding wings to facilitate carrier stowage, but reports of trials aboard the first US Navy carrier *Langley* in 1927 are unconfirmed. Most of the T2D-1's career was spent operating on floats with Patrol Squadron 1 out of Pearl Harbor.

To avoid friction with the US Army over the operation of land-based bombing aircraft, 18 T2D-1 developments were ordered in June 1930 as P2D-1s. They differed from their predecessors mainly in having curved twin fins and rudders in place of the large single fin and rudder and were powered by twin 575-hp Wright R-1820 Cyclones with Townend rings. They also operated mainly on floats, with Patrol Squadron 3 based at Coco Solo, Panama Canal Zone, remaining in first-line service until 1937. Greater fuel capacity increased range from the 730 km (454 miles) of the T2D-1 to 1625 km (1010 miles).

(T2D-1 seaplane) *Span:* 17.37 m (57 ft) *Length:* 13.51 m (44 ft 4 in) *Gross weight:* 5151 kg

A Douglas T2D-1 torpedo-bomber of the US Navy. The type usually operated on floats and was part of the Pearl Harbor-based Patrol Squadron 1

(11 357 lb) *Maximum speed:* 201 km/h (125 mph) at sea level

(P2D-1 seaplane) *Span:* 17.37 m (57 ft) *Length:* 13.38 m (43 ft 11 in) *Gross weight:* 5802 kg (12 791 lb) *Maximum speed:* 217 km/h (135 mph) at sea level

---

T2V, Lockheed US Navy advanced trainer aircraft **See Shooting Star**

T.3, Tellier

French reconnaissance flying boat. The T.3 was designed by Alphonse Tellier to replace his T.2 prototype which had crashed during trials in mid-1916. The Tellier flying boats were evolved, along with FBA, Donnet-Denhaut and Coutant types, to supply the vast expansion programme begun by the French navy in 1915. France began the First World War with just a handful of seaplanes, and as the war at sea progressed there was an ever-increasing need for aircraft for coastal-patrol and antisubmarine work.

The type was alternatively known as the Tellier 200 hp, after the power of its Hispano-Suiza 8 Ba water-cooled engine. Pilot and observer were normally seated side by side in the forward hull, and in the bow was another cockpit with a ring mounting for a light machine-gun; access to the bow cockpit was via the hull. The rudder was of unusual configuration with a semicircular leading edge. There was considerable dihedral on the lower wing, which was of smaller span than the upper. Wing bracing was by means of three pairs of parallel struts either side, the outer two pairs being in V form. The engine, which drove a two-bladed pusher propeller, was set between the wings. These were supported by six struts, the forward pair connecting with the hull at points just forward of the pilot's cockpit.

At least 96 T.3s were delivered to the Marine Nationale, later examples being built at Nieuport factories. Later Tellier flying boats were distinctive in that they had tall rectangular rudders braced at the bottom to the end of the hull and at the top by struts attached to the rear of the upper wing. All these later Tellier designs, including the Tc with a 47-mm (1.85-in) cannon, and various twin- and three-engine designs, were built in association with the Nieuport company.

Most were built in only small quantities, but it is reported that 55 examples of the Tc were completed.

The Telliers did a worthwhile job in the English Channel and the Mediterranean during 1917-18. A number were flown from Le Croisic by US Navy crews and a single example was evaluated in the United States.

Span: 15.6 m (51 ft 2 in) *Length:* 11.8 m (38 ft 9 in) *Gross weight:* 1700 kg (3748 lb) *Maximum speed:* 145 km/h (90 mph) at sea level

T3M/T4M/TG, Martin

US carrier-based torpedo-bomber. The Glenn Martin company made a successful bid to meet a US Navy requirement of 1925 for a new carrier-borne torpedo-bomber to equip the new giant vessels *Lexington* and *Saratoga*. Drawing on experience gained in building the Curtiss-designed SC machines, Martin fulfilled a contract to build 24 T3M-1s. As with the SC, the upper wing of the single-bay biplane had a slightly shorter span than the lower wing and both the wings were braced to the fuselage top and bottom by pairs of parallel struts. It differed from the

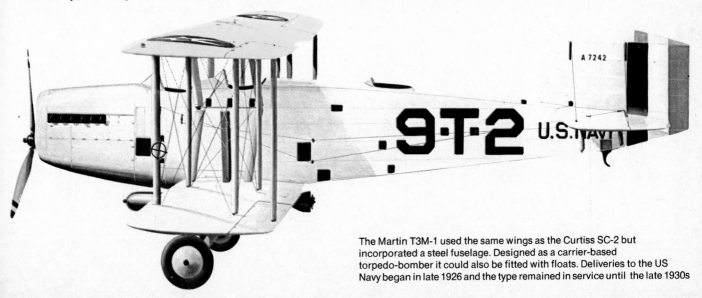

The Martin T3M-1 used the same wings as the Curtiss SC-2 but incorporated a steel fuselage. Designed as a carrier-based torpedo-bomber it could also be fitted with floats. Deliveries to the US Navy began in late 1926 and the type remained in service until the late 1930s

T-IVW, Fokker

Curtiss design in having a welded steel-tube fuselage. The pilot and torpedo-man sat in open side-by-side cockpits in front of the wing with the observer-gunner's cockpit well to the rear, fitted with a single 0.30-in (7.62-mm) machine-gun on a ring mounting. Offensive load comprised a single torpedo (or the equivalent in bombs) on racks beneath the fuselage between the independent main wheels of the undercarriage.

Most of the T3M-1s flew as twin-float seaplanes and it was left to the T3M-2, 100 of which were delivered from March 1927, to equip Torpedo Squadrons 1 and 2 aboard *Lexington* and *Langley* respectively. They differed from the T3M-1s in having equal-span wings, 710-hp water-cooled Packard 3A-2500 engines with radiators either side of the nose, replacing the T3M-1's 575-hp Wright T-3B which had a large single radiator rigged between fuselage and upper wing. The torpedo-man and pilot were seated in tandem cockpits with the torpedo-man in front. The first T3M-2 was tested with an uncowled Pratt & Whitney Hornet radial as the XT3M-3, and then with a Wright R-1750 Cyclone as the XT3M-4. The XT4M-1 was ordered in April 1927. It had the Hornet engine and featured wings of reduced span and a larger balanced rudder. Tests were satisfactory and 102 production aircraft followed, first deliveries occurring in early 1928. Like the T3M-2, the T4M-1 was operated on both wheel and floats and became standard equipment of both coastal- and carrier-based torpedo squadrons of the US Navy.

The Great Lakes corporation took over Martin's Cleveland plant in October 1928, and soon afterwards received a contract for 18 TG-1s. These resembled the T4M-1s apart from a 525-hp Pratt & Whitney R-1690-28 Hornet and a modernized undercarriage; 32 TG-2s followed, powered by 620-hp Wright R-1820-86 Cyclone radials. TG-2s were operational with Squadron VT-2 until 1937. The Great Lakes and Martin biplanes had represented typical reliable and slow naval equipment for a decade. Final examples were passed on to reserve units and finally to navy training stations. These ungainly giants were the first practicable torpedo-bombers able to operate from United States aircraft carriers.

(T3M-2) Span: 17.25 m (56 ft 7 in) *Length:* 12.6 m

(41 ft 4 in) *Gross weight:* 4310 kg (9503 lb) *Maximum speed:* 175 km/h (109 mph) at sea level

(T4M-1) Span: 16.15 m (53 ft) *Length:* 10.85 m (35 ft 7 in) *Gross weight:* 3661 kg (8071 lb) *Maximum speed:* 183 km/h (114 mph) at sea level

(TG-2) Span and *Length:* as T4M-1 *Gross weight:* 4189 kg (9236 lb) *Maximum speed:* 204 km/h (127 mph) at sea level

T-IVW, Fokker

Dutch twin-float twin-engined seaplane. Twelve were ordered from the Fokker company by the Dutch navy in 1926. The first made its maiden flight on June 7, 1927, and the remaining machines were delivered soon afterwards. In its original form the mixed-construction T-IVW was powered by two 450-hp Lorraine Dietrich water-cooled engines. It had open bow and midships gunners' cockpits, and side-by-side open cockpits for the pilot and copilot immediately in front of the leading edge of the shoulder wing. A third defensive gun position was located in a stepped position in the underside of the fuselage. The T-IVW had a large single fin and rudder and a strut-braced horizontal tailplane. Defensive armament normally comprised three single 7.9-mm (0.311-in) machine-guns, but twin mountings were sometimes fitted over the bow and dorsal cockpits. There was provision for up to 900 kg (1984 lb) of bombs.

The orginal T-IVWs, serialled T-1 to T-12, operated mainly in the Dutch East Indies where they gave long and faithful service. Their reputation for reliability was such that in 1935 the design was revised and modernized, 12 T-IVWa aircraft, serials T-13 to T-24, being ordered by the Dutch navy. More powerful 750-hp Wright Cyclone SR-1820-F52 radials were installed and the design was generally revised to achieve improved aerodynamic form and greater structural strength. The pilot's cabin was enclosed and set in a raised fairing above the original top fuselage line; glazed panels were fitted in the nose and the dorsal gun was enclosed in a manually operated turret. Most machines also had a nose turret. Maximum offensive

load remained 18 50-kg (110-lb) bombs, with a torpedo as an alternative. Maximum range was raised from 1100 km (684 miles) to 1560 km (969 miles).

Eleven of the type were still engaged on regular patrol duties, operating out of Morokrembangan seaplane station, when Japan invaded the Dutch East Indies in January 1942. They were utilized mainly for air-sea rescue and reconnaissance work around Soerabaya, the main Dutch naval base in the Far East. None survived the Japanese occupation. Two were sunk at Soerabaya on February 3, 1942, and all remaining Dutch floatplanes in the East Indies were scuttled on March 1, 1942.

(T-IVW) Span: 25.8 m (84 ft 8 in) *Length:* 17.6 m (57 ft 9 in) *Gross weight:* 6700 kg (14 771 lb) *Maximum speed:* 200 km/h (124 mph)

(T-IVWa) Span: 26.4 m (86 ft 7 in) *Length:* 17.8 m (58 ft 5 in) *Gross weight:* 7200 kg (15 873 lb) *Maximum speed:* 260 km/h (162 mph)

T-V, Fokker

Dutch heavy bomber aircraft. The Fokker T-V was originally intended to meet a Dutch military air arm (LVA) twin requirement for a long-range fighter which could also operate as a bomber. The fighter concept was soon, however, abandoned and 16 T-Vs were ordered in 1935. As with most other Dutch military aircraft orders in the interwar period, no prototype as such was built and the first flight of the initial T-V delivered took place on October 16, 1937. Although not possessing outstanding manoeuvrability, the T-V had a good performance for its time, reaching an impressive maximum speed and cruising at an acceptable 348 km/h (216 mph). It was a monoplane of mixed construction with a mid-wing which had considerable dihedral outboard of the twin 925-hp Bristol Pegasus XVI radial engines. The deep, slab-sided fuselage had a flat, glazed nose which accommodated the bomb aimer and a single 20-mm (0.79-in) Solothurn cannon on a free mounting. Behind the enclosed control cabin was a dorsal cockpit with a retractable windshield and covered by a sliding hatch. The dorsal gunner had a single 7.9-mm (0.311-in) FN-Browning machine-gun; other single Browning guns

A Fokker T-IVWa seaplane of the Royal Netherlands Air Force. Eleven of the type saw action in the Dutch East Indies patrolling and in an air-sea-rescue role operating from the seaplane station at Morokrembangan. None survived the Japanese occupation in early 1942

Fokker-VFW

were operated from the glazed tail cone fitted aft of the twin fins and rudders, from lateral windows and through a ventral trap. The bomb bay accommodated a 1000-kg (2205-lb) load. Main undercarriage legs retracted backwards to lie fully enclosed in the engine nacelles. The tail wheel was non-retractable.

When the Germans invaded the Netherlands on May 10, 1940, only nine T-Vs were serviceable, with the BomVa (bombing group) at Schiphol. They participated in a number of operations, aircraft serial 856 making an unsuccessful attack on the Moerdijk bridges over the Maas escorted by two Fokker G-1 twin-boom fighters. Other T-Vs attacked German aircraft on Waalhaven airfield with greater success. All but one of the T-Vs were destroyed during the German invasion, including at least one shot down by Dutch antiaircraft fire.

Span: 21 m (69 ft) *Length:* 16.5 m (54 ft 2 in) *Gross weight:* 7550 kg (16 645 lb) *Maximum speed:* 417 km/h (259 mph) at 3000 m (9842 ft)

A Fokker T-V heavy bomber escorted by two Fokker D XXI fighters. Nine T-Vs saw limited action against the Germans during the invasion of the Netherlands and Belgium in May 1940

T-6, North American US advanced trainer aircraft   See **Texan**

T-VIIIW, Fokker

Dutch bomber-reconnaissance floatplane. The Fokker T-VIIIW was built to a Dutch navy requirement of 1937 intended to find a replacement for the antiquated T-IVW floatplane. The first of an initial order for five T-VIIIW/G aircraft flew for the first time on February 22, 1939. The 'G' in the designation indicated that the aircraft was of mixed construction with the rear fuselage of wood. A further 26 aircraft were ordered by the Dutch naval air arm, the final 12 to be of all-metal construction and designated T-VIIIW/M.

The T-VIIIWs bore registrations R-1 to R-31, but by the time of the German invasion of the Netherlands in May 1940 only the first 11 had been delivered. The T-VIIIW was a medium-sized mid-wing monoplane with a long rounded nose, the upper half of which was glazed, and a long glazed canopy for the three crew members. Defensive armament comprised two FN-Browning 0.303-in (7.7-mm) machine-guns, one fixed to fire forward in the nose, offset to port, and the other on a free mounting in the rear of the raised crew canopy. The horizontal tailplane was mounted halfway up the single fin and was braced either side by a pair of V struts. The large twin floats were independently braced, and a long weapons bay accommodated a torpedo or 600 kg (1323 lb) of bombs. All initial production aircraft were powered by 450-hp Wright Whirlwind R-975-E3 radial engines.

The machines in Dutch service were used for antisubmarine patrols, operating from French bases after Holland had been overrun. Eight later took refuge in England, where they formed 320 (Dutch) Squadron RAF. During 1940 three aircraft were lost in operations, and by the end of the year the remainder had been taken out of service, largely due to lack of spares.

Production for the German Luftwaffe was continued at the Fokker factory. As well as the remaining 20 low-powered machines, five

examples originally intended for export to Finland, and powered by 890-hp Bristol Mercury XIs, also went into service for reconnaissance and air-sea rescue duties over the North Sea and the Mediterranean, the latter with 1/S.A.Gr.126. The Finnish contract had originally called for aircraft capable of being fitted with wheel, ski, or float undercarriages. One aircraft was originally completed as the T-VIIIL with fixed landing wheels.

Span: 18 m (59 ft 1in) *Length:* 15.2 m (49 ft 10 in) *Gross weight:* 4600 kg (10 141 lb) *Maximum speed:* 285 km/h (177 mph)

T-IX, Fokker

Dutch experimental heavy bomber. Although the prototype Fokker T-IX bomber flew for the first time on September 11, 1939, with the LVA registration 970, it was in fact intended for production to equip the air arm in the East Indies, replacing the Martin bombers which had been standard equipment there for several years. The T-IX retained the general mid-wing twin-fin-and-rudder configuration of the T-V, but was nevertheless an entirely new design of greater dimensions. It was of all-metal construction and was powered by

two 1375-hp Bristol Hercules radial engines. The fuselage was cut down aft of the dorsal- and ventral-gunners' positions. The nose turret and bomb-aimer's position were of entirely new design, and the tailplane had a different configuration from the T-V. There was a single machine-gun in each of the nose, dorsal and ventral positions and the bomb load of 2000 kg (4409 lb) was carried internally.

During tests the undercarriage collapsed, and in April 1940 the prototype collided with a hangar door. Thereafter no further flights took place. No steps had been taken to initiate quantity production before the German invasion put a stop to all development.

Span: 24.7 m (81 ft) *Length:* 16.1 m (52 ft 10 in) *Gross weight:* 11 200 kg (24 690 lb) *Maximum speed:* 440 km/h (273 mph)

T-10

Soviet heavy tank. The T-10 was the last of a family of heavy tanks built on the IS and KV chassis. In the early 1950s the existence of the T-10 was reported in the West and in 1957 a T-10M was identified, but these do not appear to have gone into mass production.

The first Fokker T-VIIIW floatplane (R-1), of which only 31 had been built by May 14, 1940

The T-10 was very similar to the IS-IV, but had an extra bogie on each side. It had a 122-mm (4.8-in) gun with 50 rounds, and the T-10 had a 12.7-mm (0.5-in) machine-gun, replaced by the 14.5-mm (0.57-in) gun in the T-10M. Front armour was angled to give the equivalent of 150 mm (5.9 in) at 60°. The suspension was by torsion bar with seven double road wheels, three return rollers and rear sprocket drive. An additional identification feature was a splash guard across the glacis plate which protected the driver from some of the effects of driving across rough country. On the T-10M the inverted-V glacis plate extends to the full width of the vehicle. The T-10M has a five-baffle muzzle brake whereas the T-10 has a two-baffle version.

(T-10M) *Weight:* 44.9 tonnes *Length:* 10.31 m (33 ft 10 in) *Width:* 3.51 m (11 ft 6 in) *Height:* 2.41 m (7 ft 11 in) *Armour thickness:* 273 mm (10.7 in) *Armament:* 1 122-mm (4.8-in) D-25 M-1943 (improved) DP, 50 rounds *Powerplant:* V-12 diesel, 690 hp at 2000 rpm *Speed:* 19 km/h (12 mph) *Range:* 225 km (140 miles) on road *Crew:* 4

T.22

German torpedo boat class, built 1941-44. The weakness of the *T.1* Class was their small size and weak gun armament, and so in 1939 a further 15 torpedo boats or light destroyers of enlarged design were authorized. *T.22-36* were all built by Schichau at Elbing and were very close to the destroyer category in other navies. Known erroneously to British intelligence as the 'Elbing' type they were flush-deckers with two widely spaced funnels, and had one gun forward and two aft.

As with the *T.1* Class they saw much action in the Baltic, North Sea and English Channel. *T.25* and *T.26* were sunk by gunfire from the British cruisers *Glasgow* and *Enterprise* in the Bay of Biscay on December 28, 1943. *T.29* was sunk by gunfire from three Canadian 'Tribal' Class destroyers off Ushant on April 26, 1944, while three days later *T.27* was driven ashore near by HMCS *Haida*; the wreck was subsequently destroyed by a British MTB and aircraft on May 7. On June 20, 1944, *T.31* was mined and then torpedoed by a Soviet MTB in the Gulf of Finland. *T.22, T.30* and *T.32* were all mined in Narva Bay on August 18, while *T.34* was mined west of Arcona on November 20. On August 24, *T.24* was driven ashore near Le Verdon by RAF rocket-firing aircraft. The last casualty was *T.36,* mined and bombed by aircraft off Swinemünde on May 4, 1945.

T.23 and *T.28* were seized by the Royal Navy and in 1946 became the French *Alsacien* and *Lorrain. T.35* became the US Navy's *DD.935* and was handed to France to be cannibalized for spares in 1947. *T.33* became the Soviet *Primierny* in 1946.

A repeat class, *T.37-51* was ordered in 1941 from Schichau but never came into service. The principal improvement was the provision of a director control tower on the bridge and better light AA. Only *T.37, T.38* and *T.39* were near to completion when the war ended, and they had to be scuttled. *T.38-43* were scuttled at Elbing in March 1945, while *T.44-51* were scrapped on the slip.

Displacement: 1294 tons (standard), 1754 tons (full load) *Length:* 102 m (334 ft 9 in) oa *Beam:* 10 m (32 ft 9 in) *Draught:* 3.2 m (10 ft 6 in) *Machinery:* 2-shaft geared steam turbines, 32000 shp=33.5 knots *Armament:* 4 10.5-cm (4.1-in) L/45 (4×1); 4 37-mm (1.46-in) AA (2×2); 7/9 20-mm (0.79-in) AA (1×4, 3/5×1); 6 53-cm (21-in) torpedo tubes (2×3) *Crew:* 206

T-26

Soviet light tank. The T-26 was one of the most widely produced AFVs before the Second World War. Its chassis, derived from the Vickers 6-ton, was first used for a twin-turret hull with two machine-guns, and then for a gun tank with one turret and a 37-mm (1.46-in) and then a 45-mm (1.77-in) gun. Other T-26s carried flame throwers. A large number were still in service when Germany invaded the Soviet Union in 1941, and they proved easy targets for the experienced German tank crews. The principal types are as follows:

T-26A-1 Two water-cooled Vickers 7.62-mm (0.30-in) machine-guns in twin turrets, bought from Vickers.
T-26A-2 Two air-cooled 7.62-mm machine-guns.
T-26A-3 One 12.7-mm (0.5-in) machine-gun in right-hand turret, one 7.62-mm in left-hand turret.
T-26A-4 One 27-mm (1.1-in) gun in right-hand turret, one 7.62-mm air-cooled machine-gun in left-hand turret.
T-26A-5 One 37-mm long-barrelled gun in right-hand turret, one machine-gun in left-hand turret.
T-26B-1 One 37-mm gun in early models; one 45-mm gun in later models.
T-26B-1 (V) Commander's model with frame radio antenna and radio in turret overhang. Two subsequent models of the commander's tank included small improvements such as pistol ports, AA machine-guns and lightweight bogie rollers.
AT-26 Artillery version of T-26B-1 with 76.2-mm (3-in) gun and coaxial 7.62-mm machine-gun for artillery support for cavalry tanks.
AT-1 Glider version of the T-26B-1 which had two small tail booms fitted to the rear hull and one-bay biplane wings. Flaps were used to reduce the landing speed.
T-26B-2 Improved turret, mounting a 45-mm gun and coaxial machine-gun. The commander's version had a welded turret.

The variations in the type reflected the local improvements by the different factories assigned to building these tanks.

OT-130, a flame-thrower version of the T-26B, saw action against the Japanese in Manchuria, and later against the Finns and finally the Germans. The main gun was replaced with flame equipment and was mounted in either a T-26B-1 turret or a T-26B-1 (V) commander's turret.

The T-26S, introduced in 1938, reflected the experience of tank fighting in the Spanish Civil War. It had an increased armour basis with electrically welded plates. The suspension was strengthened to carry the extra armour. The most important improvement was a conical turret with a machine-gun at the rear and pronounced overhang. All T-26Ss were equipped with radio. Some T-26Bs were retrofitted with the new turret, though retaining a frame antenna in contrast to the T-26S

which sported a whip antenna. The fuel capacity was increased, but despite these considerable improvements the interior layout was unchanged from that of the T-26B. Tanks fitted with elevation stabilizers for the 45-mm gun became T-26E. The T-26S hull was also used for a flame-thrower version, designated OT-133, which saw action in the Soviet-Finnish war. Like the other flame-throwing versions of the T-26 it had a compressed-air operated gun with 400 litres (90 Imp gal) of fuel in the turret on the left-hand side. Under good conditions the OT flame equipment could reach up to 36 m (40 yards).

The bridge-laying version of the T-26, the IT-26 was turretless, with a lightweight lattice-construction bridge fitted. In action the tank drove into the gap to allow the following vehicles to pass over it. Some T-26s were built with a box-like unarmoured personnel compartment in place of the turret and were used as artillery tractors.

(T-26A) *Weight:* 7.1-8.6 tonnes *Length:* 4.8 m (15 ft 9 in) *Width:* 2.39 m (7 ft 10 in) *Height:* 2.06 m (6 ft 9 in) *Armour thickness:* 15 mm (0.6 in) *Armament:* 2 7.62-mm (0.30-in) machine-guns *Powerplant:* GAZ T-26 8-cylinder gasoline, 88 hp *Speed:* 35 km/h (22 mph) *Range:* 140 km (87 miles) on road *Crew:* 3

(T-26B-2) *Weight:* 9.4 tonnes *Length:* 4.6 m (15 ft 1 in) *Width:* 2.45 m (8 ft 1 in) *Height:* 2.54 m (8 ft 4 in) *Armour thickness:* 16 mm (0.6 in) *Armament:* 1 45-mm (1.77-in) L/46 antitank gun, 165 rounds; 2 7.62-mm (0.30-in) machine-guns *Powerplant:* as T-26A *Speed:* 28 km/h (17.5 mph) *Range:* 346 km (215 miles) on road *Crew:* 3

(T-26S) *Weight:* 10.5 tonnes *Length:* 4.65 m (15 ft 3 in) *Width:* 2.44 m (8 ft) *Height:* 2.33 m (7 ft 8 in) *Armour thickness:* 25 mm (1 in) *Armament:* as T-26B-2 *Powerplant:* as T-26A *Speed:* 27 km/h (17 mph) *Range:* 346 km (215 miles) *Crew:* 3

T-28

Soviet medium tank. The T-28 prototype was designed and built at the Leningrad Kirov plant in 1932. It reflected the thinking of the period which envisaged some tanks as mobile gun platforms, 'independent' vehicles which would advance across a trench line and suppress enemy machine-gun and gun positions. Each tank would have three/five turrets armed with low- or high-velocity guns or machine-guns and would therefore be able to defend itself as well as attack. Experience in the West had shown that these vehicles were often too slow and cumbersome, and though there were a few available in 1939-40 they saw little action. The USSR, however, developed a number of marks of T-28, and they were committed against the Germans in 1941.

The first prototype with three turrets was armed with a 45-mm (1.77-in) gun in the main turret and two machine-guns mounted in the auxiliary turrets. Armour thickness varied between 30-20 mm (1.2-0.8 in) and it had a maximum speed of 60 km/h (37 mph). The production version had a 76.2-mm (3-in) gun in the main turret with one of the machine-guns in a ball mounting beside the gun. The centre of gravity was well forward, which enabled the tank to cross trenches up to 2.7 m (9 ft) wide. The three turrets could give a very wide spread of fire and the tank was a stable platform for the main gun. The engine and transmission were in a compartment to the rear of the hull behind a fire-proof bulkhead. The gasoline was stored in two armoured tanks above the tracks to minimize fire risk. The tank was gas-proof. The commander's model had a radio with frame antennae and smoke generators. Some tanks had a 45-mm gun in the right-hand subsidiary turret in place of a machine-gun.

A second model which appeared in 1933 had improved suspension which had 12 bogie rollers and four exposed track-support rollers. Known as the T-28A, it also had slightly thicker frontal armour.

The T-28B, which appeared in 1938-39, had a more powerful 76.2-mm Model L/10 (L/26) gun. Some models also had a machine-gun in the rear of the turret.

Experience in Finland showed that the earlier T-28s were unsatisfactory. The hull and turret armour was increased to 80 mm (3.15 in) and the sides and rear to 40 mm (1.6 in) by the addition of armoured 'screens', and all were rearmed with the new 76.2-mm gun. Thus modified, the T-28C performed satisfactorily in Poland in 1939 and in Finland in February 1940. All later models were equipped with radios and smoke generators.

A bridge-layer version was produced in limited numbers; it consisted of a lattice-construction bridge in place of the main turret. The two machine-gun turrets were retained in the hull. To launch the bridge the tank halted and the bridge was pushed forward over the hull. The operation could be carried out without the crew leaving the vehicle. A flame thrower, the OT-28, was reported by the Germans.

After suffering badly from tank and dive-bomber attacks in the early months of the war in the East the remaining T-28s were withdrawn. Production had ceased in 1940.

(T-28B) *Weight:* 31.5 tonnes *Length:* 7.45 m (24 ft 5 in) *Width:* 2.8 m (9 ft 2 in) *Height:* 2.82 m (9 ft 3 in) *Armour thickness:* 36-10 mm (1.4-0.4 in) *Powerplant:* M-17L Liberty V-12 gasoline, 500 hp *Armament:* 76.2-mm (3-in) L/26, 40 rounds; 3 7.62-mm (0.30-in) machine-guns *Speed:* 23 km/h (14.4 mph) *Range:* 177 km (110 miles) *Crew:* 6

T-28, North American US basic trainer and light attack aircraft **See Trojan**

T-29, Convair US trainer aircraft **See Samaritan**

T-34

Soviet tank. Many weapons have been favoured with the description 'war-winning' but few have deserved it as much as the Soviet T-34 tank. It made such an impression on the Germans that they considered building their own version, and when they encountered the US Sherman in large numbers called it 'the T-34 of the West'. Captured T-34s were operated by the Germans for antitank training and even in the field. The T-34's pioneering sloped armour held few shell traps, increasing its effectiveness. Though Soviet wartime tanks were generally very crudely finished, some lacking any opti-

cal equipment and requiring the gun to be laid by eye, they were effective nevertheless. Their wide tracks allowed them to cross snow and soft mud which was impassable for the German vehicles with their narrow tracks. Soviet tank losses did not reflect the quality of the equipment but rather the lack of crew training. During the fighting at Stalingrad the Tractor Works produced T-34s which drove off the production line into action, crewed by the men and women who had built them.

After the war the T-34 remained in service with the Soviet and Warsaw Pact forces and was first encountered in action by the West in Korea. The UN forces were more prepared for them than the Germans on the Eastern Front in 1941, who discovered that their 3.7-cm (1.46-in) antitank guns were so ineffective that they nicknamed them 'door knockers'. They were only stopped when the 8.8-cm (3.46-in) Flak 18 firing AP40 shot was brought forward, and even 10.5-cm (4.1-in) leFH 18 field guns were pressed into service, firing shells intended for use against reinforced concrete. Eventually the Germans developed some very powerful antitank guns which were effective against Soviet armour, and their work on the Panther and Tiger was pressed forward with greater urgency.

The T-34 began its career in August 1939.

The Soviet Main Military Council accepted a design by a team headed by Mikhail Koshkin and Alexsandr Morozov and assisted by Nikolai Kucherenko, who designed the hull. Koshkin died in September 1940, but Morozov survived to receive the title Hero of Soviet Science and see 39 698 T-34 tanks built up to the end of the war.

The first production T-34/76A had a rolled-plate turret and a short 76.2-mm gun mounted in a distinctive cast contoured cradle welded to a flush external mantlet. The first 115 produced had a ball-mounted DT machine-gun in the turret rear as well as the hull gun. The hull was welded throughout with only three different thicknesses of armour plate. There was only one bulkhead separating the fighting and engine compartment. There was no turret basket and the fighting compartment led directly onto the driving compartment. The wheels varied during the war: some had steel-tired bogie wheels, others rubber-tired wheels, and some had a mixture. The suspension was of Christie type, with five large double road wheels with a gap between the second and third wheels. Drive came from a sprocket at the rear. The tracks were designed for quick removal.

The engine mounted in the rear was identical to that of the KV tank. A V-12 water-

Above: The T-34/76A medium tank with its distinctive cast contoured cradle welded to the flush external mantlet. *Below:* A T-34/76B the second production T-34 with a welded turret, the commander showing clearly the problems of the large turret hatch as he peers around it.

The T-34/85 was first issued to the elite Guards Armoured Divisions in the spring of 1944. It mounted an 85-mm (3.35-in) gun derived from the prewar M-1939 85-mm AA gun. The Russians claimed that with an Arrowhead AP round the T-34/85 could penetrate the 100-mm frontal armour of a Panther

cooled diesel developing 493 hp at 1800 rpm, it was derived from the engine intended for the BT-7M tank. There was trouble with early transmission assemblies and it was not uncommon to see a tank going into action with a spare transmission unit secured to the engine-compartment deck.

The chief defect in the design was the turret which had a considerable overhang and a large hatch. The hatch, which occupied almost the entire rear half of the turret, blocked the commander's view and left an opening big enough through which a cool-headed soldier could throw a grenade. If the hatch was closed an alternative tactic was to climb onto the hull and wedge a Teller mine under the overhang. Both these defects were removed from later models.

The T-34/76B which appeared in 1941 was a commander's version of the model A. Its main armament was a more powerful M1940 76.2-mm L/41.5 gun which was mounted in an angular bolted gun cradle which became standard in later models.

The T-34/76C was an improved model B with a cast turret. It had two hatches for the commander and gunner in place of the large single turret hatch. An improved hull machine-gun was installed, with twin episcopes for the driver in place of the single one, and the right-hand periscope was removed from the turret. Improved webbed and studded tracks were introduced.

The T-34/76D had a radically different turret, a cast hexagonal design which had no vulnerable overhang. The gun cradle was modified with a flush mantlet which rode in a prominent bulge at the turret front.

The T-34/76E had a new cupola which gave improved observation when the tank was closed down. The lubrication and air-cleaning system was improved.

The T-34/76F was the last production model of the T-34 76-mm gun tank. The turret was a cast version of the Model D. The major change was in the engine and transmission. The main clutch was improved and the four-speed gearbox replaced with a five-speed type, which made for easier gear changing and a faster tank. Cast wheels and an improved track were added, and this increased the speed which had hitherto fallen with each successive mark.

The T-34/85-I was designed in the summer of 1943. In place of the 76-mm gun it mounted a gun derived from the 85-mm (3.35-in) M-1939 AA gun. The tank was based on an improved T-34 (designated T-43) which retained the original armament. The turret ring of the T-34/85-1 was larger, which allowed an extra crew member to assist the commander and gunner. Soviet historians state that the T-34/85-I was superior to the Panther, but battlefield performance should also be judged in the light of the numbers produced: the Soviet factories were making 2½ T-34/85-Is for every Panther.

After the war a T-34/85-II appeared with improved transmission, armour arrangement and sophisticated fire-control and vision devices. It saw extensive service in Korea and remained in production during 1947-64. Some 12 000 were built and supplied to Soviet and allied armies.

Given the enormous number of T-34 chassis available, it is not surprising that it was used for bridging, tank recovery, mine clearing and as a flame thrower. Turretless versions with a boom were built as ARVs and cranes for mobile workshops. They were designated TT-34 and were derived from the SU-85, SU-100 and SU-122 as well as the T-34 gun tank. In addition to the boom they had earth anchors and winches.

During the war some T-34s were equipped with fascines and heavy matting to assist crossing antitank ditches and trench lines. However it was not until after the war that T-34 bridging tanks were developed. These included a rigid ARK type which was driven into the gap and adjusted according to the banks. The T-34/MTU had a 12-m (39 ft 6-in) lattice-steel bridge which could be launched over a roller and boom at the front. The bridge could take loads of up to 40 tonnes. A Czech scissor-type bridge was hydraulically operated by a motor within the turret and could span 20 m (65 ft) and carry 35 tonnes.

T-34s were also adapted as mine clearing vehicles with rollers, snakes or bulldozer blades. There were two roller-equipped tanks, one with a single axle with A-shaped beaters attached to the edges of the discs, while the split-axle version was designated T-34/PT-3. The snake-equipped tank either fired an explosive filled hose or pushed a

Bangalore torpedo across wire or minefield obstacles.

Most models of the T-34 were fitted with a manual or hydraulic bulldozer blade which could be used for mine clearing or general engineering work. T-34/STUs, as these were known, were particularly useful clearing snow. They retained their main armament and so were often used to spearhead the Soviet assaults during the winter of 1941-42 and 1942-43.

Flame-throwing versions followed the British practice of retaining the main gun and mounting the flame gun in the hull. The first flame system ATO-41 was replaced by the ATO-42; the earlier system had 100 litres (22 Imp gal) capacity while the OT-34 (ATO-42) held 200 litres (44 Imp gal). It could reach 80-90 m (89-98 yards) with unthickened fuel and under ideal conditions, with thickened fuel, up to 110 m (120 yards). The flame gun was in the hull machine-gun position and operated by electric pump with a 20-mm (0.79-in) cartridge for ignition. The gun had a 5° traverse off centre and had six two-second shots.

Some T-34s were equipped for deep wading with a sealed hull and breathing tube for the engine and crew compartments.

(T-34/76A) *Weight:* 26.7 tonnes *Length:* 6.58 m (21 ft 7 in) *Width:* 3 m (9 ft 10 in) *Height:* 2.44 m (8 ft) *Armour thickness:* 45-15 mm (1.8-0.6 in) *Armament:* 1 76.2-mm (3-in) L/30.5 (Mod 38) *Powerplant:* V-2-34 V-12 diesel, 500 hp at 1800 rpm *Speed:* 50 km/h (31 mph) *Range:* 450 km (280 miles) on roads with additional fuel tanks *Crew:* 4

(T-34/76C, D, E, F) *Weight:* 31.4 tonnes *Length:* 6.58 m (21 ft 7 in) *Width:* 3 m (9 ft 10 in) *Height:* (C) 2.58 m (8 ft 5 in); (D, E, F) 2.44 m (8 ft) *Armour thickness:* 70-18 mm (2.8-0.7 in) *Armament:* 1 76.2-mm (3-in) L/41.2 (Mod 40) *Powerplant:* V-2-3-34 V-12 diesel, 500 hp at 1800 rpm *Speed:* 50 km/h (31 mph) *Range:* 370 km (230 miles) on roads with additional fuel tanks *Crew:* 4

(T-34/85-I, II) *Weight:* 32 tonnes *Length:* 7.5 m (24 ft 7 in) *Width:* 3 m (9 ft 10 in) *Height:* 2.38 m (7 ft 10 in) *Armour thickness:* 75-18 mm (2.8-0.7 in) *Armament:* 1 85-mm (3.35-in) M-1944 ZIS-S53 L/51.5 *Powerplant:* V-2-3-34 V-12 diesel, 500 hp at 1800 rpm *Speed:* 50 km/h (31 mph) *Range:* 355 km (220 miles) on roads with additional fuel tanks *Crew:* 5

T-34, Beechcraft US training aircraft
See **Mentor**

Men of the Royal New Zealand Artillery with a dump of 18-pdr shells near Albert in September 1916. Coloured clips protect the base of the shell cases and indicate the nature of the shell—HE, Gas or Smoke. The tapes assist gunners unloading the limber

Cartridges for artillery weapons come in two basic forms: the cased type, contained in a metal (usually brass) case, or the bagged type, the propellant being carried in a tubular cloth bag. The type of cartridge a particular gun uses is dependent on many factors, but as a general rule cased and bagged charges are used respectively above and below 152-mm (6-in) calibre.

Cased charges

The primary reason for having a cartridge case is to seal the rear end of the gun, so that all the explosive gas generated by the propelling charge is usefully employed in pushing the shell out of the muzzle. Using a case makes the design of the breech mechanism easier, since the gun designer does not have to concern himself with making a gas-tight seal, this being attended to by the case. This advantage was so persuasive to the German designers that they employed cased charges right up the scale to the very largest weapons; even the massive 80-cm (31.5-in) 'Gustav' gun used a metal case, which was 130 cm (51.2 in) long and 96 cm (37.8 in) in diameter.

In addition to its sealing task, the metal case also preserves the charge from damp, carries the method of ignition, and can be used to position or even ram the shell into place. Set against these advantages are the drawbacks: the metal case is heavy, it uses up precious raw materials, and time and effort are consumed in transporting it back to the factory to be either refilled or melted down to be remade.

In an endeavour to ease the raw material problem, the Germans developed a number of designs of steel cartridge cases during the Second World War. Since steel has different properties from brass, simply taking a brass case design and producing it in steel was not good enough, and composite cases were produced with solid case heads and spirally-wrapped thin steel bodies which would expand on firing to seal the chamber but which would then contract so as to be easily extracted. Similar designs were developed in Britain and the US. The British designs were never put into service, but the US designs were extensively used. Since the war, work has been done on plastic and glass-fibre cases, though without much success.

Cased cartridges may be subdivided into three classes. Firstly the 'fixed round' in which the case and shell are firmly attached to each other—rather like an overgrown rifle cartridge—and are loaded in one piece. This is particularly advantageous when a high rate of fire is required, together with rapid and fumble-free loading, as, for example, in antiaircraft and antitank guns.

The second class is the separate round, in which shell and cartridge are two distinct units and are loaded in sequence. This is advantageous when the complete round would be too big or heavy to be easily handled, or where it is necessary for the gunner to have access to the propelling charge so as to be able to adjust it before firing.

The third class is a compromise, known as the 'semi-fixed' round, in which the shell is a push-fit into the mouth of the cartridge case. It can be removed to allow the gunner to adjust the charge, but is then replaced and the complete round loaded as one unit. Examples of these are the British 3.7-in (94-mm) and 90-mm (3.5-in) antiaircraft guns for fixed, the 25-pdr for separate, and the 105-

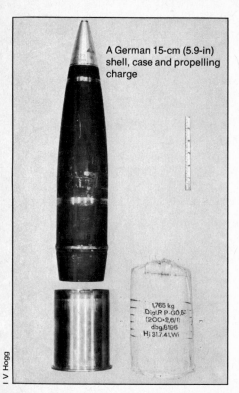

A German 15-cm (5.9-in) shell, case and propelling charge

1,765 kg
Dig!R P-G0,5¹
(200x2,6/1)
dbg.8196
Hi 31.7.41.Wi

mm (4.1-in) US howitzer for semi-fixed cases.

The propelling charge itself is of smokeless powder. During the Second World War most British powder was 'Cordite', a mixture of nitro-cellulose and nitro-glycerine formed into long cords. These could be bundled together to the required weight and placed in the cartridge quite simply. American, German and Russian propellant was a nitro-cellulose mixture made up in the form of 'grains', short cylindrical portions generally perforated so as to control their burning and thus obtain the desired ballistic characteristics. The size of the grain varied with the gun: for a 76-mm (3-in) weapon they might be about 10-mm (0.39-in) long and 3 mm (0.1-in) in diameter; for heavy guns, up to 30 mm (1.2 in) long and 10-mm diameter. These grains would simply be poured into the case and the shell inserted on top. Where adjustable charges were needed the propellant would be placed in small bags, colour-coded or numbered, and these placed in the case. To adjust the charge to give lesser range or a different trajectory, the gunner could remove certain of the bags to give the combination he required.

The charge in the case was ignited by a 'primer', screwed or pressed into the base of the case. This contains a sensitive explosive and, usually, a charge of gunpowder. When the cap of the primer is struck by the firing pin of the gun, or in some cases given a surge of electric current, the sensitive material ignites, setting off the gunpowder, and this in turn ignites the smokeless powder.

Bagged charges

Bagged charges are simply the requisite amount of smokeless powder contained in a cloth bag. The selection of the cloth is important, since it must preserve the contents from damp but at the same time be easily consumed in the explosion so that no smouldering shreds are left in the gun after firing. Should such shreds be left, there is the danger that they might ignite the next cartridge when it is loaded and before the breech can be closed. Heavy coast and naval guns frequently incorporate a 'wash-out' jet through which water is sprayed into the gun chamber as soon as a shot has been fired and before the breech is opened, so as to quench any lingering portions.

Cordite was easy to make up into bagged charges, since the sticks could be bundled and they were rigid, enabling the charge to be easily handled. Granular powder is less handy for the gunner, though easier to fill in the factory, and in large calibres it can mean

British 3.7-in AA guns in action against German positions on the Gothic Line in Italy. A quick-fire mission in support of an infantry and tank attack consumes large amounts of ammunition, as these positions show. Antiaircraft guns were used in a ground role at the end of the Second World War when the Luftwaffe had ceased to be a threat to Allied ground forces

a floppy bundle which is hard to handle. When it is necessary to adjust charges, as with howitzers, the charge is subdivided into a number of smaller bags which are supplied tied together in one unit; the gunner can then untie and remove those bags which he does not require.

Bagged charges are ignited by a 'tube' or 'primer' which resembles a rifle's blank cartridge and is inserted into a small breech mechanism, known as the firing lock, attached to the gun's breech block. From this lock a vent or tube leads through the breech to the gun chamber, so that when the lock is operated it fires the primer (either by a firing pin or by electricity) and the flash passes through the vent to the gun chamber to strike the bag of the charge. To ensure thorough ignition the bag charge always has an 'igniter', a flat package of gunpowder stitched to its base end so that the gunpowder is struck by the flash from the tube.

The bagged charge cannot seal the gun breech, and this had to be done by the breech mechanism. This is usually carried out by a resilient pad which presses firmly against the rear end of the gun chamber. In most cases it is so designed that when the charge is exploded the pad is pressed even more firmly in place, so that leaks of gas around this type of breech are extremely rare.

Above, left to right: Shell cases for the 15-cm leFH, brass, wrapped steel and built-up steel.
Below: The case and (bottom) shells and shaped ballistic caps for the German 38-cm Max E gun

A Royal Marine gunner with a 15-in shell near Acheux in July 1916. Slogans were not standard

As gunners never tire of pointing out, it is the shell which is the weapon of the artillery and not the gun, and during the course of the present century a great deal of work has been done in developing shells of greater efficiency in order to widen the operational scope of the artillery arm.

First World War

At the start of the First World War two shells were standardized in most armies; a shrapnel shell for field guns, to be used for antipersonnel tasks, and a high-explosive shell for howitzers, to be used for antimaterial tasks.

The only other projectile given consideration was the high-explosive armour-piercing shell used with coast defence artillery and intended for the attack of warships.

The shrapnel shell consisted of a number of lead-antimony balls packed inside a hollow casing. Beneath them was a small charge of gunpowder, and the shell was completed by fitting a time fuze. This was set by the gunner so as to burst the shell above and in front of the enemy troops. As the fuze functioned, it ignited the gunpowder charge, and the explosion of this blew the balls out of the shell body in a shot-gun effect. As might be imagined, this gave excellent results against unprotected columns of troops. In 1915, however, the troops disappeared into trenches and took advantage of overhead cover, and the shrapnel shell became less effective.

In order to overcome light cover, the high-explosive shell began to assume greater importance. This was simply a steel casing packed with high explosive and fitted with an impact fuze. Beneath the fuze would be an 'exploder system' of carefully selected explosive substances calculated to react to the detonation of the fuze and then amplify this impulse to ensure effective detonation of the main filling. It will be appreciated that the acceleration when a shell is fired places considerable strain upon the shell's contents, and the selection of the explosive to go into

A British 60-pdr shrapnel shell. Fitted with a time fuze, it was designed to scatter its contents of about 1000 balls in a downward cone. Against troops in the open, shrapnel was deadly, but once under overhead cover, infantry could survive even the heaviest shrapnel bombardment

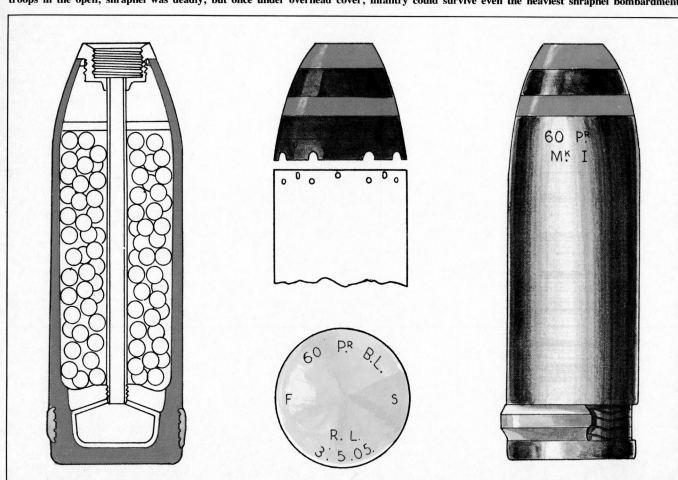

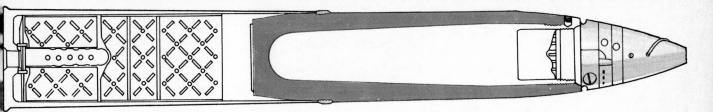

An American 75-mm HE shell M48 showing the Primer M1B1A2, Case M5A1 and the fuze Time and Super-Quick M54 with booster M20A1

the shell must be done with this stress in mind: too sensitive an explosive will result in premature functioning, while too inert an explosive will raise difficulties in transferring the fuze impulse. The general choice for a high-explosive shell filling during the First World War was TNT, but due to production problems various adulterated mixtures such as Amatol (a mixture of TNT and Ammonium Nitrate) were adopted.

The choice of explosive for the antiship armour-piercing shell was even more difficult, since the object of these shells was

A British 18-pdr QF phosphorus smoke shell

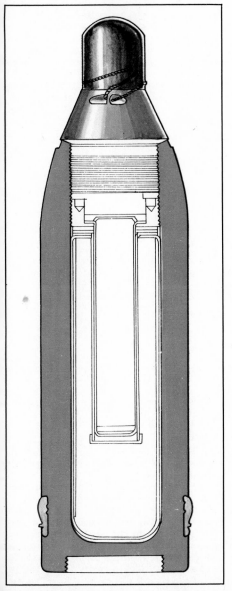

to penetrate a considerable thickness of armour *before* detonating; therefore the explosive had to be particularly resistant to the sudden deceleration as the shell struck the armour. Picric Acid or Ammonium Picrate were generally chosen for this application.

An interesting compromise adopted by the German army prior to 1914 was the Universal Shell, a shrapnel in which the balls were packed in powdered TNT. When used with a time fuze in the normal way, the powdered TNT was ignited and gave a puff of smoke, useful for spotting. If, however, the fuze was set to percussion and used as an impact fuze, it then detonated the TNT to burst the shell and scatter the fragments and balls as well as giving blast effect. Like most compromises it failed to completely fill the bill in either role, and the additional expense led to its rapid abandonment under the pressures of wartime ammunition expenditure.

The shells of this period were generally

An American M84 base-ejection smoke shell

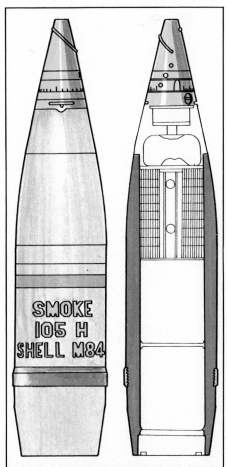

SMOKE
105 H
SHELL M84

blunt-nosed and square-based, largely for ease of manufacture and in order to get the maximum explosive inside them. But wartime experiments showed that by tapering the nose and base—'streamlining' shells—it was possible to make considerable improvements to accuracy and maximum range without making any alterations to guns or propelling charges. This development was continued in postwar years, so that by 1939 the streamlined shell was in almost universal use.

The First World War also saw the start of the 'carrier' shell, a shell designed to carry some substance or device to its point of application and there release it, the actual shell then being discarded and having no tactical effect. The first of these was the smoke shell, intended to release smoke clouds to conceal the movement of troops. This was achieved by taking a high-explosive shell body and filling it with white phosphorus which, when released by bursting open the shell on impact, would spontaneously ignite on contact with the air and give a cloud of dense white smoke.

Next came the gas shell; working along the same lines as the smoke shell, but the nature of the contents (usually highly corrosive and, if not lethal, certainly incapacitating) meant that the shells had to be carefully lined, sometimes with glass, and sealed to prevent the contents from leaking during storage and transport.

A third class of shell brought into prominence during 1914-18 was the star (now known as 'illuminating') shell. This originally contained a number of pyrotechnic candles which were released in the sky by bursting the shell by means of a time fuze.

During the interwar years a great deal of development took place to iron out the defects in wartime shell designs. The phosphorus smoke shell, for example, developed a great deal of heat as it burned; this heated the surrounding air which then rose, carrying the smoke with it, so that instead of a low-lying cloud the 'screen' became a series of dispersed pillars. The high-explosive shells, due to failure to match the contents with the grade of steel used for the casing, gave large jagged fragments; whereas the ideal would be a large number of small but lethal fragments. The pyrotechnic candle type of star shell did not give sufficient light and did not last very long after bursting.

The solution to the carrier problem was worked out by the British Chemical Warfare research station at Porton in the early 1930s and became known as the 'base ejection' shell. Instead of using phosphorus as a smoke compound, a mixture of hexachlorethane and zinc was pressed into steel containers. These were then placed inside a hollow shell body and retained there by a lightly-screwed-in baseplate. The nose of the shell carried a time

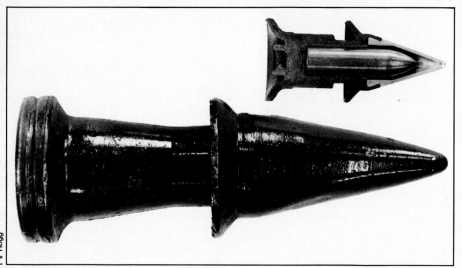

A German Panzergranate 40 tungsten-cored antitank shot showing its sabot configuration

A German 15-cm (5.9-in) fin-stabilized 'mine shell' developed towards the end of the war

An American M67 HEAT shell which uses the shaped charge principle to penetrate armour

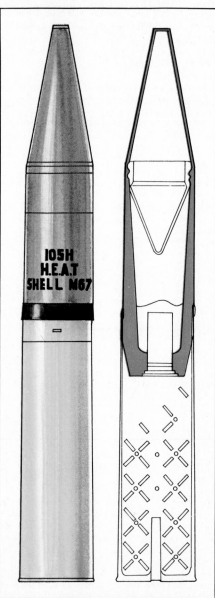

105H
H.E.A.T
SHELL M67

fuze and a gunpowder expelling charge; in many respects it was like a shrapnel shell turned upside down. When the time fuze functioned, it lit the gunpowder charge, which exploded. This lit the smoke compound in the canisters and also blew out the baseplate and ejected the canisters, which fell to the ground. There they burned, giving off dense white smoke, but with a cooler reaction than that of phosphorus and thus the smoke clung to the ground to give a more effective screen.

In a similar fashion, the star shell was made by taking the same body and inserting a metal container and a parachute. The metal canister held a brightly burning magnesium composition which was ignited by the gunpowder charge as both canister and parachute were ejected.

Second World War

The Second World War brought new types of shell into the field in order to satisfy particular demands. Most of them (incendiary for setting fire to buildings or standing crops, coloured flare for marking targets at night, coloured smoke for the same task by day, propaganda for dispersing leaflets) were little more than adaptations of the base ejection principle. One application, however, demanded fresh thinking: that was the attack of tanks. First thoughts on this led to scaled-down armour-piercing shells based on the designs used for the attack of ships; pointed, hard steel, with a small filling of high explosive in the base and a base fuze. Some armies, notably the British, felt that the

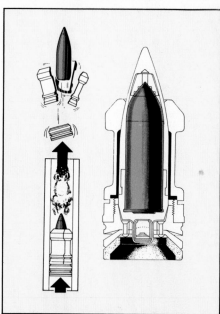

An APDS shell showing the effect of the sabot. The energy of the propellent charge is concentrated behind the alloy or plastic sabot which encloses the hardened shot. When the gun fires the shot and sabot are driven up the barrel until they reach the muzzle. Here the sabot sections fall away and the smaller shot continues propelled by the energy of the charge that was behind the sabot sections. On hitting a tank the kinetic energy of the shot is therefore greatly enhanced particularly if the shot is tungsten-hardened

complications of putting high explosive and fuzes into small shells were not worth the effort, and they relied almost entirely upon inert steel shot to smash into the tank and damage it by ricochetting around inside as well as breaking off pieces of the tank's armour to act as missiles. But as tank armour became thicker and the guns they mounted became more powerful, engagement ranges became longer so that the simple answer no longer sufficed and new methods of dealing with the new generation of tanks had to be found.

The attack of tanks resolved itself into two methods: kinetic energy and explosive energy. The kinetic energy attack meant throwing a hard substance as fast as possible to smash through the plate. Steel could no longer do the job, and tungsten carbide became the universal material. Since this was much heavier than steel it was necessary to make composite projectiles in which a tungsten core was supported by a lightweight body so as to permit high velocities to be attained. These were known as Panzergranate 40 to the Germans, AP Composite Rigid to the British, and Hyper-velocity AP to the Americans. They were effective at short and medium ranges but less so at long ranges due to the progressive falling-off of the projectile's velocity.

The answer was to modify the shape of the projectile somehow. It had to be large in diameter and light in weight as it accelerated up the gun barrel, but small in diameter and heavy as it flew through the air so as to retain its velocity and striking power. The first solution was provided by the German taperbore guns which squeezed the shot diameter down during its travel up the gun barrel. This was effective but demanded extremely careful manufacture of both shot and gun barrel. The better solution was the British Discarding Sabot shot in which the tungsten core was supported in the barrel by a light alloy sleeve which, as the shot left the muzzle, was discarded, leaving only the tungsten to fly to the target propelled by the full force of the exploding cartridge.

The chemical energy attack was used in guns which could not attain high velocities, generally field and medium guns which required an antitank projectile for self-protection. The hollow-charge shell was widely used by Germany, Russia and the US in this application. Here the shell had a hollow nose concealing a metallic cone backed by an explosive charge. On impact with the tank, the explosive blast was focused by the cone; at the same time the cone metal was melted, and a fast-moving stream of gas and molten metal blasted a hole through the armour. Although widely used, particularly by Germany, experience showed that spun shells were not the best vehicle for hollow charge, since centrifugal force dispersed the jet's effect. In the latter stages of the war hollow charge was used more and more with fin-stabilized projectiles such as those of the Bazooka and Panzerfaust rocket launchers.

A more effective projectile was developed in Britain as the 'wallbuster' shell. This used a thin-walled shell to carry a filling of plastic high explosive, together with a base fuze. On striking the tank, the plastic HE was deposited on the armour like a poultice; the base

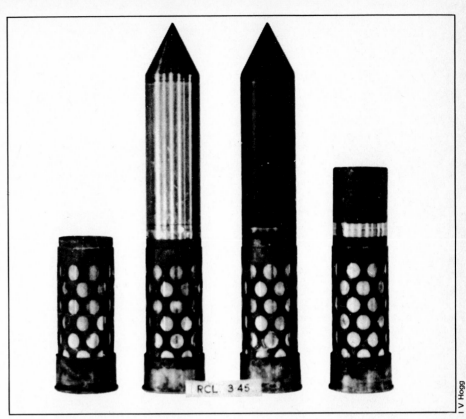

The cartridge case, wall-buster round, practice shot and proof shot developed for use in recoilless guns towards the end of the Second World War. The principle of the wall-buster shell was later used in 'squash-head' tank ammunition which proved very effective against AFVs

fuze then detonated it, and the shock wave, travelling through the thickness of the armour, tore off a sizeable slab from the inside face of the plate and whirled it around inside the tank.

In post-1945 years, the wallbuster was gradually improved to become the HESH or HE Squash-Head, known in US parlance as the HE-P for HE Plastic, and it is currently a secondary tank-destroying shell. The primary tank killer is still the discarding sabot shot, though present practice is to use depleted uranium as the core instead of tungsten, to give a heavier projectile.

Modern Development

In general, projectile development in the last thirty years has been relatively unsung, but great improvements have been made. The high-explosive shell has had its shape slightly improved so as to give better flight characteristics. Carrier shells, in general, have shown little change from wartime designs except in matters of detail. Recent developments include carrier shells which are loaded with small antitank or antipersonnel bombs, so as to be burst over troop concentrations at long ranges. In the antitank field, much work has gone into the development of fin-stabilized projectiles, both of hollow-charge pattern and discarding sabot. The prime object here is firstly to do away with the centrifugal degradation of the hollow-charge jet, and, in the case of APDS, to boost the velocity by using smoothbore guns. The greatest difficulty in both these fields has been to bring the accuracy of fin-stabilized projectiles up to that of spun projectiles.

Relative accuracy figures are among the most closely guarded secrets of current ammunition development, but the recently announced German adoption of a smoothbore 120-mm (4.7-in) gun for their latest main battle tank would seem to be an indication that the desired degree of accuracy has at last been achieved.

The most innovative postwar projectile has, of course, been the nuclear shell. The technical problems of containing the nuclear device within the restricted compass of an artillery shell, securing it against the acceleration forces, ensuring its absolute safety prior to firing and its absolute certainty of action on reaching the target have all been difficult to solve, but they have all been achieved. Fuzing of the nuclear shell has probably been the greatest difficulty, generally solved by highly complicated multiple fuzes. One difficulty has been that the nuclear shell, due to its shape, balance, and weight, ranges quite differently to any other projectile, and it has been necessary to develop equivalent spotting shells filled with an explosive and dye mixture and weighted and balanced identically with the nuclear shell. This spotting shell is fired in order to establish the range and fuze setting prior to firing the nuclear shell.

This brief survey is confined to what might be called 'conventional' shells insofar as these projectiles rely entirely on the propelling charge for their flight characteristics. It is possible to modify the shell trajectory and flight by rocket or ramjet assistance. These applications are covered in a separate entry under Rocket-assisted Shells.

See also Gerlich.

Fuzes

A gunner fuzes 5.5-in (140-mm) shells during a fire mission in Italy in the summer of 1944

Impact Fuzes

These fit into the nose or base of the shell and rely upon the deceleration of the shell as it strikes the target. In the simplest case, the nose fuze, a striker is poised above a detonator so that as the shell strikes, so this striker is forced back to hit the detonator. The impulse from this detonator is then passed to a larger charge of explosive, the 'magazine' of the fuze, which, in turn, detonates the shell filling. An alternative approach, used where slight delay is required so that the shell can penetrate light cover such as a house, is to mount the striker in a heavy metal block and allow this to be thrown forward by the sudden deceleration so that it strikes a fixed detonator. The time required for the block to travel forward gives a fraction of a second's delay to the functioning. It will be appreciated that this system is mandatory in base fuzes, since the positioning of the fuze prevents direct impact from being used.

Having determined these basic systems of operation, it is then necessary to introduce safety devices to prevent the striker or block moving under the effect of the shell's acceleration up the gun barrel when fired, or under the effect of the shell being dropped or roughly handled during transport. The most usual method is to interpose some sort of positive obstruction to the striker's travel and arrange for this to be withdrawn by the centrifugal force developed as the shell takes up spin during its passage through the gun's rifling. This is adopted since the high rate of spin can never be duplicated by any form of rough handling.

A refinement of this basic design is to introduce some form of adjustable delay into the fuze so that, for example, it can be used as an impact fuze against targets in the open, or as a delay fuze against targets with light protection. The most usual method of achieving this is to incorporate both the direct

A shell fuze has been described as 'a combination lock, the key to which is firing from a rifled gun', a definition which sums up the designer's problem.

In short, the fuze must burst the shell at the required place and time, but prior to that it must withstand every sort of shock or impulse due to handling, transport, and being fired from the gun.

These conflicting demands lead to a difficult design problem; not for nothing has one critic observed that the British make a safe fuze and then spend ten years trying to make it work, while the Americans make a fuze which works and then spend ten years trying to make it safe.

Fuzes fall into three categories: impact, time and proximity. They can be further subdivided into nose and base types, depending upon their position in the shell.

A Fuze, Percussion, Base, Large, Bronze, No 16 Mk IV (L). Versions of this fuze with a delay were effective against bunkers and trenches

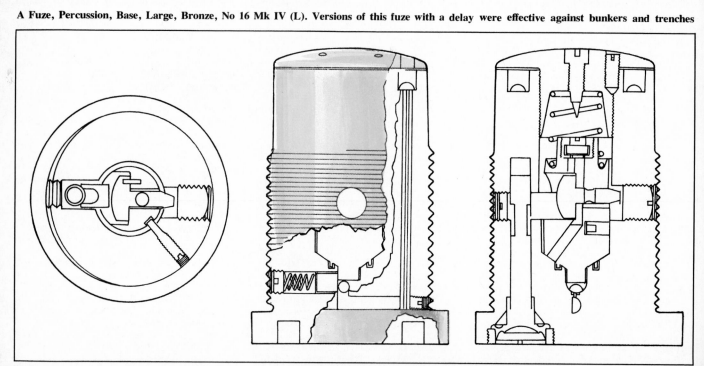

striker and the floating block into the fuze mechanism and then arrange to cut one of them out by some form of externally operated switch. In the US M51 series, for example, an external screw-head controls a centrifugal shutter. When set to Superquick, this shutter is withdrawn under spin and as the shell strikes, a needle in the nose is driven on to a detonator. This flashes down the centre of the fuze and sets off the fuze magazine. When set to Delay, the shutter is locked in place in the central channel and prevents the flash from reaching the magazine. Instead, a block, carrying a detonator, runs forward under deceleration, strikes a detonator which ignites a short channel of gunpowder, and this finally ignites a second detonator to set off the magazine. The effect of this is to delay the fuze operation by about 0.25 seconds.

Time Fuzes

Ever since the seventeenth century, time fuzes have relied upon the burning of a predetermined length of gunpowder, ignited by the explosion of the cartridge. With the advent of rifled guns the primitive beechwood peg with a length of powder down its centre was replaced by more sophisticated metal fuzes in which the gunpowder train was pressed into metal rings arranged around the centre stem of the fuze. One ring was fixed, the other moveable, and by moving this ring the total length of powder between an initiating detonator and the fuze magazine could be altered. On firing, the acceleration force caused a needle to 'set back' and strike a detonator, igniting the gunpowder train. This then burned round the rings until it met a powder-filled channel leading to the fuze magazine and thus set off the shell. The object behind all this was to burst the shell in the air, over the enemy's head, in order to shower him with shrapnel balls.

When the high-explosive shell began to

A Fuze, Percussion, Delayed Action No 117

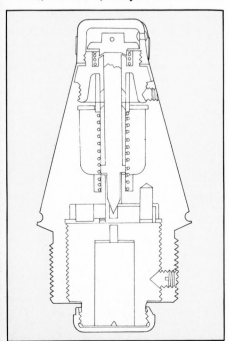

Fuzing shells for the first truck-mounted 18-pdr AA gun during an alert near Nieppe in 1914. *Below:* A typical time and percussion fuze made an effective proximity or impact shell

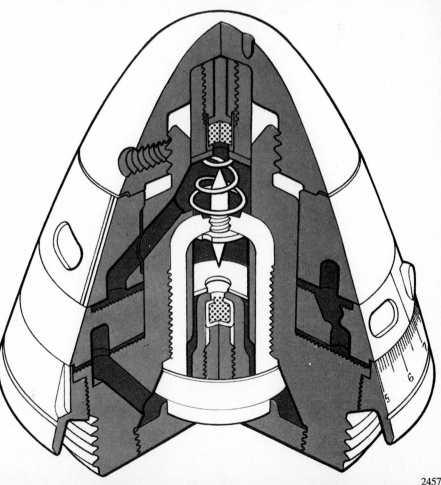

Fuzes

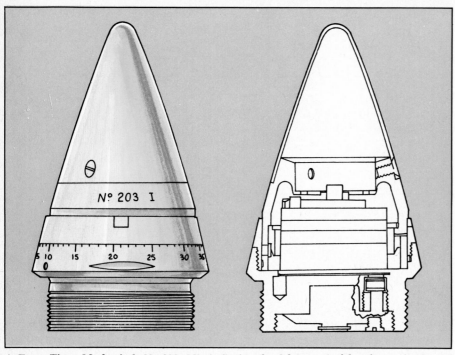

A Fuze, Time, Mechanical, No 203, Mk 1. Setting the delay was quick using a simple tool

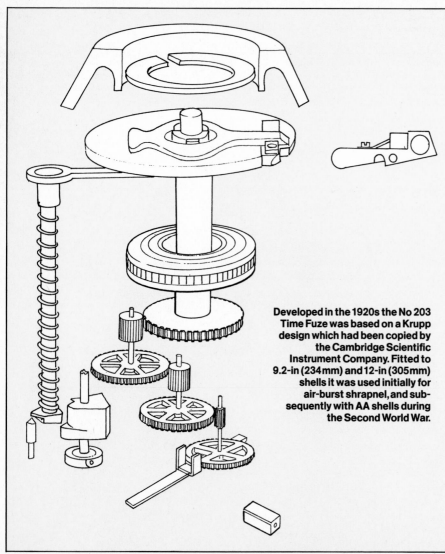

Developed in the 1920s the No 203 Time Fuze was based on a Krupp design which had been copied by the Cambridge Scientific Instrument Company. Fitted to 9.2-in (234mm) and 12-in (305mm) shells it was used initially for air-burst shrapnel, and subsequently with AA shells during the Second World War.

take over from the shrapnel, the time fuze went into a decline, since there seemed to be little object in bursting an HE shell in the air. But with the arrival of antiaircraft gunnery, the time fuze again became important and fuzes for use with high-explosive shell began to be designed. One great difference was the incorporation of safety devices, since a premature detonation with an HE shell was far more dangerous than one with a shrapnel shell.

Antiaircraft gunnery also revealed many defects of powder-burning fuzes which had not previously been apparent, largely because in this new application the fuze was passing through rarefied layers of air in the upper altitudes. This led to fuzes failing to operate since the powder failed to burn evenly. It also pointed up the considerable zone of error in such fuzes, due to the impossibility of making a length of gunpowder burn for precisely the same period every time. As a result, efforts were made to improve powders and, at the same time, to investigate other methods of making fuzes work.

Mechanical fuzes had attracted inventors for many years. One method of operation was the 'distance' fuze in which a train of gears counted the revolutions made by the spinning shell. If the rate of spin, due to the twist of rifling and velocity of the shell, was known, then it would be possible to correlate the number of turns made to the distance travelled, and thus arrange to burst the shell at the correct point. In theory this is true, but in practice it has never been made to work. The velocity is not constant after leaving the muzzle, the mechanism invariably jams under the acceleration force, and it is not possible to make a gear train sufficiently accurately to detect a single turn and detonate the shell precisely.

The only alternative is to use a conventional clock mechanism, a system pioneered by Krupp in the early years of this century. This was perfected and the German army introduced clockwork time fuzes in 1917 for long-range shrapnel firing against Allied observation balloons. The mechanism relies on a prewound clock spring, a train of gears, and a lever escapement to regulate the speed. At the end of the set time a striker is released to hit a detonator and set off the shell. By careful positioning of the gears and careful design of the bearing, centrifugal force and set-back effects are reduced to a minimum and the fuze can be made remarkably accurate—certainly much more accurate in its timing than a powder-filled fuze.

This type of fuze was widely adopted in the interwar years, but another type, developed by the German firm of Junghans, was also popular. This used the same basic gears and timing mechanism but relied upon two weights being flung outwards by centrifugal force to provide the motive power. In general, the British preferred the spring drive type, the Americans the centrifugal, while the Germans used both.

Other methods of operating time fuzes have been put forward from time to time, but few have proved practical. One system developed during the Second World War in Britain relied upon a resistor-condenser circuit. It is well known that if a suitable resistor and condenser are linked together and given

an electrical charge, they will form a timing device by virtue of the condenser's charge passing through the resistor. The time depends upon the values of the resistor and condenser and upon the voltage placed into the circuit. In the British Fuze, Time, No 717 this charge was given by a contact wire at the gun muzzle which wiped across the fuze as it left the gun. By setting a regulator against the desired time, the correct voltage was thus induced and the timing circuit activated. This fuze was introduced into the Royal Navy in small numbers, but its development was abandoned when the proximity fuze became a practical proposition.

Proximity Fuzes

The difficulties inherent in antiaircraft gunnery were many and varied, but one of the greatest was the problem of arranging for the shell to burst close to its target—for it was generally accepted that to try for a direct hit was impractical. Provided an HE shell could be burst within lethal distance, however, the effect on the target would be sufficient and

An early proximity fuze with its complex cells and batteries which have been replaced by smaller, more reliable printed circuits

Above: **Fuzing 13-pdr shells at St Vaast in March 1918. The mounting is a Mk IV Truck.** *Below:* **A 40-mm (1.57-in) Bofors proximity fuze bursts above a dummy missile. The missile shows approximately 250 penetrations. These shells are effective against sea-skimmers**

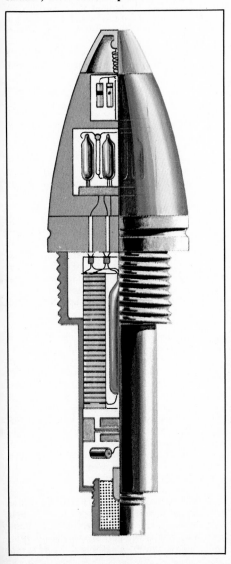

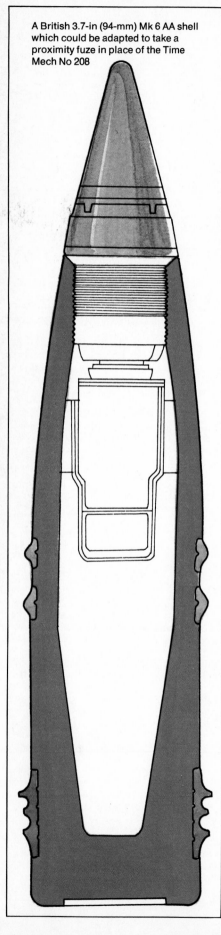

A British 3.7-in (94-mm) Mk 6 AA shell which could be adapted to take a proximity fuze in place of the Time Mech No 208

the gunnery would be easier. Time fuzes were the accepted solution, but they were not perfect, since the inherent tolerances in the mechanisms or in the burning powder meant that the shell might burst anywhere within 60-90 m (200-300 ft) of the set point on the trajectory. The ideal would be to have a shell which could detect the target and burst within lethal distance.

One of the first solutions offered was a Swedish design, published in 1938. In this the shell was fitted with lights shining outwards and with a fuze carrying photo-electric cells. The light was reflected from the target to strike the cells and thus function the fuze. Whether this idea was studied in Britain or not, the fact remains that at that time British designers had produced a prototype PE-cell fuze for rockets which relied upon the shadow of the aircraft to function the fuze, and this went into service in 1940. Rockets, however, presented less of a problem for fuze designers since they did not have the same acceleration forces, and attempts to fit a PE fuze into shells continued to prove unsuccessful.

At about the same period, British engineers developing radar began to study the prospect of a fuze which would pick up the tiny amount of energy reflected from the aircraft by the radar and use this to detonate the shell. At this stage of radar development, however, it demanded a truck-load of equipment to detect and amplify the radar reflection and, again, condensing this into a fuze was impractical. From this, thoughts turned to placing a complete radio transmitter and receiver unit into a fuze and using the fuze's own signals to reflect from the target. This promised better results and the design was thoroughly worked out theoretically, but by the time it was perfected in 1940, there was no hope of having it built in Britain since the entire British electronic industry was committed to work on radar.

In 1940 the Tizard Mission to the US took the proximity fuze plans and gave them to the Americans. The US Navy took charge of the development. Eastman Kodak became the prime contractors, with component development subcontracted to such firms as Sylvania, GEC and Exide. By early 1943 a working fuze was produced and in June of that year it was first used in combat when the USS *Helena* shot down a Japanese aircraft. After that it was brought into service for army AA guns, playing a vital part in the defence of Britain against FZG-76 (V-1) flying bombs in 1944. Antiaircraft batteries on the Channel coast, firing proximity-fuzed ammunition, accounted for large numbers of V-1s, and on the last day of large-scale flying bomb attacks 68 out of 90 which reached the coast were shot down. Proximity fuzes were later used in field artillery to give air-bursts with HE shells.

The proximity fuze as developed during the war was a large device which, though presenting the same outward shape to the nose of the shell as a conventional fuze, had a long shank which extended deep into the shell and thus demanded a special shell filling and reduced the amount of explosive. This was countered by using more powerful types of explosive. The size was due to the many components necessary. The head carried a transmitter and antenna, beneath this was the

receiver and firing circuitry, in the shank was a wet battery, and beneath this a number of electrical and mechanical safety devices and the fuze magazine. On firing, the shock broke a glass ampoule of acid inside the battery, which began delivering power to the various units. The transmitter sent out a signal, and, due to the design of the antenna, this signal's area covered the lethal area of the bursting shell, so that anything reflecting the signal stood to receive the benefit. The reflected signal was detected by the receiver, and as the reflection built up, indicating the proximity of the target, the circuit triggered the fuze at the optimum point. Should the fuze not come within lethal distance of a target, then a self-destruction device blew up the shell before it could come back to the ground. Fuzes designed for field artillery use incorporated an impact switch to detonate the shell as it struck the ground if it failed to function on reflection.

The wartime fuzes relied upon the state of the electronic art as it then was. They used glass valves and fairly large components. Since then, however, transistors and, more recently, integrated circuits, have allowed the designers to reduce the size of the proximity fuze until it is no larger than any other type. Currently, work is being done in several countries on developing a PPD (proximity-percussion-delay) fuze. This will, within one unit, cover all the required functions of impact, delay action or proximity and thus result in one single fuze which, by a simple adjustment, will be capable of doing almost every job.

Special-purpose Fuzes

While the standard fuzes outlined above will cater for the majority of tasks, there are occasions when fresh designs are needed to meet some peculiar demand. For example, contemporary hollow-charge shells are designed for use in smoothbore guns. In these cases, the standard artillery fuzes, which rely upon spin to arm, are useless. Moreover, a heavy fuze with large metal parts can interfere with the functioning of the hollow-charge jet. The almost universal solution to this is the piezo-electric fuze. Here a piezo-electric crystal is fitted in the tip of the shell and connected by wire to an electric detonator in the base of the explosive charge. The impact on the target crushes the crystal and this generates an electric current which is sufficient to set off the detonator. The active tip of this sort of fuze can be very small and thus will not interfere with the hollow-charge effect.

Probably the most unusual fuze ever to go into an artillery shell was the British Fuze No 620 developed in 1940. This resembled the standard Fuze Percussion No 117, but contained an ampoule of acid and a striker held by a thin wire. It was fitted into a shell, and the shell placed at the bottom of a stack. In the event of a hurried withdrawal, the protective cap of the fuze was screwed down tight, breaking the acid ampoule. This gradually eroded the safety wire until it failed, permitting the striker to go down on to the detonator. At anything between 48 and 72 hours after the stack had been abandoned, the fuze operated and the whole dump of ammunition was destroyed in the subsequent detonation.

Above: **The Coventry Ordnance Works (COW) gun installed in a Westland COW gun fighter**

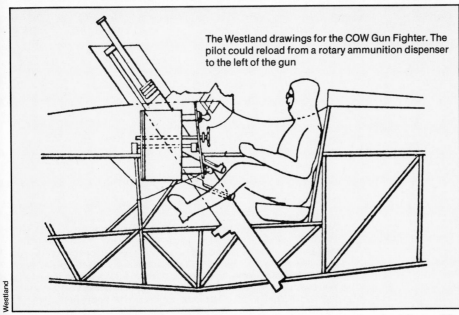

The Westland drawings for the COW Gun Fighter. The pilot could reload from a rotary ammunition dispenser to the left of the gun

Below: **The Vickers COW gun pusher fighter**

The attempt to arm an aircraft with something heavier than rifle-calibre weapons began during the First World War, the principal concern being that of damaging a Zeppelin, since rifle bullets appeared to have little effect. In general, these attempts took the form of mounting short-barrelled cannon of 37-40 mm (1.46-1.57 in) calibre in the front observer's cockpit of pusher aircraft such as the Henri Farman and FE2 biplanes.

One of the first to be tried in this role was the Maxim 37-mm (1.46-in) Pom-Pom, but it was rejected for being too heavy and powerful for the aircraft of the time, and a special short-barrelled version, the 1-pdr Mk 3 firing reduced-charge ammunition, was developed and formally adopted by the Royal Flying Corps in 1917.

Another proposal was the 1½-pdr COW (Coventry Ordnance Works) gun, which was simply an over-sized gas-operated machine-gun fed with five-round clips. This saw little wartime use but it lingered in service right through to the Second World War, being most used in the ground defence of airfields, though it is reported that a small number were also mounted in Sunderland flying boats in the early part of the war.

Vickers produced the Crayford Aeroplane and Trench Gun in 1918, a single-shot 37-mm weapon with a hand-operated breech which must have been highly inconvenient to operate in a manoeuvring aircraft. As the name implies, it was proposed for use either as an infantry trench gun (similar to the French M1916) or an anti-Zeppelin weapon, but by the time it went into production the Zeppelins had given up raiding Britain.

The most notable development of this period was the Davis Non-Recoil Aeroplane Gun. This had been invented in 1913 by Commander Davis, USN, and was the first practical recoilless weapon. Davis' idea was the ultimate in logic; he obtained recoillessness by placing two opposite-facing barrels on a common chamber. The forward barrel fired a projectile, while the rear barrel fired a countershot. Since both these weighed the same and moved at the same velocity, the recoil force on each barrel countered that of the other and the weapon was recoilless. The prospect of firing a sizeable gun without having to worry about the effect of recoil on the aircraft attracted the Royal Naval Air Service, and early in 1915 the Director of Naval Ordnance purchased a specimen Davis gun from the Ordnance Development Company of America. Tests showed that it worked and, under licence from Davis, a 2-pdr (40-mm), a 6-pdr (57-mm) and a 12-pdr (76-mm) were developed. It seems that the RNAS envisaged a wide spectrum of possible uses for the guns, since high explosive, incendiary and case-shot projectiles were developed and approved for service in 1918, suggesting that they had in mind antisubmarine, anti-Zeppelin and ground-strafing roles. A limited number of these guns were made and put into service, but no record has been found of the results of their employment (probably because they were classified 'Secret') and they were declared obsolete in April 1919.

The postwar years saw little development of heavy armament for aircraft. The 20-mm (0.79-in) cannon, as promoted by Oerlikon and Hispano-Suiza, became popular and was the largest calibre weapon generally contemplated, though there was considerable argument over whether cannon might not be less effective than multiple machine-guns.

In the early 1930s, however, the Rheinmetall company in Germany had begun working on recoilless guns in which a proportion of the propellant gas was directed to the rear through a venturi, so producing a thrust which countered the recoil force. The principal result of this line of work was the 'light gun' developed for ground use by airborne and mountain troops, but the weight-saving characteristic of the RCL gun gave promise of a potent aircraft weapon, an up-to-date version of Davis' idea.

Work on prototypes in 37-mm (1.46-in) and 75-mm (2.95-in) began in 1936. The experimental guns were fitted beneath the fuselage of a Messerschmitt Bf 110 which was supported during trials at a height above the ground sufficient to avoid blast reflections. Results were not encouraging, the undersurface of the fuselage, reinforced by 3 mm (0.12 in) steel plates, was severely deformed, the side panels were buckled, and equipment inside the aircraft was damaged; a pipe added to the jet nozzle made little difference.

Work then began on an 88-mm (3.46-in) version, known now as the Dusenkanone (jet gun) or DUKA, intended for use in attacking tanks or ships. In order to bring the jet efflux out at right angles to adjacent surfaces, two jets were used, one discharging below the aircraft and one above. One advantage of this layout was that a normal breech could be used, and this encouraged the design of an automatic loader, a revolver drum holding ten rounds and driven by an electric motor. The jets took gas from the chamber at a point just behind the projectile, and to allow for this a special cartridge case was developed with a plastic forward section which burst under pressure to release gas to the jets. The equipment weighed about one ton.

The gun was successfully developed and

installed in a Junkers Ju 88 aircraft in about 1941, but by that time the priority had fallen and opinions as to the weapon's worth were mixed. The designers later claimed that no damage to the aircraft was experienced, but other engineers concerned in the work said that every time the gun was fired, rivets popped from the aircraft's structure. Whatever the truth of the matter, the DUKA 88 was not accepted for service.

Meanwhile, Rheinmetall engineers had looked again at the Davis countershot principle. The Luftwaffe had asked for a heavy

The Henschel Hs 129 mounted a 75-mm (2.95-in) BK7.5, derived from the Pak 40 L/46. In an aircraft it was particularly effective since the 3.2-kg (7-lb) AP40 ammunition which could penetrate 115 mm (4.5 in) of armour at 460 m (500 yards) had no trouble penetrating the thin deck armour covering tank engines. The Hs 129 saw some action in North Africa, but the bulk of its tank kills were in Russia. The pilot sat in a tiny armoured cockpit with very thick cockpit canopy and optic sight mounted in the nose. This protection was essential since the aircraft normally flew within range of small-arms fire on an attack mission

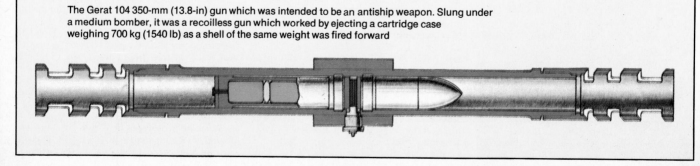

The Gerat 104 350-mm (13.8-in) gun which was intended to be an antiship weapon. Slung under a medium bomber, it was a recoilless gun which worked by ejecting a cartridge case weighing 700 kg (1540 lb) as a shell of the same weight was fired forward

The COW gun mounted in the nose of a Westland Westbury. The gunner is dwarfed by the 37-mm (1.46-in) gun with its magazine clip of five rounds. The mount designed by Vickers allowed the gun to be fired in flight at a broadside angle despite its 907-kg (2000-lb) recoil force

weapon for the attack of warships; armour-piercing bombs did not have sufficient striking velocity, and a rocket-assisted bomb under development was wildly inaccurate. Rheinmetall developed a 335-mm (14-in) gun which fired a Naval armour-piercing shell weighing 700 kg (1540 lb) at 328 m/sec (1000 ft/sec). The gun was a simple tube slung beneath the aircraft and loaded before takeoff with the shell and a cartridge case of steel which weighed the same amount as the shell. The aircraft could fire the gun only once, having to return to base to reload. On firing, the shell was shot forward while the steel cartridge case was shot backward at the same velocity so as to achieve recoillessness. The whole weapon was 11.2 m (37 ft) long and weighed 3400 kg (7500 lb) and was slung beneath a Dornier Do 217.

Experimental firings, with reduced charges, showed that the backblast as the case was ejected caused severe damage to the aircraft, buckling the fuselage and tearing the skin. Deflectors were fitted, and the fuselage lined with steel plates, but work on the idea was eventually stopped when it was apparent that the radio-controlled bomb was offering a better solution to the problem.

The Davis gun principle was later applied to a number of 'Sonder Gerat' (special equipment) installations for fighter aircraft. Here a tube (or battery of tubes) was installed vertically in the aircraft fuselage and loaded with a projectile and cartridge case. The projectile used depended upon the application of the equipment. The SG 110, for example, used a 45-mm (1.77-in) armour-piercing shot and was fired downwards against tanks; the SG 116 fired a 30-mm (1.2-in) high-capacity, high-explosive shell upwards and was for the attack of bombers. In both cases the discharge of the shot was counterbalanced by the discharge of the steel cartridge case, in the opposite direction via the tube. Usually the cartridge case weighed more than the projectile and this, by the balance of forces, allowed a suitably high velocity to be developed. The largest of these SG devices was the SG 113A or Jägerfaust, which fired a 77-mm (3.03-in) piercing shell downwards at 650 m/sec (2130 ft/sec) against tanks; it had not

been perfected before the war ended. Some upward-firing SG installations were installed in fighters and tried against Allied bombers.

The jet gun idea was revived in 1944 with the development of the MK115 a 55-mm (2.16-in) recoilless gun intended for the future armament of high-speed fighters. This gave a velocity of 800 m/sec (2625 ft/sec) and with an auto-loading mechanism was expected to produce a cyclic rate of fire of 300 rpm. The jet was tapped from the forward end of the chamber by two pipes which led around the breech and then joined up to run to a single efflux set well to the rear of the aircraft so as to discharge safely away from the fuselage. The cartridge case used with this equipment had a steel base and nitrated paper walls which were consumed during firing. By the end of the war the gun had successfully fired in the single shot mode, but the auto-loader had not completed development. A similar weapon was under development by Skoda as the war ended.

To turn now to the Allied side, in 1936 the Royal Air Force had begun investigation of large-calibre guns and eventually decided that nothing smaller than a 0.9-kg (2-lb) shell would be effective, a decision which ruled out the COW gun. Development work began

in 1938 and Vickers-Armstrongs produced a modernized version of the Maxim Pom-Pom which became the 40-mm (1.57-in) gun Class S, while Rolls-Royce made a recoil-operated cannon which became the 40-mm gun Class BH. The S gun was adopted by the RAF, while the BH was taken for Naval Air Service use. Although the original intention had been to use them as air-to-air weapons, in fact they saw little of this except for some experimental mountings in a dorsal position on bombers. The majority of these guns were used to equip fighters and were extensively used in the Middle East in 1941-42 for ground strafing and the attack of tanks.

In 1942 the Molins company, who had exhibited considerable talent for devising automatic loading mechanisms for AA guns, were asked by the army to develop a suitable auto-loader for use with the 6-pdr antitank gun in a self-propelled mounting (the original Firefly). It was perfected in a matter of five months, but by the time it was ready the 6-pdr was no longer adequate as a ground antitank gun and the requirement for the auto-loader no longer existed.

The Royal Navy, at this time, were using the 40-mm BH gun on coastal motor-boats but were dissatisfied with its performance.

Aircraft Ordnance

As the army began to turn over to 17-pdr antitank guns, numbers of 6-pdr guns became surplus and the Navy decided to take the gun and the Molins auto-loader and fit it to coastal craft. Molins, appreciating the reasoning behind the navy's request, did the job, and at the same time began to explore the possibility of mounting the 6-pdr with auto-loader into an aircraft, against the day when, inevitably, the RAF would decide that the 40-mm S gun was no longer effective against armour. The RAF were already experimenting with a 47-mm (1.85-in) gun, but it seemed that before they would ever get it into service the German tanks would have thickened their armour yet again. In mid-1943 Molins produced their automatic 6-pdr just at the time when the RAF were having second thoughts about their 47-mm gun, and the idea was quickly taken up. A test installation in a Mosquito proved satisfactory and 36 guns were ordered. By the end of 1943 three aircraft fitted with the guns had been placed in service, their purpose being to attack U-Boats in the Western Approaches; a further nine had been authorized, but before more could be built the Air Ministry decided against the gun and placed its faith in rockets for the future. The three Mosquitos operated successfully, claiming at least one U-Boat, but once the 3-in (76-mm) rocket came into service the 6-pdr was withdrawn.

For reasons not entirely clear at this late date, in April 1944 the RAF decided to try using the 32-pdr antitank gun in an aircraft. Its prime use, it was claimed, would be air-to-air firing, though air-to-ground would also be tried. In order to keep the recoil of such a massive weapon within bounds, it was to be fitted with a 'Galliot' muzzle brake, a device of great complexity but great efficiency which would keep the trunnion pull (or recoil stress) to seven tons. A Molins auto-loader was also specified. Design work went ahead; it is not clear whether a trial barrel was actually fired from an aircraft or not, but in any event the difficulties which arose were enormous, particularly the construction of the complex muzzle brake, and in November 1945 the project was cancelled.

In the United States, interest in big guns began in 1937 with the issue of a specification for a 75-mm (2.95-in) weapon suitable for arming aircraft. This resulted in 1942 as the 75-mm Gun M4, a variation of the Tank Gun M3 provided with additional recoil cylinders. It was a hand-loaded weapon firing the standard tank gun ammunition, and it was installed in the nose of the Mitchell B25G bomber for use in ground or sea attacks. This proved to be an extremely effective gun against all sorts of targets. So far as is known, however, no other type of gun was seriously considered for aircraft mounting.

Since 1945 very little work has been done in this field; in view of the speed of aircraft today and the brief firing times available, the accent has been upon developing smaller-calibre guns with extremely high rates of fire so as to deliver as many projectiles as possible within an engagement, which has led to the Gatling-type Vulcan and similar weapons. Moreover, postwar development of accurate rockets, guided missiles and 'smart' bombs has removed the requirement for a gun solution to ground targets.

See also COW, Davis Gun, Dusenkanone.

A Davis gun mounted on a US Navy Curtiss HS-1. The gun has a Lewis machine-gun mounted coaxially as a spotting rifle. Once the tracers were on target the Davis gun would be fired, a cheap and effective ranging method used in modern tanks

US Navy

Below: The Galliot muzzle brake was designed for an airborne 32-pdr. The spiral slots had to be very accurately machined and several engineering firms rejected the job as too complex and expensive. The project was shelved in November 1945 after many trials

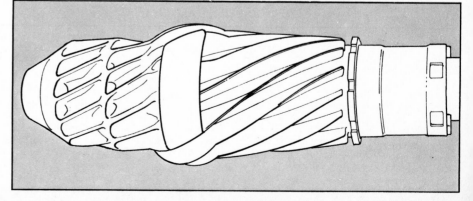

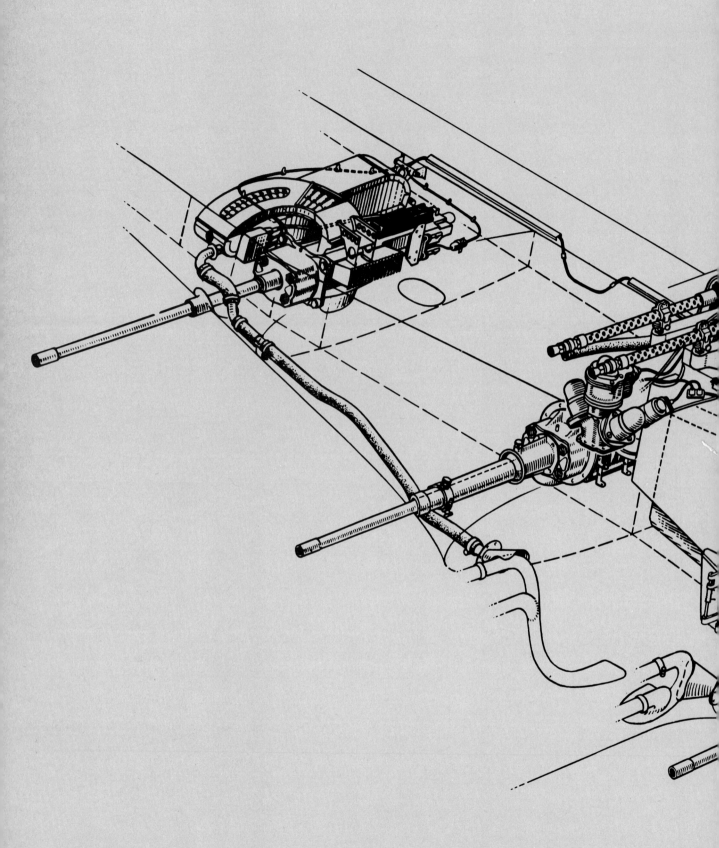